Engaged
Marryin

Welc

Switched
at the ALTAR

Four best-selling authors bring you
fabulous stories about brides-to-be with a
very bad case of wedding jitters!
They have *two* men in their lives
and *one* very big decision:
Who should be their groom?

And some of them leave it until
the very last minute to make
up their minds…

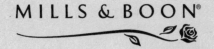

MILLS & BOON®

Switched
at the ALTAR

Last-minute change of...man!

Miranda Lee
Susan Napier
Leigh Michaels
Rebecca Winters

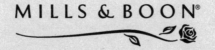

MILLS & BOON®

*MILLS & BOON and MILLS & BOON with the Rose Device
are registered trademarks of the publisher.
Harlequin Mills & Boon Limited,
Eton House, 18-24 Paradise Road, Richmond, Surrey TW9 1SR*

SWITCHED AT THE ALTAR
© by Harlequin Enterprises II B.V., 2002

*Something Borrowed, Vendetta, Some Kind of Hero, For Better, For Worse
were first published in Great Britain by Harlequin Mills and Boon Limited in
separate, short story anthologies*

Something Borrowed © Miranda Lee 1992
Vendetta © Susan Napier 1995
Some Kind of Hero © Leigh Michaels 1991
For Better, For Worse © Rebecca Winters 1993

ISBN 0 263 83192 2

*Set in Times 10.5 on 12 pt. by
Rowland Phototypesetting Limited
Bury St Edmunds, Suffolk*

24-0102

*Printed and bound in Spain
by Litografía Rosés S.A., Barcelona*

SWITCHED AT THE ALTAR

Something Borrowed

by
Miranda Lee

MIRANDA LEE is an Australian, living near Sydney. Born and raised in the bush, she was boarding-school educated and briefly pursued a classical music career before moving to Sydney and embracing the world of computers. Happily married, with three daughters, she began writing when family commitments kept her at home. She likes to create stories that are believable, modern, fast-paced and sexy. Her interests include reading meaty sagas, doing word puzzles, gambling and going to the movies.

Look out for Miranda Lee's new linked books in Modern Romance™!

A SECRET VENGEANCE
February 2002
THE SECRET LOVE-CHILD
March 2002

CHAPTER ONE

'JAMES hasn't seen your dress, has he?' Kate asked, glancing at the magnificent satin and lace bridal gown hanging on the wardrobe door. 'You know that's considered unlucky.'

Ashleigh put down her mascara and smiled at her chief bridesmaid in the dressing-table mirror. 'No, Miss Tradition. He hasn't. Not that it would worry me if he had,' she added with a light laugh. 'You know I don't believe in superstitions. *Or* fate. *Or* luck. People make their own luck in life.'

Kate rolled her eyes. 'You've become annoyingly pragmatic over the years, do you know that? Where's your sense of romance gone?'

It was killed, came the unwanted and bitter thought. A lifetime ago. . .

Ashleigh felt a deep tremor of old pain, but hid it well, keeping her mascara wand steady with an iron will as she went on with her make-up.

'Just look at you,' Kate accused. 'It's your wedding-day and you're not even nervous. If I were the bride my hand would be shaking like a leaf.'

'What is there to be nervous about? Everything is going to go off like clockwork. You know how organised James's mother is.'

'I wasn't talking about the wedding. Or the reception. I was talking about afterwards. . . You know. . .'

'For heaven's sake, Kate,' Ashleigh said quite sharply.

9

'It's not as though I'm some trembling young virgin. I'm almost thirty years old, and a qualified doctor to boot. My wedding-night is not looming as some terrifying ordeal.'

Oh, really? an insidious voice whispered at the back of her mind.

Ashleigh stiffened before making a conscious effort to relax, letting out a ragged sigh. 'I'm sorry,' she apologised. 'I shouldn't have snapped at you like that.'

'You *are* nervous,' her friend decided smugly. 'And you know what? I think it's sweet. James is a real nice man. Much nicer than. . .' Kate bit her bottom lip and darted Ashleigh a stricken look. 'Oh, I. . .I'm sorry. I didn't mean . . . I. . .'

'It's all right,' Ashleigh soothed. 'I won't collapse in a screaming heap if you mention his name.'

'Do you. . .ever think of him?' Kate asked, eyes glittering with curiosity.

Too damned often, came the immediate and possibly crushing thought.

But Ashleigh gathered herself quickly, refusing to allow Jake—even in memory form—to mar her wedding-day.

'Jake's as good as dead as far as I'm concerned,' she stated quite firmly. 'As far as *everyone* in Glenbrook is concerned. Even his mother doesn't speak of him any more.'

'What about James?' the other girl asked. 'I mean. . .he and Jake are twins. Doesn't he ever talk about his brother?'

'Never."

Kate frowned. 'I wonder what Jake would think of his quieter half marrying his old girlfriend. Does he know, do you think? They say some twins, especially identical ones, have a sort of telepathy between them.'

Ashleigh's fine grey eyes did their best to stay calm as she turned to face her old school-friend. 'Jake and James never did. As far as Jake knowing. . .' She gave a seemingly offhand shrug. 'He might. His mother insisted on sending him a wedding invitation. God knows why, since she doesn't even know where he's living now. She posted it to his old solicitor in Thailand, who once promised to pass on any mail. Naturally, she didn't receive a reply.'

Ashleigh sucked in a deep breath, then let it out slowly, hoping to ease the constriction in her chest. 'Jake wouldn't give a damn about my marrying James, any-way,' she finished. 'Now. . .perhaps we'd better get on with my hair. Time's getting away.'

Kate remained blessedly silent while she brushed then wound Ashleigh's shoulder-length blonde hair into the style they'd both decided on the previous day. Even though Ashleigh appeared to be watching her hairdresser friend's efficient fingers, her mind was elsewhere, remembering things she shouldn't be remembering on the day she was marrying James.

Jake. . .holding her close, kissing her.

Jake. . .undressing her slowly.

Jake. . .his magnificent male body in superb control as he took her with him to a physical ecstasy, the like of which she doubted she would ever experience again.

A shiver reverberated through her.

'You're not cold, are you?' Kate asked, frowning.

Ashleigh tried to smile. 'No. . . Someone must have walked over my grave.'

Her friend laughed. 'I thought you didn't believe in

stuff like that. You know what, Ashleigh? I think you're
a big fibber. I think you believe in fate and superstitions
and all those old wives' tales as much as the next person.
And I'll prove it to you before this day is out. But, for
now, sit perfectly still while I get these pins safely in. I
don't want to spear you in the ear.'

Ashleigh was only too happy to sit still, her whole
insides in knots as a ghastly suspicion began to take hold.
Was she marrying James simply because of his physical
likeness to Jake? Could she be indulging some secret
hope that, when James took her to bed tonight, her body
would automatically respond the same way it had to his
brother?

She hadn't thought so when she'd accepted James's
proposal. Ashleigh believed she was marrying him
because he was the only man she'd met in years who
seemed genuinely to love her, whom *she* liked enough
to marry, and who wanted what she was suddenly wanting so very badly: a family of her own. Sex had not
seemed such an important issue.

Now. . .with her wedding-night at hand. . .it had suddenly become one.

Perhaps she should have let James make love to her
the night he'd asked her to marry him. At least then
she would have known the truth. Looking back to that
occasion, she had undoubtedly been stirred by his
unexpectedly fierce kisses. Why, then, had she pulled
back and asked him to wait? Why? What had she been
afraid of? As she'd said to Kate. . .she was hardly a
trembling virgin.

Ashleigh mentally shook her head, swiftly dismissing
the possibility that her body—or her subconscious—
might find one brother interchangeable with the other.

She had *never* confused James with Jake in the past. Others had, but never herself. The two were totally different in her eyes, regardless of their identical features.

They'd been in the same class at school since kindergarten, she and Jake and James, though the boys were almost a year older than her. The three had been great mates always, spending all their spare time together. It wasn't till the end of primary school that their relationship had undergone a drastic change. The three of them had seemed to shoot up overnight, Jake and James into lithe, handsome lads, and Ashleigh into a lovely young woman with a figure the envy of every girl in Glenbrook.

By the time they had finished their first year in high school the more extroverted, aggressive Jake had staked a decidedly sexual though still relatively innocent claim on Ashleigh. She'd become his 'steady', and from then on James had taken a back seat in her life, even though she had always been subtly aware that he was equally attracted to her, and would have dearly liked to be in his brother's shoes.

But she'd had eyes only for Jake.

How they had lasted till their graduation from high school before consummating their relationship was a minor miracle. Oh, they'd argued about 'going all the way' often enough, with Jake sometimes becoming furious with her adamant refusal to let him. But she had seen the way other teenage boys talked about girls who gave sex freely, and had always been determined not to give in till Jake had proved he wanted her for herself, not her nubile young body.

Ashleigh almost smiled as she remembered the first time Jake had made real love to her, the day after her eighteenth birthday, two weeks after they'd graduated.

What an anticlimax their first effort had been. Jake had been furious with himself, knowing he'd been too eager, too anxious.

'Too damned arrogant and ignorant,' were *his* words.

Jake had gone out then and there and bought a very modern and very progressive love-making manual, then quickly became the most breathtakingly skilful lover that any mortal male could become, mastering superb control over his own urgent young body, thrilling to the way he'd eventually learnt to give the girl he loved such incredible pleasure.

Or so Ashleigh had romantically imagined at the time. She should have known that it was just Jake being his typical obsessive self. She certainly should have begun to doubt the depth of Jake's love when he announced in the New Year that he was going overseas—*alone*—for a couple of months. She'd stupidly believed his story about his rich Aunt Aggie's giving him the holiday as a reward for his great exam results and insisting he go immediately, saying it would broaden his mind for his future writing career. He'd promised Ashleigh faithfully to be back in time to go to university with her in March.

But by March Jake had been in prison in Bangkok, awaiting trial for drug trafficking and possession, after trying to board a plane home with heroin in his luggage. Though greatly distressed, Ashleigh had flown over to support her boyfriend, certain he was innocent. The penny hadn't dropped till after Jake had been found guilty and given a life sentence. He had looked her straight in the eye from behind those filthy bars and told her quite brutally that *of course* he was guilty. What in hell did she think he'd really come over for?

But it had been his subsequent personal tirade against

her that had shattered Ashleigh completely. His cruelly telling her that he had grown out of their puppy love during his weeks abroad; that he found her blind faith during his trial suffocatingly laughable; that she was boring compared to the *real* women he'd enjoyed since leaving home and that he didn't want to see her pathetic face again, let alone receive any more of her drippy, mushy love letters.

Ashleigh had returned home to Australia in a state of deep despair and disillusionment, having had to defer her entry into medical school till the following year due to her emotional state. In truth, she had almost succumbed to a nervous breakdown over Jake. Yet still some mad, futile hope had made her keep on writing to him. Not love letters. Just words of forgiveness and encouragement. Every day she had gone out to the mail box, hoping against hope for a letter back.

It had never come.

In the end, she'd crawled out of her crippling depression and gone on without Jake.

But the scars left behind from her disastrous teenage romance had plagued her personal life, spoiling every relationship she'd tried to have. Always she'd compared the man with Jake. His looks, his personality, his drive, his lovemaking. . .

They'd all failed to measure up. Which was crazy! For what had Jake done to her? Let her down. Let his family down. Let *everyone* down.

'What made you come home to Glenbrook to practise medicine?' Kate asked all of a sudden, startling Ashleigh from her reverie. 'From what you've told me, you were doing well down in Sydney.'

'Very well,' Ashleigh agreed. 'But the city can be a

lonely place, Kate, without your family or someone special to share your life. I remember I spent my twenty-ninth birthday all alone, and suddenly I was homesick. Within a week I was back here in Glenbrook.'

'And in no time you found James. God, life's strange. There you were in Sydney for years, where there must be hordes of handsome, eligible men, and what do you do? Come home and find your future hubby in good old Glenbrook.'

'Yes. . .' Ashleigh recalled the night she'd answered an emergency call from the Hargraves home where Mr Hargraves senior had unfortunately suffered a fatal heart attack. It had been James who'd opened the door. . .

'I suppose there's no hope of you-know-who coming back to town, is there?' Kate probed carefully.

'I wouldn't think so. It's been over three years now.'

Three years since the Thailand government had unexpectedly pardoned a few foreign prisoners during a national celebration—one of them being Jake—and Ashleigh had still foolishly started hoping he'd come home to her.

Well, he had come home all right. For less than a day, apparently, his visit only to ask for money before he went back to the very country that had almost destroyed him! He hadn't come to see her, even though she'd been home at the time.

One would have thought that such callous indifference should have made it much easier for Ashleigh to see other men in a more favourable light. But somehow. . .it hadn't.

A type of guilt assailed Ashleigh. James deserved better than a bride who spent her wedding-day thinking about another man, especially his own brother.

She gave herself another mental shake. She wouldn't

do it any more. Not for a second! And if tonight there were fleeting memories of another time, and another lover, she would steadfastly ignore them.

I will be a good wife, she vowed. The very best. Even if I have to resort to faking things a little. . .

'Well, what do you think?' Kate asked after one last spurt of hair-spray.

Ashleigh swallowed, then glanced in the mirror at the way her wayward blonde hair was now neatly encased in a sleek French roll. 'That's great,' she praised. 'Oh, you're so clever!'

'*You're* the clever one, Dr O'Neil,' came her friend's laughing reply.

A hurried tap, tap, tap on the bedroom door had both women glancing around. The door opened immediately and Nancy Hargraves, James's mother, hurried into the room.

'Goodness, what are you doing here, Nancy?' Ashleigh exclaimed, getting to her feet. 'Has something gone wrong? Don't tell me it's raining down at the park!'

The actual ceremony was to take place in a picturesque park down by the river, James having vetoed his mother's suggestion they have the wedding at a church neither of them attended. Ashleigh had happily gone along with his idea of a marriage celebrant and an open-air wedding, choosing the local memorial park as a setting. Nancy, though not pleased, had acquiesced, warning them at the time that if it rained it would be their own stupid fault!

'No, no, nothing like that,' she muttered now in an agitated fashion.

Ashleigh was surprised at how upset James's ultra-cool and composed mother seemed to be. Her hands were twisting nervously together and she could hardly look Ashleigh in the face.

'Could I speak privately to Ashleigh for a minute or two?' she asked Kate with a stiff smile.

'Sure. I'll go along and check that the others are nearly ready.' The others being Alison and Suzie, Ashleigh's cousins—the second bridesmaid and flower girl respectively.

'Thank you,' Mrs Hargraves said curtly.

Kate flashed Ashleigh an eyebrow-raised glance before leaving the room, being careful not to catch the voluminous skirt of her burgundy satin bridesmaid's dress as she closed the door behind her.

Ashleigh eyed her future mother-in-law with both curiosity and concern. It wasn't like Nancy to be so flustered. When she'd offered to help with the wedding arrangements Ashleigh had very gratefully accepted, her own mother having died several years before. She imagined not many women could have smoothly put together a full-scale wedding in the eight weeks that had elapsed since the night she'd accepted James's proposal. But Nancy Hargraves had for many years been Glenbrook's top social hostess, and all had been achieved without a ruffle.

Ashleigh got slowly to her feet, taken aback to detect red-rimmed eyes behind the woman's glasses.

'What's happened?' she said with a lurch in her stomach.

'I. . . I've heard from Jake,' came the blurted-out admission.

Ashleigh felt the blood drain from her face. She clutched her dressing-gown around her chest and sank slowly down on to the stool again. It was several seconds before she looked up and spoke. 'I presume he rang,' she said in a hard, tight voice. 'There's no mail on a Saturday.'

The other woman shook her head. 'He sent me a letter through a courier service. It arrived a short while ago.'

'What. . .what did he say?' she asked thickly.

'Apparently the wedding invitation only just reached him,' Nancy said with the brusqueness of emotional distress. 'He. . .he sends his apologies that he can't attend. He. . .he also sent this and specifically asked me to give it back to you today *before* the wedding.'

Ashleigh stared at the silver locket and chain dangling from the woman's shaking fingers. Her own hand trembled as she reached out to take it, a vivid memory flashing into her mind.

'What's this?' Jake had asked when she'd held the heart-shaped locket out between the bars of his cell the night before the verdict had come down.

Her smile had been pathetically thin. 'My heart,' she'd said. 'Keep it with you while you're in here. You can give it back to me when you get out, when you come to claim the real thing.'

'I could be here for years, Leigh,' had come his rough warning. Jake always called her Leigh, never Ashleigh.

'I'll wait. . .I'll wait for you forever.'

'Forever is a long time,' he'd bitten out in reply. But he'd taken her offering and shoved it in the breast pocket of the shabby shirt he'd been wearing.

Now she stared down at the heart-shaped locket for a long, long moment, then crushed it in her hand, her eyes closing against the threatened rush of tears.

'I'm sorry to have upset you, Ashleigh,' Nancy said in a strained voice. 'I know what Jake once meant to you. But believe me when I say I wanted nothing more than to see you and James happily married today. I did not want to come here with this. But I had to do what my son asked. I just *had* to. I. . .'

She broke off, and Ashleigh's wet lashes fluttered open to see a Nancy Hargraves she'd never encountered before. The woman looked grey, and ill.

Anger against Jake flooded through her, washing the pain from her heart, leaving a bitter hardness instead. How dared he do this, *today*, of all days? How *dared* he?

Ashleigh pulled herself together and stood up, the locket tightly clasped within her right hand. 'It's all right, Nancy,' she stated firmly. '*I'm* all right. I have no intention of letting Jake spoil my wedding-day. Or my marriage. You haven't told James about the letter, have you?'

Nancy's blue eyes widened, perhaps at the steel in Ashleigh's voice. 'N. . .no. . .'

'Then everything's all right, isn't it? I certainly won't be mentioning it. By tonight, James and I will be driving off on our honeymoon and he'll be none the wiser.'

She was shocked when her future mother-in-law uttered a choked sob and fled from the room.

CHAPTER TWO

ASHLEIGH stood there for a few moments in stunned silence, her thoughts in disarray. But she soon gathered her wits, renewing her resolve not to let Jake spoil her marriage to James. No doubt Nancy would soon collect herself as well and present a composed face at the ceremony in little over half an hour's time.

'Mrs Hargraves gone, I see?' Kate said as she breezed back into Ashleigh's bedroom. 'What on earth did she want? She looked rather uptight.'

'Yes, she did, didn't she?' Ashleigh agreed with a deliberately carefree air. Kate was a dear friend but an inveterate gossip, the very last person one would tell about the correspondence from Jake. Everyone in Glenbrook would know about it within a week, with suitable embellishments. It had been Kate who had furnished Ashleigh with the news of Jake's fleeting visit over three years before, the information gleaned from Nancy Hargraves's cook, a talkative lady who had her hair done at Kate's salon every week.

Ashleigh smiled disarmingly at her friend. 'It proves that even someone like James's mother can be nervous with the right occasion. I thought something must have gone wrong there for a moment. But she just called in to give me this to wear today.' And she held up the locket and chain. 'Must be one of your mob, Kate. An upholder of old traditions. This is to be my *something borrowed*.'

The irony of her excuse struck Ashleigh immediately, but she bravely ignored the contraction in her chest. She'd lent Jake her heart, and now he'd given it back to her.

Good, she decided staunchly. I'll entrust it to James. He'll take much better care of it, I'm sure.

With a surge of something like defiance, she slipped the chain around her neck. 'Do this up for me, will you?' she asked her chief bridesmaid.

'Will do. But what are you going to do for the something old, something new and something blue?'

'No trouble,' Ashleigh tossed off. 'My pearl earrings are old, my dress is new, and my bra has a blue bow on it.'

'Spoil-sport,' Kate complained. 'I had a blue garter all lined up for you.'

'OK. I'll wear that too. Now help me climb into this monstrosity of a dress, will you? The photographer's due here in ten minutes.'

'You're suitably late now, Miss O'Neil, ' the chauffeur of the hire-car informed. 'Shall I head for the park?'

'God, yes,' her father grumbled from his seat beside her. 'If we go round this damned block one more time I'll be in danger of being car-sick for the first time in my life!'

'Kate insisted I be at least ten minutes late,' Ashleigh defended, feeling more than a little churned up in the stomach herself. But it wasn't car-sickness. Much as she had maintained a cool exterior since the perturbing encounter with Nancy, inside she was a mess. And it was all Jake's fault. The whole catastrophe of her personal life so far had been Jake's fault!

But no longer, she decided ruefully. She was going to marry James and be happy if it killed her!

She slanted her father a sideways glance, thinking wryly that he was far from comfortable in his role as father of the bride. He was a good doctor, but an anti-social man, whose bedside manner left a lot to be desired.

Ashleigh believed she'd contributed a lot to his practice since joining it, always being willing to lend a sympathetic ear, especially to women patients. They certainly asked for her first. She planned to continue working, at least part-time, even if she did get pregnant straight away, which was her and James's hope.

Thinking about having a baby, however, brought her mind back to the intimate side of marriage, and the night ahead of her. Another attack of nerves besieged her stomach. Dear heaven, she groaned silently. She hadn't realised that going to bed with James would loom as such an ordeal.

Her hand fluttered up unconsciously to touch the locket lying in the deep valley between her breasts.

Any worry over her wedding-night was distracted, however, when the park came into view. Oh, my God, she thought as her eyes ran over what Nancy had arranged for her favourite son's wedding.

A rueful smile crossed Ashleigh's lips. James's vetoing a church service clearly hadn't stopped his mother's resolve to have a traditional and very public ceremony. Right in the middle of the park under an attractive clump of trees sat a flower-garlanded dais, with an enormous strip of red carpet leading up to it, on either side of which were rows and rows of seats, all full of guests. But the *pièce de résistance* was the electric organ beside the dais, which seemed to have a hundred extension leads running from it away to a van on which two loud speakers were placed.

Ashleigh shook her head in drily amused resignation. Serve herself right for giving James's mother *carte blanche* with the arrangements.

'Trust Nancy Hargraves to turn this wedding into a social circus,' her father muttered crossly as the white Fairlane pulled up next to the stone archway that marked the entrance to the park. A fair crowd of onlookers were waiting there for the bride's arrival, not to mention several photographers and a video cameraman. 'Thank God I've only got one daughter. I wouldn't want to go through all this again.'

Ashleigh felt a surge of irritation towards her father. Why did he always have to make her feel that her being female was a bother to him?

If only Mum were still alive, she thought with a pang of sadness. She would have so loved today. Not for the first time Ashleigh wondered how such a soft, sentimental woman had married a man like her father.

People always claimed she took after her mother. She certainly hoped so.

'I've been thinking,' Edgar O'Neil went on curtly while they sat there waiting for the chauffeur to make his way round to Ashleigh's door. 'It's as well Stuart will be joining the practice next year. You're going to be too busy having babies and dinner parties to be bothered with doctoring. And rightly so. A woman's place is in the home.'

Ashleigh was too flabbergasted to say a word. She had always known that her father was one of the old brigade at heart. Also that her younger brother would be joining the practice after he finished his residency. But her father spoke as if her services would be summarily dispensed with!

As for her giving dinner parties. . . Nancy Hargraves and her late husband might have been the hub of Glenbrook's social life, the Hargraves family owning the logging company and timber mill which were the economic mainstays of the town. But James was not a social animal in the least, and Ashleigh didn't anticipate their married life would contain too much entertaining.

She had planned to go on working, babies or not. Or at least she *had*. . .till her father had dropped his bombshell just now. Her heart turned over with a mixture of disappointment and dismay, though quickly replaced by a prickly resolve. She would just have to start up a practice of her own, then, wouldn't she?

Alighting from the car, Ashleigh had to make a conscious effort to put a relaxed, smiling face on for the photographers and all the people avidly watching her every move. Heavens, but it looked as if the whole town had turned out to see their only lady doctor getting married.

Or was there a measure of black curiosity, came the insidious thought, over her marrying the wrong brother?

Stop it! she breathed to herself fiercely. Now just you stop it!

'Doesn't she look beautiful?' someone whispered as she made her way carefully up the stone steps and through the archway, her skirt hitched up slightly so she didn't trip.

'Like a fairy princess,' was another comment.

Ashleigh felt warmed by their compliments, though she knew any woman would look good in what she was wearing. The dress and veil combined had cost a fortune,

Nancy having insisted she have the very best. Personally she had thought the *Gone With The Wind* style gown, with its heavy beading, low-cut neck, flounced sleeves and huge layered skirt, far too elaborate for her own simpler tastes. But Nancy had been insistent.

'It's expected of my daughter-in-law to wear something extra-special,' she had said in that haughty manner which could have been aggravating if one let it. But Ashleigh accepted the woman for what she was. A harmless snob. James had a bit of it in him too, but less offensively so.

Jake had been just the opposite, refusing to conform to his mother's rather stiff social conventions, always going his own way. Not for him a short back and sides haircut. Or suits. Or liking classical music. Jake had been all long, wavy hair, way-out clothes and hard-rock bands. Only in his grades had he lived up to his parental expectations, being top of the school.

Irritation at how her mind kept drifting to Jake sent a scowl to her face.

'Smile, Doc,' the photographer from the local paper urged. 'You're going to be married, not massacred.'

Ashleigh stopped to throw a beaming smile the photographer's way. 'This better?'

'Much!'

'Come, Ashleigh,' her father insisted, taking her elbow and shepherding her across the small expanse of lawn to where the imitation aisle of red carpet started and her attendants were waiting. 'We're late enough as it is.'

Her chief bridesmaid thought so too, it appeared. 'Now that's taking tradition a bit too far for my liking,' Kate grumbled. 'I was beginning to think you'd got cold feet and done a flit.'

'Never,' Ashleigh laughed.

'Well, stranger things have happened. But all's well that ends well. I'll just give the nod for the music to start and the men to get ready. I think they're all hiding behind the dais. Still nervous?' she whispered while she straightened her friend's veil.

'Terrified,' Ashleigh said truthfully, a lump gathering in her throat as all the guests stood up, blocking out any view of the three men walking round to stand at the base of the dais steps.

'Good. Nothing like a nervous bride. Nerves make them look even more beautiful, though God knows I don't know how anyone could look any more beautiful than you do today, dear friend. James is going to melt when he sees you.'

'Will you two females stop gasbagging?' the father of the bride interrupted peevishly.

'Keep your shirt on, Dr O'Neil,' Kate returned, not one to ever be hassled by a man, even a respected physician of fifty-five. Which could explain why, at thirty, she'd never been a bride herself. 'We'll be ready when we're ready and not a moment before. Your father's a right pain in the neck, do you know that, Ashleigh?'

'Yes,' came the sighing reply.

The organ started up.

Kate grinned. 'Knock 'em dead, love.'

'You make this sound like the opening night of a show,' Ashleigh returned in an exasperated voice.

Kate lifted expressive eyebrows, then laughed softly. 'Well, it is, in a way, isn't it?'

Heat zoomed into Ashleigh's cheeks.

'Aah,' the other girl smiled. 'That's what I wanted to see. The bridal blush. She's ready now, Dr O'Neil.'

As ready as I'll ever be, Ashleigh thought with a nervous swallow.

The long walk up the red carpet on her father's arm was a blur. The music played. Countless faces smiled at her. It felt almost as if she were in a dream. She was walking on clouds and everything seemed fuzzy around the edges of her field of vision.

Only one face stood out at her. Nancy's, still looking a little tense, and oddly watchful, as though expecting Ashleigh to turn tail and run at any moment.

And then the men came into view. . .

First came James, looking tall and darkly handsome in a black tuxedo, his thick, wavy hair slicked back neatly from his well-shaped head. And next to him was. . .

Ashleigh faltered for a moment.

For the best man *wasn't* Peter Reynolds, the new accountant at Hargraves Pty Ltd and James's friend since college, but a perfect stranger!

Her father must have noticed at the same time. 'Who the hell's that standing next to James?' he muttered under his breath to her.

'I have no idea. . .' The man was about thirty with rather messy blond hair, an interesting face and intelligent dark eyes. After a long second look Ashleigh knew she'd never seen him before in her life.

Her eyes skated down to the other groomsman. Stuart, her brother. He smiled back reassuringly, after which she swung her gaze back to James. Their eyes locked and for one crashing second Ashleigh literally did go weak at the knees. For James was looking at her as if she were a vision, an apparition that he could scarcely believe was real, as if he couldn't tear his eyes away from her.

All thought of mysterious best men fled, her breath

catching at the undeniable love and passion encompassed within James's intense stare. He'd never looked at her like that before, even when he'd said she was the only woman he'd ever loved, the only woman he could bear marrying. His stunningly smouldering gaze touched her heart, moved her soul. *And* her body.

Ashleigh was startled to find that suddenly the night ahead did not present itself as such an ordeal after all. Her eyes moved slowly over her husband-to-be and her heart began to race, her stomach tightening, a flood of sensual heat sweeping all over her skin.

The raw sexuality of her response shocked her. She hadn't felt such arousal since. . .since. . .

Quite involuntarily one trembling hand left her bouquet to once again touch the locket.

James's deeply set blue eyes zeroed in on the movement—and the locket—and her hand retreated with guilty speed. Surely he didn't know anything about the locket, did he? Surely Nancy hadn't told him about it, and the letter from Jake?

James was frowning now, all desire gone from his gaze.

'Keep moving, Ashleigh,' her father ordered in an impatient whisper.

Haltingly she took the remaining few steps that drew her level with the still frowning James. For a second she didn't know what to do, where to look, but as she gazed up into James's face she was distracted from her emotional confusion by the dark circles under his eyes. She peered at him intently through her veil, and saw how tired and strained he looked, as though he hadn't had much sleep the night before.

A possible solution to the mystery of the missing best

man catapulted into her mind. Peter had taken James out on a stag night last night, *against* everyone's advice. Maybe they'd really tied one on and something had happened to Peter in the process. A severe hangover, perhaps?

James reached out his left hand towards Ashleigh. Still rattled, she almost took it without first handing her bouquet over to Kate. Turning to do so, she caught a glimpse of Kate and the others, staring and frowning, first at the strange best man, then at her. Ashleigh shrugged, handed the bouquet to Kate then turned back to place her hand in James's. When his right hand moved to cover it she looked down and almost died, her mouth falling open as she stared down at the bruised knuckles, the badly grazed skin.

Her eyes flew to his. 'James,' she husked. 'What happened to your hand? What—?'

'Ssssh,' he hushed. 'Afterwards. . . The celebrant's ready to start.' And he urged her up on to the wide step, where they would be in full view of the guests.

'We are gathered here today to celebrate the marriage of. . .'

Ashleigh found it hard to concentrate on the ceremony, her head whirling with questions. The image of James in a physical fight was so out of character that she couldn't even think of what possible reason there could be for it. And whom had he been fighting with, anyway? Surely not Peter?

Peter was even less physically inclined than James, being older and much slighter in build, as well as a connoisseur of the finer things in life. Art. . .the theatre. . .fine wines. . . Ashleigh often wondered what he was doing in a small timber town like Glenbrook. He didn't appear to like the place any more than he liked *her*.

Not that he ever said as much openly. But she had seen the coldness in his eyes when he looked her way, and he rarely let an opportunity go by to slip in a mildly sarcastic comment about women in general, even though Ashleigh knew they were really directed at one woman in particular. Namely herself.

In fact, Peter Reynolds was the one dark cloud on the horizon of her future with James, one made all the darker because she hadn't been quite able to pin down the reason for his antagonism towards her. Usually she got on well with men on a social level. Better than with women, who seemed threatened by her being a doctor.

Except for Kate, of course, Ashleigh thought warmly. Kate was never threatened by anything.

'Till death us do part.'

'A tight squeeze on her fingers snapped Ashleigh back to the present.

'I. . .I do,' she said shakily, and flashed James an equally shaky smile.

He didn't smile back.

Ashleigh stared. At his grim mouth; his hooded eyes; his clenched jaw.

It was at that moment she realised something was dreadfully wrong. James had not been involved in some silly male spat with Peter after drinking too much. It was something much more serious than that. Not only serious. But somehow dangerous.

To her. . .

CHAPTER THREE

PANIC clutched at Ashleigh's insides, making her heart-rate triple and her thoughts whirl.

But not for long. Ashleigh was a logical thinker and she quickly calmed down, accepting that she was being ridiculous and fanciful. The events of the day so far had clearly unnerved her.

James would *never* do anything to hurt her, or cause her to be in any danger. She was mad to even think so. He was too kind, too caring, too gentle. As for his having been in a physical brawl with Peter. . . The very idea was ludicrous! There had to be some other reason for his damaged hand. Certainly something *had* happened to Peter, but probably no more than the hangover she'd first envisaged. Meanwhile she refused to let her imagination run away with her.

Lifting her chin slightly, she turned her eyes to the front. But, despite all her inner lectures, an uneasy churning remained in her stomach.

A long shuddering breath of self-exasperation trickled from her lungs, which brought a sharp glance from the groom, *and* the celebrant, who was about to start James's vow.

She let her eyes drop away from both of them, staring uncomfortably at the floor while the celebrant's deep male voice rolled on.

'Do you, John James Hargraves, take. . .?'

Ashleigh's eyes jerked up, her lips parting in protest.

For John James was what *Jake* had been christened, the exact reverse of James's names.

But as the celebrant continued, loud and clear, she reconciled herself to the mistake and shut her mouth again. Why make a fuss? These things happened all the time at weddings. Nevertheless, she hoped James didn't mind the mix-up.

Apparently not, for his 'I do' at the end was strong, even if there was a decided raspiness in his voice.

The doctor in Ashleigh automatically diagnosed that he was getting a cold—the result, no doubt, of a heavy night out and whatever else James had been up to last night.

Truly, she thought somewhat irritably, never being at her sympathetic best when it came to male drinking bouts, let alone indulging in one the night before getting married.

Ashleigh was mulling over this uncharacteristic lack of consideration in her husband-to-be when James reached out and abruptly took her left hand, almost crushing her fingers within his as he drew it across her towards him. Her eyes flew up in startled alarm, meeting his steely blue gaze with a definite contraction in her chest.

This was a side of James she had certainly never seen before—a tougher, harder, much more macho side. It came to her astonished self that perhaps he was more like Jake than she'd realised.

And why wouldn't he be? inserted the voice of ruthless reason. They were identical twins, weren't they? They had probably started out with identical natures, till the stronger of the two personalities stamped his presence more loudly, forcing the other to adopt a more passive, compromising role. Maybe, once Jake had gone from the

Hargraveses' household, James had been able to crawl out from under the shell his brother's dominance had forced around him, even though the gentle, less assertive manner he'd adopted over the years had by then become a habit.

Today, however, the pressure of the wedding and the mishap over Peter was probably bringing his basic male aggression to the fore.

To be frank, Ashleigh wasn't sure if she liked this more masterful James or not. Perhaps she didn't want to be faced with the prospect of his becoming more and more like Jake. Perhaps she was more comfortable with their remaining totally different.

'The ring?' the celebrant asked of the best man.

The stranger with the fair hair and dark eyes extracted the ring from his pocket and handed it over. Only the one ring. James had resisted Ashleigh's attempts to make him wear one, saying he didn't like to wear jewellery of any kind. Which was quite true.

Lifting her hand, he began sliding the wide gold band on to her ring finger, saying the traditional words as he did so. 'With my body I thee worship. . .'

Ashleigh's heart caught at the fierce emotion James was putting into his vow. Unless, of course, it was the oncoming cold bringing that huskily thickened quality to his voice.

Her eyes lifted to his and she knew instantly that that was not so. The earlier steel had melted to a swirling blue sea of desire, drawing her gaze into its eddying depths, seducing her with the silent promise of a passion she had never dreamt James capable of. But it was there in the eyes holding hers, in the hand wrapped securely around her fingers, in the chemical electricity which was surging from his hand to hers.

'And with all my worldly goods I thee endow,' he concluded, his eyes dropping to caress first her softly parted lips, and then her lush cleavage.

Ashleigh was shocked, a shaming heat stealing into her cheeks. Surely this was not the right moment for open seduction?

Flustered, she yanked her hand away from James's disturbing touch, not daring to look at him in the process. Instead, she concentrated her regard on the celebrant, who cleared his throat and announced pompously, 'I pronounce that they be Man and Wife together.' Beaming widely at them both, he added, 'And now, Mr Hargraves, you may kiss your lovely bride.'

Oh, God, Ashleigh thought with a flip-over of both her stomach and heart. Instant nerves had her holding her breath as James turned her to face him before slowly lifting the thin layer of netting back over her head. Quite deliberately she didn't look up into his eyes, focusing her attention on his chin. But slowly and inexorably her eyes were drawn upwards till they were right on his mouth. She watched, heart pounding, as those well-shaped lips opened slightly.

And then he was bending his head.

Ashleigh froze till contact was made, suppressing a gasp of dismay to find that his lips were oddly cold and lifeless on hers. Somehow, after his smouldering scrutiny, she'd been expecting—no, *hoping*—for more. A possessive, hungry kiss. An explosion of passion. A sample of what was to come.

But when James's mouth lifted from hers she was left

feeling desolate, a jagged sigh of disappointment wafting from her lungs.

The sigh brought another incisive glance from her brand-new husband. This time Ashleigh wasn't quick enough to avoid returning his look.

There was no longer any promise of seduction in his silent stare, only an unreadable implacability that sent a deep shiver reverberating through her. For, though the expression in his eyes seemed impassive on the surface, there was a razor's edge lurking within those cool blue depths. One got the impression of suppressed violence, of wild forces, barely tamed behind a civilised façade.

Ashleigh had a vivid mental picture of James tonight, ripping her clothes from her then taking her with a savagery bordering on rape. She sucked in a startled breath, her glossed lips gasping apart, her breasts rising and falling in a bemused agitation, caused as much by her own reaction to such a vision as the vision itself.

Was she appalled, or aroused?

If the latter, how could that be? She had never been a woman to indulge in rape fantasies. She had consistently shrunk from sexually aggressive men over the years. They reminded her too forcibly of Jake, who, though never violent, had exploited her own sexual vulnerability towards him with a frightening ruthlessness.

Would James turn out to be of the same ilk?

Her agitation was just about to rocket into fully fledged panic when the dangerous light disappeared from his gaze and he was turning away from her to accept his best man's congratulations, leaving Ashleigh wondering if she was imagining things again.

Of course you are, her high degree of common sense argued, seemingly for the umpteenth time that day. James is a gentleman. A *gentle* man. Now you stop this non-sense this very second!

But it still crossed Ashleigh's mind as the celebrant led the wedding party up on to the dais for the signing of the marriage certificate that not once, so far this after-noon, had James smiled at her.

Now that wasn't like him at all!

While the adolescent James had been a shy, sensitive lad who didn't make friends all that easily, especially with girls, maturity had developed in him a more relaxed, easygoing personality which was quietly successful with women. In fact, there wasn't an attractive girl in Glen-brook who hadn't at some stage been dated by the very eligible and handsome James Hargraves.

He had, however, gained a reputation for being a bit fickle, never staying with one girl for too long. It had also been rumoured that he had a mistress stashed away somewhere, accounting for his many weekends spent away from the town, probably in Brisbane or the Gold Coast. Though Glenbrook was in New South Wales, it wasn't far across the Queensland border, and only a couple of hours' drive to that state's capital and the nearby tourist Mecca of Surfer's Paradise.

But the weekends away had lessened with the added responsibility that fell on James's shoulders after his father's death, and Ashleigh hadn't given James's sup-posed mistress—or his sex-life—a single worrying thought.

Till now. . .

Could he still be seeing this woman occasionally? Was that why he had almost meekly accepted her wish not to make love before their marriage?

Unsettling doubts besieged her, but she quickly

brushed them aside. Any reason James had for seeing another woman would no longer be valid after tonight. She would make sure of that! Meanwhile, she *did* need to have explained some of the things that had bothered her this afternoon. Peter's absence and James's hand, as well as his swinging moods.

'James,' she whispered as they sat down side by side at the special signing table. 'You must tell me what's going on.'

'Regarding what?' he said slowly, turning an annoyingly bland face her way.

'What happened to Peter, for one thing?' she went on agitatedly.

Now James smiled, a sardonic grimace that did nothing to ease Ashleigh's peace of mind. 'You might say Mr Reynolds and I didn't see eye to eye on a particular subject,' he muttered.

'You mean me, don't you?'

He nodded. 'I found it necessary to impress on him quite forcibly that it would be in his best interests to leave Glenbrook forthwith.'

Ashleigh's mouth fell open. 'Then you did. . .hit him?'

James's smile showed great satisfaction. 'Several times.'

'Oh, my goodness. . . Oh, James. . .I'm so sorry.'

'Don't be. I enjoyed it.'

'You. . .*enjoyed* it?'

James must have seen her shock, for his hand moved swiftly to cover hers, his eyes holding hers with the first real warmth and affection he'd bestowed on her since she'd arrived today. 'Forget Peter. He's not worth thinking about.'

She jumped when Kate touched her on the shoulder.

'You're supposed to be signing,' her friend said with a teasing laugh, 'not having an intimate little tête-à-tête. Keep that for later.'

James flashed Kate a smile that was more like his usual self, and Ashleigh let out a long-held breath.

'Whatever you say, Kate,' James agreed. 'Has Rhys explained about Peter's sudden attack of appendicitis?'

Ashleigh only just managed to stifle her astonished gasp at this cool delivery of the obviously prearranged excuse. Goodness, but James was constantly surprising her today. Who would have thought so many faces were hiding behind his usually bland façade?

'Yes. It was a real shame, wasn't it?' Kate returned with blithe indifference. Peter Reynolds was not one of her favourite people, either. 'You were lucky to have someone else to step in at the last minute who could fit into Peter's clothes.'

'You're so right. Well, let's get on with this.' And, picking up the pen, he started to sign.

Ashleigh stared down over his shoulder with a peculiar feeling of tension invading her chest. When she saw the words 'James John Hargraves' form in James's usual conservative hand an unmistakable wave of relief flowed through her, bringing a measure of exasperation. For heaven's sakes! What had she been expecting?

'Smile, Mrs Hargraves,' Nancy's hired photographer said, crouching down in front of the desk and snapping away. 'Now one while you're signing. . .'

Finally she was finished, and settled back in her chair to watch both Kate and this Rhys person sign, happy for her heartbeat to get back to normal.

It was impossible to mind Peter's not being one of their witnesses, as she was only then realising how much

she'd despised the man. Still, she couldn't imagine what
he'd said or done to turn James against him so vehe-
mently. They'd been such close friends for so long. But,
whatever it was, she sure as heck hoped James had
smacked him one right on his supercilious moosh.

Yes, now that she'd had time to mull it over, she
wasn't at all upset by this turn of events.

The substitute witness finished signing, startling her
with a surprisingly warm smile as he turned to step away
from the desk. She got the oddest feeling he knew a
darned sight more about her than she did about him.
When the celebrant also stepped up to put his name
to the official documentation of her marriage Ashleigh
glanced down at the best man's signature. Rhys
Stevenson. . .

A jab of recognition tickled her brain. The name was
familiar. But why? She glanced over her shoulder to
where he was standing, talking very amiably to Kate.
No, she didn't recognise him at all, yet the name still
rang a vague bell.

'I'm sorry I have to dash away,' the celebrant was
saying, a widely apologetic smile on his face. 'But I have
another engagement this evening and you were—er—a
little late getting here. My hearty congratulations, and I
hope everything turns out very well. Might I say you
both did splendidly? No one would have guessed that—'

'All finished here?' Rhys interrupted, leaving Ashleigh
wondering what it was no one would have guessed. 'You
have to go now, don't you, Mr Johnson?' he directed at
the celebrant. 'You did a great job. A really great job.'
He pumped the man's hand then pressed an envelope
into it, which no doubt contained the prearranged fee.

A big one, judging by Mr Johnson's huge grin as he departed.

A triumphant wedding march suddenly burst forth from the nearby speakers.

'Shall we go, darling?' James said, getting to his feet. Smiling, he picked her bouquet up from where it was lying on the table and handed it towards her.

Ashleigh took it with a trembling hand, his calling her darling leaving her unexpectedly breathless. It was not an endearment James had ever used with her before, but, goodness, the word had sent a ripple of sexual response quivering down her spine.

And what's wrong with that? came the voice of logic. He's your husband now. And, after tonight, your lover. . .

With a little shiver she hooked her arm through his offered elbow and allowed herself to be propelled down the dais steps and along the red strip of carpet to the clapping and congratulations of the guests.

Ashleigh would have liked to dive straight into the waiting Fairlane, but she was obliged to go through the motions of posing for photographs in various locations around the park, all the while hotly aware of her new husband beside her, of his hand taking her hand, of his arms encircling her waist, his eyes on hers every now and then.

Yet every time she felt her pulse-rate leap it was accompanied by the most peculiar stab of dismay. For with this new and unexpected desire for James she was irrevocably and finally abandoning what she'd once felt for Jake. For how could she pretend to herself that she still treasured her teenage love while she yearned for his brother's body?

She couldn't, she finally accepted. This would be the

end of Jake. The real end. Once she physically surrendered herself to James, there would be no going back,
even in her mind.

The thought depressed, then confused her. But
then. . .a lot of things had confused her today. Maybe
that was the prerogative of nervous brides.

But she gave voice to one of her minor confusions as
soon as they were semi-alone in the back of the hire-car
and on the way to James's house for the reception. 'Who
is this man Rhys Stevenson? I have the strangest feeling
I should know him.'

'He's an up-and-coming Australian film director.
You've probably seen his name on the screen, or on
television, and absorbed it subconsciously.'

'But how did you meet him and what was he doing
at our wedding?' she persisted, not entirely satisfied.
'Don't tell me he was invited, because I saw the list of
guests and he wasn't on it.'

'I asked him personally, only a couple of days ago.
Lucky I did, as it turned out,' he finished drily.

'Well, yes, but—'

'Are you going to talk about Rhys all the way to the
house?' James interrupted, startling her by disposing of
her bouquet on to the floor then sliding an arm around
her waist and pulling her close. 'I'd much rather tell you
that you're the most stunningly beautiful woman God
ever put breath into,' he rasped, 'and then do this.'

There was nothing cold and lifeless about his kiss this
time. Far from it. . .

Ashleigh found it difficult, however, to forget the
chauffeur behind the wheel, who was possibly watching
then in the rear-view mirror. She squirmed under the

hot possession of her husband's mouth and hands, an embarrassed heat flushing her cheeks.

Squirming, however, was not the best activity for a woman in the close embrace of a man she'd been becoming more sexually aware of all day. Her chest rubbed against his dinner-suit jacket, a button scraping harshly over one already hardening nipple.

Her lips fell open in a silent gasp, and immediately James's probing tongue found its mark, filling her mouth with a hungry thrust that sent the blood whirling in her head. Dazed, she clung to the lapels of his dinner-jacket, and all thoughts of chauffeurs vanished. There was only that ravenous mouth crushed to hers, and its insatiable tongue, feeding on the sweetness it found behind her own panting lips.

When James finally abandoned her mouth it was to kiss her neck, to mutter unintelligible words against her flushing skin. Ashleigh's head tipped back in a raw response, her whole body drowning in a flood of warmth and heat. The drum-beat of desire began pounding in her heart, and her head, making her oblivious to her surroundings, making her a willing victim to her husband's passion. Already James's mouth was back on hers, taking her down deeper and deeper into maelstrom of need and yearning.

'Damn it,' he rasped when the car turned the corner that led up the hill to his home. 'We won't be staying at this reception late,' he growled. 'I've already waited too long for this night. Far too long.'

Ashleigh shivered at the darkly intense resolve in James's voice and face. But it was a shiver of excitement, not fear. She wanted him as much as, if not more than, she'd ever wanted Jake. Such a realisation ripped through all her preconceived ideas on what she felt for the two brothers. Before it had been love and desire for one. Liking and respect for the other. Now Ashleigh was forced to accept this wasn't so any longer. She had *never* felt this kind of desire before without love. That was why no man had ever reached her since Jake, simply because she'd never loved any of them.

She lifted a trembling hand to James's face and held it there, tears swimming in her eyes. 'I love you, James,' she whispered. 'I really, really love you.'

His head jerked back and he stared at her. For a second Ashleigh was taken aback, unsure if the frozen mask on his face meant he was appalled, or merely deeply sceptical. With a sigh of understanding she realised it had to be the latter.

'I know I said I didn't love you when I agreed to marry you,' she rushed on in a low whisper as the car pulled into the long driveway that led up to the Hargraveses' house. 'To be brutally honest, I thought that, underneath, I was still in love with Jake.'

She felt the muscles in his jaw flinch, though his eyes didn't waver.

'There's been no one else, you see, and I always believed. . .' Her hand trembled against his skin. 'But, when you kissed me just now and I responded the way I did, I knew it had to be true love.'

There was no doubting the relief that zoomed into those blue eyes, or the emotion behind the husky, 'I knew it. I *knew* it!'

And he kissed her again, deeply and hungrily.

He only released her when the car pulled up at the house. 'Just as well,' she murmured with an embarrassed laugh. 'If we keep this up I'll get your cold.'

'My. . .cold?' His puzzlement was only momentary. 'Oh, you mean my raspy voice. Don't concern yourself, my darling. It's not a cold. Let's say I—er—did a fair bit of shouting last night and it affected my vocal chords. Now, take that frown off your lovely face and don't let that bastard Reynolds spoil things for us.'

Ashleigh blinked her amazement. That bastard Reynolds? Astonishing. Only last week James had been telling her what a wonderful friend Peter had always been and how grateful he had been for his help with the financial side of the company since his father's death.

She might have liked to take the discussion further— such as exactly what Peter had said to cause the blow-up between them—but the chauffeur's opening the back door for her to get out put paid to that. Putting her hand in the chauffeur's, and a blush of lingering embarrassment on her face, she alighted at the base of the wide steps, glancing up at the house where she would have to live for a while till she and James found something suitable around Glenbrook in which to set up their own home. Perhaps something with enough room for her to have a small attached practice, she thought, since Nancy would hardly let her turn any of the Hargraveses' home into a surgery.

Two-storeyed and in a Cape Cod design, the house had a setting suited to the family's status in Glenbrook, grandly overlooking the town from the crest of a hill. Tall English trees stood in elegant clumps of shade over the surrounding lawns, upon which a large marquee had been erected for the reception.

The guests had not yet arrived, but soon the nearby area would be full of parked cars. Even the photographer hadn't made it yet, having stayed behind to snap some more pictures of the bridesmaids and guests.

All of a sudden Ashleigh recalled what James had said to her in the car, about how they would leave the reception early. She turned to watch him stride around the white Fairlane to join her, a splendid male figure in his tuxedo, his well-tailored clothes highlighting his wide-shouldered, lean-hipped frame.

He caught her staring at him, and an amazingly confident smile caressed his mouth. It jolted her. For there had only ever been one male who'd been so sexually sure of himself with her. Only one. . .

'Jake,' she whispered on a breathless note, and her fingers fluttered up to the locket.

But the man beside her wasn't Jake. It was his brother, his brother who had finally taken Jake's place in every possible way. . .

James had stiffened at her uttering his brother's name. He stared down at her, then at the locket, the muscles twitching in his strong jaw. Ashleigh stopped breathing, certain now that he suspected the locket had something to do with Jake. Which was why he had stared at it earlier on.

She opened her mouth to try to explain why she'd chosen to wear the thing today, but he cut her off.

'Do not speak that name again,' he rasped, 'or I won't be responsible for what happens.'

He drew in then expelled a ragged breath.

'Now,' he went on sternly, 'go inside and replace your lipstick. The others will be here soon and it wouldn't do for everyone to think I'd been ravaging you already. My mother, particularly, might find that thought. . .unnerving. She isn't quite herself today, as I'm sure you've already realised.'

It was at that precise moment that Ashleigh realised James knew not only about the locket, but Jake's letter as well.

CHAPTER FOUR

'YOU know, don't you?' Ashleigh confronted James. 'About Jake's writing to your mother, about his sending me back this locket?'

James's blue eyes grew watchful beneath a dark frown. 'I am acquainted with my mother's visit to you before the wedding,' he admitted slowly.

'Good God!' Ashleigh gasped. 'Why did she have to tell you? What point was there?' She shook her head in agitation. 'I suppose you think I wore this damned thing because I was still pining for Jake. I wasn't. I wore it in defiance of his rotten arrogance and lack of tact in wanting me to have it on the very day I was marrying his brother!'

'I see,' James said somewhat drily. 'To be honest, I would not have thought of that reason.'

'It's the truth.'

'I don't doubt you.'

'You did believe me when I said I loved you, didn't you, James?'

There was no mistaking the flash of painful irony in his eyes. 'I think you might be a touch confused, my dear, in these unusual circumstances. But I'm a patient man. I know I can win your love, even if it takes me the rest of my life.'

Ashleigh was distressed at the bleak intensity behind his words.

'Leave me now, Ashleigh,' he went on brusquely.

'There are cars coming up the hill. I'll stay out here and greet the guests and organise things for the photographs while you fix your face. Someone will be up shortly to collect you.'

Ashleigh didn't want to leave him. She wanted to go on explaining, reassuring. Oh, how she'd hated seeing the hurt in his face, hated feeling the withdrawal in his manner towards her. But she could hardly stand there arguing with him in front of other people, especially with smudged make-up. Reluctantly she turned and made her way up the front steps and in through the open double doors, holding her skirt up as she made her way slowly up to the bedrooms Nancy had set aside for her as a changing-room.

The door was already open and Ashleigh walked in, her mind still on James and the unhappy thought that he didn't believe she really loved him. But she did. She was sure of it! How could she convince him?

Tonight, she decided breathlessly. Tonight she would leave him in no doubt that she both loved and wanted him as she had wanted no other man, not even Jake.

Damn Jake, she thought angrily. Damn him to hell!

With an abrupt movement her hand swept up under her veil and behind her neck, where she fumbled to unclasp the now hated locket. It stubbornly refused to yield, and in the end she reefed it from her neck with a savage yank, the locket spilling on to the parquet floor and sliding under the double bed.

And that was where she left it, tossing the silver chain on to a chest of drawers.

'Something borrowed,' she scorned out loud. 'Something *buried* would be more like it!'

Ashleigh counted to ten till her breathing was back to

normal, then quite deliberately turned her back on the chain and gazed with satisfaction at her going-away outfit, all laid out ready for her on the double bed, complete with shoes and handbag.

It was an elegantly simple suit in emerald-green silk, which hugged her tall, shapely figure and proclaimed to the world that she was all woman. James would like it, she was sure. And in the packed suitcase of clothes already in the boot of James's Jaguar, awaiting their honeymoon, was an ivory satin négligé set that would make any man sit up and take notice, let alone the man who already loved her.

Picking up the black leather handbag, she carried it over to the corner dressing-table, where she opened it and drew out the make-up she'd put in there. First she touched up her foundation, then replenished her blusher and lipstick. She was just applying some perfume when Kate knocked on the open door and breezed in.

'There you are, Ashleigh. James sent me to get you. Hmmm, perhaps I could do with some more lipstick too. May I?'

'Be my guest.'

'The photographer wants to take a few shots in the garden,' Kate explained as she applied the deep pink shade to her wide mouth. 'He spied that clump of rhododendrons and thinks they'll make a splendid backdrop. There. . .all done. . .' She looked at herself critically in the mirror, then shrugged. 'Oh, well, we can't all be gorgeous. Come, oh, beautiful bride,' she said, and linked arms with her friend's. 'Your panting groom awaits!'

Laughing, the two friends made their way down the sweeping staircase and out into the mild autumn air, Ashleigh immediately expressing her gratitude that all the guests seemed to have disappeared into the marquee, and weren't waiting to besiege her on the front lawn.

'You have James to thank for that,' Kate informed her. 'I also heard him sneakily instructing the drink waiters to ply everyone with as much liquor as they could handle to keep them out of our way while the official photographs were being finished. By the time we make our grand entrance they'll be high as kites on sherry and a quite lethal fruit punch. I know: I sampled it.'

'I could do with a shot of something lethal myself,' Ashleigh said drily. Kate's ebullience hadn't totally distracted her from how she had left James a little earlier. Neither could she forget that in a couple of hours she would be driving off on her honeymoon with a husband who didn't really believe his bride loved him.

'I could do with sitting down as well,' she continued with a sigh. 'I didn't exactly have a chance to break in these shoes before today, and they're killing me.'

'Ditto repeato,' Kate groaned expressively.

Both girls looked at each other and laughed again.

'Just as well we didn't decide to become models, eh, Kate?'

Kate made a face. 'Well, I didn't have much option on that count, being five feet two and having a face that *didn't* launch a thousand ships.'

'You have a *great* face,' Ashleigh insisted, stopping to look at her friend. And she did, all her big, bold features combining well to present an arresting, vivacious image.

Kate beamed with pleasure at the compliment. 'You are so good for my self-esteem, do you know that?'

'Will you two giggling Gerties mind shaking a leg?' James called over from where the rest of the bridal group were waiting impatiently beside the pink rhododendrons. 'We're all dying of dehydration and hunger here.'

Ashleigh was astonished and relieved to see that James was actually smiling at her. Gone was his earlier scowl, his look of pained anguish. He was a totally different man, confident and positive in his manner. She heaved a happy sigh. Everything was going to be all right after all.

Walking quickly over, she slipped a loving arm through his, smiling up into his face. Clearly her gesture startled him, for he stared back down at her for a second before expelling an exasperated though good-natured sigh.

'Right,' the photographer announced. 'Everyone facing front and smiling.'

'Wait!' Kate shouted, making everyone jump. She rushed over and started straightening Ashleigh's veil where it had caught slightly on some beading on her shoulder. Suddenly she stopped and frowned down at Ashleigh's bare neckline. 'What happened to the locket?' she asked.

Ashleigh groaned silently. Trust Kate to notice and comment. She opened her mouth to voice an excuse, but nothing came to mind, and she was left looking like a flapping flounder.

'It broke,' James said coolly from beside her. 'In the car.'

'Oh, what a pity!'

'Not to worry, Kate,' Ashleigh inserted swiftly, having regathered her wits. 'I still have your garter, which was borrowed as well as blue.'

'A garter?' The new best man perked up. 'How quaint. Can I see it?'

'Certainly not while it's on,' James intervened firmly.

Rhys laughed. 'How possessive you are! But rightly so. Your bride is as lovely as you described to me. I fully understand you now, dear friend. Some things are worth any sacrifice.'

Flattered and flustered, Ashleigh lifted startled eyes to her husband, catching the end of a harsh glare thrown his best man's way.

'Do you think we could get on with this, folks?' the photographer sighed.

The session seemed interminable, as was having to keep on smiling. By the time it drew to an end Ashleigh's mouth was aching. She was also harbouring the beginnings of a headache.

'Something wrong, darling?' James murmured from her side when she put a hand to her temple.

'Only a very small headache,' she smiled softly, thinking that she did so like his calling her that.

'I'll get you something for it. Kate! Take Ashleigh over to that garden seat there while I rustle up some aspirin. Or do you need something stronger?' he directed back at his bride.

'Well. . .panadol is kinder to the stomach.'

His mouth curved into a wry smile. 'Of course. Doctor knows best.'

She flinched, knowing how men didn't like to be corrected, or told things by a woman. She could never tell her father or brother anything—even about medicine— without earning a reproachful glare or a sarcastic remark. 'Sorry,' she murmured.

'Don't be. I'm proud of your being a doctor. Kate? The seat, please. Be back shortly.' And, flashing them a parting smile, he strode off.

'I didn't realise James could be so masterful,' Kate

remarked as she led Ashleigh in the direction of the shaded seat. 'It's very attractive on him, isn't it? I mean, being nice is all very well, but a man shouldn't be too, *too* nice. If he is people walk all over him, including his wife, and then he might lose her respect, don't you agree?'

Ashleigh did.

'Rhys is a very interesting man too,' Kate raved on. 'I could talk to him all day. The places he's been and the people he's met! Fantastic!'

'Don't tell me you've finally met a man you didn't want to put solidly in his place,' Ashleigh said, amazement in her voice.

'I can't imagine anyone putting Rhys Stevenson in his place.'

'Kate! I do believe you're smitten.'

'Not at all. Just jealous.'

'Of what?'

'Of his lifestyle.'

'Well, we can't all be movie directors!'

'Why not, if that's what we'd like to be?' she said quite aggressively.

Ashleigh stopped and stared at her friend.

'Now don't go giving me one of those looks of yours,' Kate huffed.

'What looks?'

'Oh, your "one must keep one's feet firmly on the ground" looks. Life is meant to be lived, Ashleigh. And I'm not so sure I want to live the rest of mine in good old Glenbrook! Oh, forget it,' she grumbled. 'You wouldn't understand. Not only do you have a rewarding career, but you've just married a great bloke whom it's quite

clear you're mad about—and who's mad about you—
so what would you know about frustration?'

Suddenly she smiled, a sort of brave, sad smile that
caught at Ashleigh's heart. She hadn't realised her dear
friend was so unhappy. One would never have guessed.
She so wished there was something she could do.

'Just listen to me,' Kate laughed, but it had a brittle
edge to it. 'As if this is the right moment to be pouring
out all my worries and woes. Now come along and sit
down before I get into trouble for not doing as his lord
and master commanded. Heavens, if I didn't know different I might have thought it was Jake telling me what to
do. Remember how he used to boss us around at school?'

'Yes, Kate,' Ashleigh said stiffly. 'I haven't forgotten.
But I'm *trying* to.'

'Oh. . .oh, sorry, love. God, me and my big mouth. Is
your headache very bad? I guess I haven't made it any
better by my whingeing then bringing up ancient history.
Truly, Ashleigh, I'm a real clot. Forgive me?'

Ashleigh patted her friend's hand. 'Of course, but I
would rather you not talk about Jake, especially in front
of James. It's rather a sore point between us, I'm afraid.'

'I won't, believe me. The James I'm seeing today
might just bite my head off. Aah. . .here he is now. . .'

'Nurse Hargraves to the rescue,' he said mockingly,
and pressed the glass of iced water he was carrying into
her free hand. 'Now. . .give me that infernal bouquet and
hold out your other hand,' he commanded.

She did, and he dropped two white tablets into
her palm.

'Swallow them up straight away. I know you medical
people. Great at dosing others but rotten at taking things
yourself. Gone? Good. Look, I'm sorry, but we'll have

to make an appearance in the marquee. Mother is making unhappy noises.'

Ashleigh was surprised to find she quite enjoyed the feeling of being cosseted, not having had that experience since her mother died. Leaving the empty glass behind on the garden seat, she allowed James to walk herself and Kate over to the marquee, a lovely, warm sensation spreading in the pit of her stomach at having his solicitous arm around her waist.

If this was what being married to James was going to be like then she was all for it. Being married to *her* seemed to be good for him too. As Kate had rightly observed, James wasn't usually so quick to take control of situations, to taking the role of leader. Yes, he certainly was coming out from under the shadow of his brother and being his own man. And suddenly Ashleigh no longer minded.

'Oh-oh,' James whispered in her ear. 'Brace yourself. Here come the aunts and uncles and various assorted cousins to tell you how beautiful you are and how lucky I am. You'll have to kiss the men too. Convention, you know. And we must uphold all the social conventions,' he added quite testily. 'Mother would have a seizure if we didn't!'

It wasn't till they'd finally taken their adjoining seats at the main bridal table under the huge tent that a puzzling thought struck Ashleigh. James never called his mother 'Mother'. He always called her Nancy. Neither was he in the habit of using that caustic, almost cutting tone when speaking about her foibles.

A deep frown settled on to her high, wide forehead as she tried to fathom out why she was so bothered by that, since the reason for it was clear enough. Mother and son had clearly had an argument that morning about Jake's letter—hence Nancy's agitation and tears—and James was taking his anger out on her by being disdainful and aloof.

Yet it *did* bother her. Quite considerably. Perhaps because she wanted her wedding-day to be a really happy occasion.

'James,' she whispered, and he leant her way, pressing his whole side against hers.

A shivery charge zoomed through her body. 'Please don't be cross with your mother,' she said thickly.

The muscles along his arm stiffened. 'What makes you think I'm cross with her?'

'You don't usually call her "Mother" like that, for one thing. And you were. . .well, you were sarcastic when talking about her. That's not like you.'

'I see,' he murmured thoughtfully. 'And what would you like me to do about it?'

'Go and talk to her and make up. She looks so unhappy.' Which the woman did, not a smile having passing Nancy's thinnish lips all day.

'Mmmm. . .well, we can't have that, can we?' he muttered in a voice that didn't sound as conciliatory as Ashleigh might have hoped.

He got to his feet and strode off in the direction of his mother, leaving Ashleigh feeling oddly perturbed.

'God, it *is* good to be sitting down,' Kate pronounced from her right-hand side. 'Where's James off to?'

'Has to see his mother about something,' came her suitably vague answer.

'I have to give Mrs Hargraves credit where credit it due,' Kate said. 'This is all top-drawer stuff. Genuine lace tablecloths, real silver cutlery, candelabras, the finest crystal glasses. We might be out under a circus tent—if you can recognise canvas through the decorations—but it could well be a king's banquet table, judging by the accoutrements.'

Ashleigh agreed that Nancy had pulled out all stops in making sure that her son's wedding had no equal in the history of Glenbrook. Right at this moment two hundred happy, suitably intoxicated guests were busy finding their silver-embossed place-names at one of the twenty lace-covered tables, while a small orchestra played subtle wedding music and silver, white and burgundy streamers and balloons fluttered over their heads. A four-tier wedding cake stood proudly on its own table to one side, patiently awaiting its part in the celebration that was about to start. The caterers were hovering, clearly wanting to serve the first course of the meal.

Ashleigh was still glancing around when her eyes landed on James talking to his mother in a far corner. They were too far away for her to see the expressions in their eyes, but their body language reeked of a barely controlled anger, Nancy making sharp movements with her head and hands while she spoke. James's fists were balled at his side, his broad shoulders held stiffly while he stood silently and listened. Suddenly James launched into speech, and Nancy's head rocked back, as though his words were like a physical blow. She stared back at him while he raved on, her face frozen.

At last he finished speaking and they simply stood there, eyeing each other, both still obviously livid, each one seemingly waiting for the other to break first.

It wasn't James.

Quite abruptly Nancy leant forward and kissed her son on the cheek, after which she plastered a smile on her face and went about her hostess duties with the sort of serenely smiling look on her face one might have expected from Nancy, but which had been absent all afternoon.

The whole incident rattled Ashleigh, especially with James making his way swiftly across the room towards her with a black look still on his face. What on earth was going on with those two? She could understand that initially James wasn't pleased with his mother's having taken a returned gift from his brother to his bride on her wedding-day, especially when that same bride had once been besotted with that brother.

But surely, with her having discarded the locket, James could see that Jake was not going to be a threat to their relationship? Why couldn't he forgive and forget? But no, she thought irritably, he was a typical male, whose anger was not allowed to be so quickly discarded.

Ashleigh was initially astonished when, just as suddenly as his mother, James appeared to pull himself together and adopt a more pleasant expression. Yet as he drew closer there was no mistaking the hard glint remaining in his eyes, or the tension in his stiffly held arms and shoulders. Though, once he became aware of Ashleigh's reproachful eyes upon him, he shrugged and smiled.

'I'm afraid she's still not pleased with me,' he confessed on sitting down beside her, 'but she's agreed to play her part a bit more convincingly.'

'Play her part?' Ashleigh repeated, frowning. 'Isn't that an odd way of putting it? Your mother *loves* you, James. She wouldn't want there to be bad feeling between you. She—'

'For God's sake, don't start worrying about *her*,' he suddenly snapped. 'She'll survive.'

Ashleigh fell silent, truly shocked by his manner.

'Hell,' he muttered. 'This is even harder than I thought it'd be.'

Ashleigh stared at him. 'What. . .what do you mean?' she asked, totally perplexed.

He turned to lock eyes with her, his gaze penetrating and deep. 'Do you trust me, Ashleigh?' he rasped, his voice low and husky.

A dark, quivery sensation fluttered in her stomach.

'Of. . .of course. . .'

'Then don't give my mother's attitude a second thought. Take no notice of anything she says or does. Believe me when I say she isn't concerned for *your* happiness. *Or* mine. That's all you have to remember.'

'But. . .but. . .that doesn't make any sense.' Which it didn't. Nancy *adored* James. He'd always been the apple of her eye.

'I know. That's why I asked for your trust. Do I have it?' he demanded to know.

'I. . .'

'Do I have it?' he repeated in an urgent tone.

Ashleigh's heart started to pound and she knew that, with her answer, her fate would be sealed, irrevocably. Her mind flew to what she'd told Kate earlier that day, about not believing in destiny or one's fate being outside a person's own control. She still believed that. Her husband, in asking her for blind trust, was really testing her love for him, as well as her faith in the person he was.

There was really only one answer she could give.

'Yes,' she said firmly.

'Then just do as I ask,' came James's harsh answer.

Ashleigh was to remember later that night that she had deliberately chosen to place her future in this man's hands. So she had nobody else to blame but herself.

CHAPTER FIVE

'FANCY Kate catching my bouquet,' Ashleigh laughed as James drove down the hill away from the Hargraves home. 'You know what else? I think she and your friend, Rhys, really hit it off. They were chatting away together all evening.'

'I wouldn't be getting my hopes up about Kate and Rhys if I were you,' James returned drily. 'He's an incorrigible chatter-upper of women.'

'Oh?' Ashleigh frowned, a tinge of worry in her voice.

'And I wouldn't worry about your Kate either. If ever there was a female who can take care of herself it's that one!'

'I suppose so. . .'

'You don't sound convinced.'

'Kate's rather vulnerable at the moment.'

'Aren't we all?' he muttered. 'Aren't we all?'

A strained silence fell between them at this darkly cryptic remark, with James putting his foot down more solidly. The powerful car hurtled into the night, eating up the miles between Glenbrook and their destination.

Ashleigh found herself with time to ponder the not so subtle difference in James today. He was far moodier than his usual easygoing self, far more uptight. Originally she'd put it down to wedding-day jitters, plus irritation at Jake's last-minute correspondence, not to mention his doubts over his bride's really loving him or not.

But now that the reception was over and they were

off on their honeymoon Ashleigh began to wonder if there was a far more basic reason. Perhaps he was worried about tonight, about how sex between them would turn out. Was he concerned, perhaps, that she would compare his lovemaking with Jake's? And, more to the point. . .would *she*?

She honestly didn't know. All day her sexual response to James had surprised and pleased her. But it was one thing to feel a few heart flutters, quite another to experience the sort of abandon during total intimacy that she had experienced with Jake.

Not that it would overly concern *her* if they didn't achieve sexual perfection straight away. Ashleigh was a realist. She knew these things could take time. They had, even with Jake! But she had the awful feeling James would be cut to the quick if he didn't satisfy her tonight, if he thought for a moment he had failed her in bed.

Thinking about his possible disappointment and unhappiness began twisting her insides into knots. Before she could stop it a quavering sigh escaped her lips.

Hard blue eyes snapped her way. 'What's that sigh supposed to mean?' he asked in a definitely suspicious tone.

'Nothing. I. . .' Suddenly she sat up straight and blinked rapidly. 'James! What. . .what are you doing?' she gasped.

What he was doing was obvious! He was turning into a motel, a rather cheap-looking highway motel into which they were definitely *not* booked. They were supposed to be on their way to a five-star luxury hotel on the Gold Coast.

'I'm afraid this won't wait, Ashleigh,' he ground out. Ashleigh turned to stare with wide eyes at the man sitting beside her. How determined he sounded. How. . .*forceful*.

She swallowed, her mind filling with all those moments today when she'd glimpsed a James she had never seen before, a James simmering with unleashed passion. Clearly he couldn't bear to wait any longer to make love to her. She found his impatience to have her in his arms both flattering and arousing, her pulse-rate accelerating into overdrive, an excited heat flushing her cheeks.

'This isn't like you, James,' she laughed softly as he braked to an abrupt halt in front of the motel office.

His sidewards glance was sardonic. 'I realise that, believe me. Wait here,' he ordered brusquely, and climbed out from behind the wheel. 'I won't be long.'

She watched James stride purposefully into the office to book in, thinking to herself that he had a very attractive walk. Funny, she had never thought that about James before. But as he came back through the door, key in hand, her eyes were drawn to his very male and undeniably impressive body, lingering on the breadth of his shoulders before slowly working her way downwards. She didn't have to wonder what he would look like naked. Mother nature had assured that, as an identical twin, he would have the same well-shaped, muscular, virile body as Jake.

A quivering started deep in her stomach and she knew beyond a doubt that nothing was going to go wrong between them. It was going to be right. *Very* right. *Exquisitely* right. Suddenly she was as anxious as he was to be in bed together, to have the right to touch his hard naked flesh at will, to lie back and accept his body into hers as many times as it would take to assuage her rapidly soaring desire.

She smiled at him when he climbed in behind the wheel, her smile the smile of a siren. It stopped him in his tracks, his eyes glittering blue pools as they locked with hers. 'You shouldn't look at me like that,' he rasped.

'Why not?' she said thickly. 'You're my husband, aren't you? I love you and want you. I'm not ashamed of that.'

His groan startled her, as did his hands, reaching out to pull her towards him, his mouth covering hers with a raw moan of passion. His kiss only lasted a few seconds, but those few seconds burnt an indelible fact in Ashleigh's brain.

This was the man she loved and wanted. Not Jake. James.

They were both gasping when he tore his mouth away, both astonished at what had transpired between them. But somehow James did not seem as happy about it as Ashleigh was. Why that was so she couldn't work out.

He muttered something unintelligible, then whirled away to restart the engine and drive the car round to the motel units behind the main building, parking in front of door number eight. Getting out straight away, he walked briskly around to open the passenger door and help her out.

Ashleigh was slightly disconcerted when his eyes refused to meet hers, also at the way he once again turned away from her quite sharply to insert the key in the door. Pushing it open, he waved her inside.

'But what about our luggage?' she asked, staying where she was.

He went to say something, but just then another car

made its way around the back. Shrugging, he went over, opened the boot and brought the two suitcases inside, Ashleigh trailing behind with a frown on her face but a defiant resolve in her heart. As keen as she was for James to make love to her, she was not about to abandon her whole dream of a truly romantic wedding-night.

'I won't be a moment,' she said, snatching up her suitcase and disappearing into the adjoining bathroom. As she closed the door she had a fleeing glimpse of James, standing open-mouthed and exasperated beside the bed.

She was more than a moment. She was a good fifteen minutes, having a shower, powdering and perfuming her body, taking down and brushing out her shoulder-length blonde waves, then finally slipping on the ivory satin full-length nightie.

'Goodness,' she murmured to herself in the *en suite* bathroom's vanity mirror. It hadn't looked quite *this* sexy in the lingerie shop. But then she hadn't had her hair down that day, and neither had her breasts strained against the moulded bodice with nipples like hard round pebbles jutting suggestively through the satin.

Drawing the matching lace and satin robe up her long arms and over her slender shoulders didn't make the underlying nightwear any less sensuous. If anything, half covering up her full-breasted figure made the revealing garment underneath even more tantalising. She was sure that, when she walked, the overlay would flap teasingly open while the satin nightie underneath would cling to her naked stomach and thighs.

Just thinking about how James would look at her in this rig-out had Ashleigh's heart slamming madly against her ribs. But she *wanted* to send him wild with need and desire, wanted him to think of nothing but fusing his body with hers, of thrusting his hardness deep inside her already moistening flesh, of giving himself up to the pleasure she could give him.

She didn't want him to think of Jake.

He was pacing up and down across the room when she emerged, having removed nothing but his jacket and tie. He ground to a halt at the sound of the door opening, his head snapping round to glare at her. But the second his eyes raked over her provocatively clad figure his expression changed, from a black frustration to a smoulderingly stirring desire.

Hot blue eyes started on her face and hair then travelled slowly downwards, Ashleigh's skin breaking out in goose-bumps when she saw his eyes narrow on her already aching breasts.

Quite abruptly his eyes snapped back up, shocking her with the anguish in their depths.

'You don't understand, Ashleigh,' he growled, shaking his head. 'The reason I stopped here. . . It. . .'

She began undulating towards him, and any further words died in his throat. As she approached she lifted trembling hands to peel the outer robe back from her swollen breasts, letting it slip off her shoulders and flutter to the floor behind her. She kept moving, breathless but confident in her femininity, knowing that with each sinuous movement of her limbs she was ensnaring him in her web of seduction, inflaming his male need to a level that would brook no more hesitation, only action.

She drew right up to him, her lips softly parted, her head tipping back slightly as she wound her arms up around his neck. 'I don't want any explanations,' she husked, her mouth so close to his that she could feel his breath on her lips. 'I just want *you*. Right here and right now. . .'

Her fingers splayed up into his thick black hair as she leant into him, her breasts pressing flat against the hard wall of his chest.

Once again James surprised her, standing where he was without attempting to touch her back, frozen within a dangerously explosive tension. She could feel it in the corded muscles straining in his neck, in the way his breathing was silent and still. 'You think you know what you're doing, Ashleigh,' he muttered low in his throat. 'But you don't.'

A dark shudder raced through him. 'Hell. . .I wish I had the strength to deny myself this. But I haven't. It's asking too damned much!'

And, with that, his arms swept up and around her, imprisoning her against him and bending her spine back till her hair spilt free from her neck and her mouth was an open, gasping cavern. His head bent to cover that cavern with hot, ravenous lips, to fill its dark, moist depths with his tongue, to stunningly imprint upon its owner that her mouth was there primarily for his possession, to be used as he willed, to be taken and abandoned only as he ordained.

Or so it seemed. For when she struggled against such an unexpected and confusing display of male mastery— her arms retreating from his neck to push vainly at the solid wall of his chest, her head trying to twist from side to side—one of his hands slid up into her hair, grasping the back of her head and holding it firmly captive. But soon she herself was caught up in her own pleasure, giving in to his physical domination with a throaty moan of surrender.

She shuddered when he finally left her mouth to trail rapid kisses down her throat, dazedly aware she should be appalled by his semi-violence, but conceding she wasn't at all. Instead she thrilled to the savage mouth that nipped and sucked at her flesh, working its way inexorably towards her breasts and their pointed, expectant peaks.

'James,' she groaned when she felt his hot breath hover over one of her aching nipples.

His head jerked up and she stared at him with glazed eyes. 'What's wrong?' she husked in bewilderment.

She could hardly think, her whole being in a world of its own, where it was responding instinctively, without thought, without reason.

'Nothing,' he growled.

'Then touch me,' she begged. 'Here. . .' And she brushed a shaking hand over the throbbing tip.

'Oh, God,' he moaned aloud, and bent his mouth to do her bidding, suckling the tender flesh right through the nightie, drawing the whole aureole into his mouth and rubbing the satin-covered nub over and over with his tongue.

Never had she felt such electric pleasure, such tempestuous excitement. Heat swept through her, making her blood race, her limbs grow heavy with desire. She closed her eyes and let the rapture spread, her lips parting, her arms falling limply to her side.

One of his broad hands had settled in the small of her back, the other on the flat of her stomach, moving in a sensual circular motion as his mouth continued to tantalise first one breast, then the other, both bare now, the nightie having somehow been pushed off her shoulders to crumple at her waist, held up perhaps by the hand caressing her stomach.

Ashleigh became hotly conscious of that hand as it moved lower and lower. . . Of their own accord her legs shifted slightly apart in silent invitation for a more intimate caress. James obliged, his hand sliding between her legs, forcing the satin inwards with him, rubbing the silken material over her arousal till she moaned in utter abandonment and need.

James moved to assuage that need, peeling the nightie down over her hips to pool at her feet while he sank to his knees in front of her, licking the soft flesh of her inner thighs, gradually easing them wider and wider apart till he could move his mouth with exquisite intimacy over her.

Ashleigh caught her breath, her hands shooting up to close over his shoulders lest she fall. For those knowing lips and tongue seemed to know exactly what to do to send her mad, moving hotly over the core of her need before returning again to her most sensitive spot. When her soft moans turned to whimpering little cries he pulled her down on to the carpet with him, kissing her mouth while he freed his desire with frenzied movements.

For several excruciating seconds his head was lifted to look down at her naked arousal, his eyes glittering with satisfaction as they roved over the stark evidence of her passion. For Ashleigh was wanton in her desire for his possession, her body restless and open for him, her womanhood moist and swollen.

With an almost tortured groan he knelt between her legs, and, scooping up her buttocks, impaled her with a single powerful thrust.

Ashleigh gasped, her back arching up from the floor,

her arms reaching out for him to come to her in a lover's embrace. He sank down upon her with a jagged moan, gathering her tight against him.

'Oh, my darling, my only love,' he rasped, then began surging into her with a powerful, passionate rhythm. She gasped at the speed with which she found herself on the brink, then moaned as she tumbled headlong into an ecstatic release, the fierceness of her contractions hurtling James into an equally explosive climax that left him shaking uncontrollably.

Ashleigh clasped his trembling body close to her, totally unmindful of the potent seed he'd just spilt deep inside her. She certainly wasn't thinking of how she'd deliberately chosen to have her wedding-day right at her most fertile time of the month so that she might conceive straight away. All she wanted at that moment was to keep her husband's body fused with hers, to wrap her arms and legs tight around him, to kiss his sweat-covered neck, to tell him how much she loved him.

His shirt had come loose from the waistband of his trousers during their torrid mating, and she slipped her hands up underneath with a contented sigh to rove across bare flesh. But, when her fingers encountered the strangest ridges and dips in the skin on his back, she froze. James did not have scars on *his* back. It was smooth and clear and hairless. At least, it *had* been a week ago when they had gone swimming in the pool at his home.

My God! Exactly what *had* happened last night? Had he been in some sort of accident?

'James,' she whispered, her voice shaking, her whole insides shaking. 'What have you done to your back?'

She felt him stiffen, felt his shuddering sigh.

'Nothing,' he muttered. 'It's the same back I've had for years.'

Slowly he withdrew from her, easing himself back to sit on his heels and adjust his clothes. 'You see, Leigh,' he went on, raking her pale face with bleak blue eyes, 'the fact is. . .I'm not James.'

CHAPTER SIX

ASHLEIGH came as close to fainting at that moment as she had ever done in her life. All the blood drained from her face and for a few black moments her world tilted on its axis.

But the crisis passed, and when it did her first reaction was a desperate denial.

'Don't be ridiculous! Of course you're James. I mean. . .what are you trying to say?' she laughed shakily, sitting up and snatching the satin nightie from the carpet near by and somehow dragging it over her nude body. 'That you're *Jake*? If this is your idea of a sick joke, James, then. . .'

His hands shot out to grab her upper arms, his blue eyes steely as he leant over her. '*I am* Jake. Look at me, Leigh. Really look at me. You know the difference. You've always known the difference. You didn't today because I was where you and everyone expected *James* to be, dressed in James's clothes, my hair cut exactly like James's, acting like James.'

He made a scoffing sound. 'Well. . .maybe not acting *entirely* like James. Believe me, Leigh, when I say you wouldn't want me acting like him tonight.'

'Stop calling me that,' she screamed at him. 'Stop saying you're Jake. You're not! You can't be! It's impossible! Besides, I. . .I *hate* Jake! I. . .'

Her high-pitched hysterical outburst was terminated abruptly and effectively by his right hand's covering her mouth and pushing her, none too gently, flat on her back on to the carpet.

'Shut up, for God's sake, or we'll have the motel manager knocking at our door. Look, I'm sorry for how things turned out here tonight. I was going to tell you the truth earlier but, God damn it, Leigh, you've only yourself to blame. You virtually seduced me. *Me. . .Jake. . .*not James. For, even if you didn't recognise me on a conscious level, your body did subconsciously. It recognised me and responded to me, right from the first moment it set eyes on me in that park. Tell yourself you hate me all you like, Leigh, but deep down you know you don't!'

Once again her face paled, her eyes widening with horror as the truth refused to be denied.

Jake hadn't sent a letter home. . . He'd come in person. . .

It had been Jake looking at her with such inflammatory desire during the ceremony. . . Jake who'd evoked that mad response when he'd kissed her in the car. . . Jake who'd just made devastatingly rapturous love to her. . .

She stared up at him, appalled.

His hand lifted from her mouth and he sat back on his heels. 'I see you've finally accepted the facts.'

Confusion and anguish sent her hand careering across his face, slapping it hard. 'You bastard!' she cried brokenly, and then she slapped him again. 'I thought you were James. I would never have let you touch me if I'd known it was you!' She began hitting out wildly with both hands, across his face, his shoulders, his chest.

He grabbed both her wrists and ground them slowly back down on the carpet above her head, both their chests heaving as he pressed down flat on top of her. 'Is that so?' he bit out, blue eyes flashing with a very male anger. 'Well, you know who I am *now*, don't you? I'm Jake. Not James. Let's see how you respond *this* time, shall we?'

'No, Jake, *don't*,' she choked out. But even as his mouth took possession of hers she was quivering with an instant and breathless excitement.

Afterwards she wept, totally shattered by the moans of ecstasy still echoing in her ears.

'Oh, Leigh, darling, don't cry,' he murmured softly, holding her naked body close to his now equally naked body.

She almost surrendered to this unexpected and disarming tenderness, almost let it wash away the bitter shame she was feeling.

But just in time she recalled what had just happened, how he had ruthlessly exploited his knowledge of her body and its sexual weaknesses, how, when she'd been at her most aroused, he'd coerced from her an erotic intimacy she'd once given freely.

'Let me go, you. . .you. . .bastard!'

She reefed out of his arms and, scrambling to her feet, dashed into the bathroom, slamming and locking the door behind her. The sight of her reflection in the vanity mirror almost made her sick. She couldn't help staring at her puffy red lips, at her still hard nipples, at the red marks his possessive hands had made all over her flesh.

Shivers ran up and down her spine as she hugged herself in disbelief. This wasn't happening to her, she thought dazedly. It was a nightmare, and very, very soon she was going to wake up.

'Leigh?' Jake called out through the door. 'Are you all right? Answer me, Leigh!'

Groaning, she dashed into the shower, snapping on the

water, unmindful that it was cold to begin with. She washed herself feverishly, trying to get every trace of him from her body. But she couldn't erase the memory of her ultimate surrender to what he wanted. Why, she agonised, had Jake always been able to command such total submission from her? Why?

And what of James? she worried. Where was he? What had Jake done to him last night to force him to let him take his place today?

Thinking about James's predicament had the effect of making Ashleigh pull herself together. For there was more than *her* well-being at stake here. Besides, she couldn't go back in time, couldn't wipe out what Jake had made her do. What she *could* do was find out exactly what had happened where James was concerned, then make decisions from there.

By the time Ashleigh emerged from the bathroom, her nakedness covered by a large towel, she looked fully composed. Her cold gaze swept over Jake where he was sitting quietly on the side of the bed, his trousers and shirt back on, though the shirt buttons were not done up. He looked up at her, a frighteningly hard glint in his eyes.

'Can we talk now?' he asked, getting slowly to his feet. '*Properly*?'

'By all means,' Ashleigh returned frostily. 'I'm more than eager to know how you managed to bring off this despicable charade. Just how many people were in on it, besides your sidekick Mr Stevenson?'

Jake's sigh carried exasperation. 'Look, Leigh, I—'

'Just give me the bare facts, please,' she snapped. 'Nothing else.'

His eyes narrowed. 'Very well. My mother was aware

of the situation. As, of course, was James and his best man.'

'*Nancy* knew?' Ashleigh gasped. 'And she. . .let you get away with it?'

A rather bitter smile creased Jake's mouth. 'Mother was only too glad to go along with my suggestions, once I pointed out the alternative.'

'I can't imagine what you could have said or done to force her to go along with such a preposterous and disgraceful idea!'

Ashleigh swayed on unsteady feet as she recalled Nancy's visit before the wedding ceremony, at how dreadfully upset the poor woman had been. Her heart went out to the lady, to what she'd felt then, to what she must be feeling now. How a son could put his mother through such an ordeal she had no idea.

She took a few ragged steps towards him, her face pained. 'How. . .how could you do such a thing, Jake?' she rasped. 'To your mother? To me? And *why*? You don't love me. You *never* really loved me!'

And then it came to her. His return had nothing to do with love, but possession. She'd once been his, body and soul, and, while he'd been able to stand her moving on to some unknown man, he hadn't been able to bear her marrying his brother, in James enjoying the fruits—so to speak—of what he had sown.

'Oh, my God,' she groaned. 'What have you done with James? You. . .you've really hurt him, haven't you?'

Jake's eyes grew scornful at her concern for his brother. 'James is fine. At this very moment he is on his way to Europe in the company of his best man.'

She gaped, totally thrown by why James would meekly go off and let Jake pretend to marry her in his stead. 'But *why* did he let you take his place? *Why?*' she groaned, and shook her head in agitation. 'This is all madness. I. . .I can't take it in. . .'

'Peter Reynolds is James's lover,' Jake stated flatly.

Ashleigh froze, her mouth dropping open, her head whirling with what Jake had just said.

'James was marrying you as a cover to ensure his social respectability,' he went on. '*And* to have the child he always wanted.'

Ashleigh staggered over to slump down on the side of the bed. She could not speak. She felt nothing but shock and sheer disbelief.

Jake walked over and sat down beside her, picking up her chilled, lifeless hands, covering and warming them with his own. 'I'm sorry to tell you such upsetting news so bluntly, but is there a nice way for news like that? The only comfort I can give you is that he loves you as much as he is capable of loving a woman. I suppose he thought he would be able to successfully consummate the marriage. He told me he kissed you a couple of times and had been aroused enough by them. To be honest, I don't think James is truly gay. He just met the wrong man at the wrong time in his life.'

Stricken, Ashleigh searched Jake's eyes, hoping to see that he was lying. But she could see he wasn't.

'The invitation to your wedding only reached me three days ago,' he explained. 'I was on a type of holiday in the hills, you see, and the letter went all around the giddy-goat in Thailand before reaching me. I've never been so shocked in all my life. Or more upset. I've sacrificed my love for you twice, Leigh, for what I imagined noble reasons. But I could not stand by and see you marry my brother. Surely you can understand that. . .?'

Ashleigh blinked. She wasn't understanding very much at the moment. Her mind was back on what Jake had just said.

'What. . .what do you mean, you sacrificed your love for me. . .twice. . .?'

But already a suspicion was forming in her mind that startled and dismayed her.

Those beautiful blue eyes clouded for a moment as though some dark memory had leapt from the past to inflict a special kind of torment.

'I wasn't guilty, Leigh,' he rasped. 'Either of trafficking or possessing drugs. The heroin was included in my luggage by a very clever ruse. I told you I was guilty so you would go away, so you would forget me, so you wouldn't waste your lovely young life pining for a man who was facing life imprisonment in a prison system that knew no such thing as parole or mercy. . .'

A wave of emotion swelled in Ashleigh's heart as she thought of Jake in that filthy prison, making such a noble, heart-rending sacrifice. 'Oh, Jake,' she cried in genuine pity.

'How was I to know that a twist of fate would eventually set me free?' he went on in a thickened voice. 'Or that when I rushed home, hopeful you might still love me, I would once again be waylaid through treachery?'

'*Treachery*?'

'Yes. My parents'. They didn't believe me when I told them I wasn't guilty, you see. They said I had blackened their name, shamed the family. They said I wasn't wanted around Glenbrook.' His laugh was cynical. 'I rather expected my mother to react that way. She'd always been more concerned over what other people thought and said than what her children felt. But Dad really disappointed me. He didn't want me around either. When I asked about you he told me you were engaged to a medical student and that if I cared about you at all I'd go right away and leave you alone.'

'But. . .but I *wasn't*!'

'I know that now, Leigh. At the time I was shattered. And torn. I didn't know what to do. One part of me couldn't believe you had forgotten me. I longed to see you, to take you in my arms, to force you to love me. But common sense and decency demanded that if you were going to marry another man I should stay away. But I needed someone else to look me in the face and tell me you didn't care about me any more, someone I could implicitly trust. I went to Brisbane to speak to James, to the address where I was told he was spending the weekend with a friend. Mr Reynolds, as it turned out. It didn't take me long to see which way the land lay there. Naturally, I was shocked, but I tried to be open-minded about it, for James's sake. When I asked him about you and he confirmed what Dad had told me it never occurred to me he could be lying.'

'But *why* did he lie? It's not as though we were having anything to do with each other back then.'

'He obviously wanted me to leave Glenbrook too, because I knew his secret. He was worried I would stay if I thought there was a chance for me with you.'

'Oh, Jake. . . Do you realise what I thought when I'd heard you'd come home and hadn't even come to see me? Do you have any idea how I felt?'

He drew her into his arms and held her there, her face pressed against his chest. 'I hope you were devastated,' he groaned. 'I hope you wanted to kill me!'

She wrenched away from him and stood up, grey eyes

wide with bewilderment. 'But why would you want that?'

'Because it would mean you still loved me as much as I loved you,' he growled passionately. And, getting to his feet, he tried to embrace her again.

But she resisted, her heart and mind racing with a thousand tumbling, mixed-up thoughts. 'Is that what we felt for each other, Jake? Love?'

Clearly he was startled by her querying their relationship. 'Of course. . . What else?'

She shook her head in genuine dismay. 'I think there are many names one could call what we felt for each other, what we *still* feel for each other. There's an animal chemistry between us, Jake. It burns whenever we get close enough to each other to touch. But is it love?'

'Of course it is, damn it!'

'Was it love that kept you awake nights in that prison, Jake? Was it love tonight when you saw me in that satin nightie? Was it love that had to prove its power a second time, making me do things I didn't really feel comfortable with after all these years?'

Jake grimaced at the memory. 'I'm not proud of that, Leigh. My only excuse is that I was beyond reason, beyond control. I needed you to show me that nothing had changed between us, to bring to life all the things I dreamed about all these long, lonely years without you.'

Ashleigh sucked in a breath. 'Are you saying, Jake, that there hasn't been any other woman since you got out of prison?'

A slash of guilty red burnt momentarily in his cheeks. 'No, dammit, I'm not saying that,' he ground out. 'Hell, Ashleigh, I thought you were lost to me. I thought. . . For pity's sake, what do you honestly expect? I'm a normal man. Occasionally I've needed a woman in my bed. But that doesn't mean I loved any of them as I loved you, as I *still* love you. Stop trying to make out our feelings are only sexual, damn you!'

'And damn you too, Jake,' she countered fiercely. 'For thinking this was the way to handle the situation with James, for having the arrogance to take his place without telling me, for making love to me here tonight without revealing your identity first, for playing with my life and my feelings as though you're some sort of god who knows best!

'You *don't* know best,' she raved on, whirling away to pace angrily across the room, her hand clutching the towel so that it wouldn't fall. 'You never did!' She spun round to face him from the safety of distance. 'In the first place, you should never have gone on that rotten holiday without me. Then, after you were imprisoned, you should have given me the right to pine for you if I *chose*, to wait for you if I *chose*. Then, when you were released, you should have come to see me, fiancé or no, and once again given me the right to choose my own fate.

'Damn it, Jake!' she cried in real emotional distress. 'I'm not some mindless puppet. I'm an intelligent woman with, I hope, a certain degree of courage and character. Why couldn't you have treated me like one?'

Jake's teeth clenched hard in his jaw. 'Right. Well, to answer your first accusation, that holiday wasn't my idea. It was my Aunt Aggie's. You know she was my only adult confidante in those days. When I told her I wanted to marry you she thought the same as you—that our relationship was just sex. She made me a bargain. Said if I went away for a little while and still wanted to marry you when I came back she would give us some money to get started, to support us while we went through university. But I was not to tell you that. This was to see how *you* felt too after we'd been separated for a while.'

He lifted his chin with an unrepentant air and walked slowly towards her. 'Well, we've been separated over ten years, Leigh, and it hasn't made a scrap of difference to how I feel about you, or you for me. You love me, woman. Stop denying it.'

He took hold of her shoulders and looked down into her eyes. 'As for the rest of your accusations. . . The truth is, I took James's place today with the best of intentions, thinking I was saving everyone's feelings, yours included. What do you think would have happened in a small town like this if I'd revealed the truth to you last night and the wedding was called off at the last minute? The speculation and gossip would have been horrendous. This way gives us time to work something out for everyone's benefit. Oh, and, by the way, the wedding wasn't a legal union. The celebrant was an actor Rhys employed for the event.'

Ashleigh was truly taken aback. 'An actor?' she gasped. 'But how. . .why. . .I mean. . .'

'He was an innocent enough accomplice,' Jake explained dismissively. 'Rhys told him you and I had been married secretly just before we found out our family had already planned a grand social occasion, and that we didn't want to disappoint them. He was warned to keep his mouth firmly shut, but the idiot almost let the cat right out of the bag at the signing—remember?—till Rhys stepped in.'

'But. . .but. . .the certificate. . .'

'A cheap photostat copy. I've already torn it up. Believe me, Leigh, when I say I didn't enjoy going through that charade of a marriage. You must know that

I would have given my eye-teeth to marry you properly and publicly like that. Pretending to be James at your side was excruciatingly difficult. My only concession to my pride was having the celebrant read out John James instead of James John. Hardly anyone knows John is my real name and I knew they'd all think it was just a silly mistake, if they noticed at all. You were the only possible person who'd catch on, but oddly enough you didn't seem to be listening the first time Johnson said it. You were away in another world. Then the second time...'

'I thought it was just human error,' she finished wearily.

'Look, I know I deceived you, but at least I didn't break any laws.'

Ashleigh stiffened and stepped back from his hold. 'Maybe not in a legal sense, but there are moral laws, surely? Just how long had you intended waiting, Jake, before you told me the truth?'

A slash of guilty red coloured his high cheekbones again.

Understanding shocked her. He'd been going to keep it going as long as he could, at least for the duration of their wedding-night. 'That's what you were arguing with your mother about, wasn't it?' she accused shakily. 'The extent to which you were planning on taking the deception. My God, you don't have a conscience any more, do you?'

'I wish to hell I didn't!' Jake shot back at her. 'God dammit, the only reason I pulled in here was because my stupid conscience got the better of me. I was finally going to tell you the whole horrible truth—even if it meant you'd then hate me—but when you came out of that bathroom, looking so bloody beautiful, I couldn't resist you. Sure, I was a little rough that second time and I'm sorry for that. But I'm not sorry for making love to the woman I love. Not one iota. So shoot me down with words, Leigh. Tell me I'm a savage. A barbarian. Call me any names you like. They'll fit. But while you're calling me names have a look at this and think about who and what turned me into such an animal.'

And, stripping off his shirt, he spun round and showed her what his captors had done to him.

Ashleigh could have cried. She lifted trembling fingers to touch his beautiful skin, criss-crossed with the ugly scars of a savage bamboo flogging. And her heart went out to him. What must he have been through, a young, innocent man, wrongly accused and imprisoned for something he didn't do? How on earth could she stay angry with him, faced with such a heart-rending sight?

Impossible.

Which was exactly what Jake intended, she realised when he swung around and took her in his arms again.

'Leigh, darling,' he urged persuasively, 'come away with me. . .back to Thailand. . .I have a house there on one of the beaches. . . You can practise medicine in the villages near by. . . They're in desperate need of doctors there. . . You won't want for anything, I assure you. I've—'

'*No*,' she cried out, appalled at how tempted she was to just fall in with his wishes. '*No*!'

She pushed away from him, clutching the towel defensively in front of her. 'My God, Jake, you ask too much! You've always asked too much. I'm not an infatuated teenager any more, you know. I won't come running when you click your fingers. Besides, even if I did still love you—which I'm not at all sure I do!—I can't just drop everything in my life and go off with you like that. I have responsibilities here in Glenbrook. My family depends on me. I have patients here, friends. My *life* is here. You might be able to bum around on some far away beach in a grass hut for the rest of your life, but that's not how I want to live my life. I. . . I. . .'

She broke off, flustered by the slow, ironic smile that was pulling at his lips.

'And what do you think you're smiling at?' she threw at him.

'At my lovely Leigh. So grown up now. So liberated. So wrong. . .'

'I am *not* wrong!'

'Oh, yes, you are, my darling. About so many things. We belong together. We've always belonged together. Fate has decreed it so.'

'I don't believe in fate!'

'Don't you?' Again he smiled that infuriating smile. 'Well, maybe it takes being released from a hell-hole by some incredible miracle to make one believe in such romantic notions. But I don't mind you not believing in fate. I'm quite prepared to trust to your intelligence. And your love for me. I'm sure you'll finally come to the same conclusion I came to this afternoon, Ashleigh O'Neil.'

'Which is what?' she snapped.

'Which is that you're going to become my real wife in the end, come hell or high water.' His smile suddenly faded, replaced by an expression of thin-lipped determination. 'Now go and get dressed. We're going back to Glenbrook, where you can begin seeing for yourself that you're not wanted and loved and needed there as much as I want and love and need you!'

CHAPTER SEVEN

'So! You decided to bring her back, did you?' was Nancy Hargraves's scowled remark when she opened the front door in her dressing-gown. 'I presume she knows who you really are.' She turned a perceptive eye towards Ashleigh, who tried not to colour guiltily, but failed.

Jake's mother gave her a derisive look. 'Well, nothing's changed where you and Jake are concerned, I see,' she bit out. 'You were always his little puppy-dog, running along behind him, licking at his heels. I suppose you even believe all his protestations of innocence over that drug business. Yes, *you* would. But then sex does have a way of making certain women blind to certain men. I'll bet you couldn't wait to get into bed with him once you'd found out the truth, could you?'

She looked quite ugly in her contempt. 'God! You make me sick, Ashleigh O'Neil. You probably only agreed to marry James so you could close your eyes every night and pretend he was Jake!'

'Have you heard enough, Leigh?' Jake said coldly, but placing a surprisingly warm arm around her by now shivering body.

'Y . . . yes,' she stammered, stunned by Nancy's vicious attack.

'Let's go, then.'

'You can't take James's car!' his mother screamed after them.

Jake whirled. 'Just try and stop me, Mother. You're

87

damned lucky that you and your precious James are getting off this easily. I could have pulled the plug on his little scheme with a very loud pop today. But I didn't. One of the reasons I went through with that fiasco of a marriage was to save James's reputation, as well as your miserable social position in this town. But somehow I don't think you'll be quite so generous with *Ashleigh's* reputation, will you? I can hear you now, after we're gone. . .

' "You've no idea what happened on poor James's honeymoon," ' Jake mimicked in Nancy's best plum-in-the-mouth voice. ' "Ashleigh ran into Jake again and you wouldn't believe it! The wretched creature ran off with him. The poor boy is just devastated. I don't think he'll ever marry again. . ." '

'Close, am I, Mother?' he taunted.

Nancy lifted her patrician nose. 'James is not really gay. He's been led astray, that's all, by a wicked, wicked man. I have to protect him till he's himself again.'

'You know what, Mother?' Jake said wearily. 'I actually agree with you. And who knows? Maybe, in time, he'll get rid of that corrupting creep and eventually meet a girl like my Leigh and fall in love.'

Suddenly Nancy's icy control cracked. 'Do you think so, Jake?' she choked out. 'Do you really?'

Both Ashleigh and Jake looked at each other in amazement when Nancy burst into tears, her slender, almost frail body racked with heart-rending sobs.

Ashleigh's soft womanly heart was moved, and she stepped forward to take the distressed woman in her arms. 'There, there, Nancy,' she soothed, hugging her and patting her on the back. 'James will be all right. Either way he's a good man, and I love him dearly, just as you do, just as his brother does. We all want to protect him from hurt, don't we, Jake?'

Jake looked at her and sighed. 'I guess so, but not at your expense, Leigh.'

'Then why don't the three of us go inside and think of some way out of this mess? Glenbrook is our home, Jake. We want the right to be able to come here occasionally and visit, without undue scandal and gossip.'

His eyes narrowed to stare at her. 'Come back, Leigh? That suggests leaving in the first place. Does that mean. . .you *are* going to come with me?'

If Ashleigh had ever had any doubt about her love for Jake it vanished at that moment. To see him looking at her like that. So hopeful. . .so tense. . .so vulnerable. . .

This was not the same arrogant young blood she'd once known. This was a sensitive human being, who'd been to hell and back and somehow survived. But not without a great deal of damage. He was so right when he said he needed her. She could see it in his strained face, and in the way he wasn't breathing while he waited for her answer.

'Of course, Jake,' she whispered, a lump in her throat. 'You were right all along. I love you. And I want to be your wife, wherever that takes me. . .'

They stared at each other over the bowed head of his weeping mother, and neither needed to say a thing. It was all there, in the intense relief in his eyes, and the glistening love in hers.

'I hope we can come up with a damned good solution for all this mess, then,' he said in an emotion-charged voice. 'Because I want everything to be right for you, my darling. You deserve it.'

*   *   *

KATE stared at all three of them across the large kitchen table. 'I still don't believe it!' she exclaimed. 'When the telephone rang in the middle of the night I was sure there'd been some terrible accident. I would never have dreamt. . .' She darted another wide-eyed glance Jake's way, then shook her head. 'I should have known,' she muttered under her breath. 'So damned masterful. . . Not like James at all. . .'

'You weren't the only one who was fooled,' Ashleigh said, throwing an accusing though indulgent look Jake's way.

'Really?' Kate speculated. 'When did you—er. . .?'

Her voice trailed away when Ashleigh looked daggers at her.

'Yes, well. . .best I don't ask that, I think. Just as well I moved out of home and into the small flat above my salon,' she went on blithely, 'or I'd have had to explain to my mother why you were dragging me out in the middle of the night of your wedding, Ashleigh. Come to think of it, why *have* you? I mean, I'm glad you told me the rather astonishing truth about everything, and I think Jake's switching with James is rather romantic in a weird sort of way, but what can I do to help?'

'I want you to make sure the whole town knows the truth. No, not about James,' she quickly amended, hearing the gasp of shock from Nancy, 'but about Jake's having taken his brother's place at the wedding. You can act as if the families and close friends were all in on it, but didn't say anything at the last moment for fear of causing an uproar among the more elderly guests. Relay all this confidentially to some selected customers of your salon, adding that James and I were already having doubts about our marriage and that when Jake arrived home for the wedding I realised he was still the man for me. It probably won't occur to anyone to question how we got a licence so quickly, but if they do just say we told the authorities a mistake was made with the names. . .'

When Kate looked totally perplexed James explained to her about how Jake was another form of John and that he and James actually had the same names, only reversed.

'Goodness!' she exclaimed. 'Then when the celebrant said John James at the ceremony he really meant it. It wasn't just a boo-boo?'

'No boo-boo,' Jake confirmed. 'I wasn't about to promise to love, honour and cherish my darling Leigh here in another man's name.'

Kate looked very impressed.

'Then after you've spread all that around, Kate,' Ashleigh continued, 'you'd better also add that James decided he was still in love with some girl he'd been seeing in Brisbane last year and was going off to try and win her back.'

'Goodness, Leigh, how inventive you've become over the years,' Jake said with some amusement in his voice.

'Not at all, Jake,' Kate denied drily. 'She's as disgustingly practical as always. Believe me, this is her idea of forging her own destiny.'

'Sounds good to me,' he grinned. 'As long as I'm in there somewhere, she can forge away all she likes.'

'Be quiet, the both of you,' Ashleigh reprimanded. 'I'm thinking. . . Yes, and it might not be a bad idea to also let drop some "hush-hush" news about how Jake was wrongly convicted all those years ago and that was the real reason why the Thai government eventually released him. No one will bother to check, and if you tell everyone it's supposed to be a secret it'll get around like wildfire.'

'I'll tell Mrs Brown. She has her hair done on Monday.' Kate's eyes glittered with relish at the task. 'Oh, and Maisie Harrison. She's coming in on Tuesday and has just been elected president of the local ladies' guild. Don't worry. There won't be a soul in town who won't know everything within a day or two.'

'Now, Nancy. . .' Ashleigh turned to the woman sitting next to her. Jake's mother was still very pale, though she had pulled herself together once she'd known Kate was on her way over. 'You'll have to ring my father in the morning and get him over here on a house call. Say you feel ill. That way, when you tell him the truth about James and Jake and everything, he won't be able to tell anyone because of his having to keep your confidence. I'll write a letter as well that you can give him, explaining my feelings for Jake and that I've gone off with him. I think he'll be understanding.'

Privately Ashleigh knew her father wouldn't be too broken up over his daughter's leaving Glenbrook, other than how he and his partner would be inconvenienced till Stuart joined the practice next year. In her letter she would suggest he hire a woman locum to fill in, warning him that if he didn't watch out a smart woman doctor would set up practice in Glenbrook and steal half his patients.

'But where will you and Jake go?' Kate asked.

Ashleigh looked at Jake. 'Darling? Where are we going?' she smiled at him, and when he smiled back an incredible sensation of bonding wrapped tentacles around her heart. He was so right. They did belong together. How could she ever have doubted it? Here in Glenbrook or out the back of Bourke or over in a small village in Thailand in an old grass hut. It didn't matter, as long as they were together.

'To Brisbane first, I think,' he said. 'I'll ring Rhys—he's staying at the Glenbrook Hotel. He'll drive us to Brisbane Airport, where we can see about booking tickets to Thailand. Have you got a current passport?'

'Yes.' Ashleigh tactfully declined mentioning that part of her honeymoon had been arranged for Hawaii. 'It's in my black handbag in the car.'

'Good, then there's no reason why we can't fly out to Bangkok straight away. My home is not far from there. Oh, and, by the way, it's far from a grass hut. It's quite grand, in fact. You see, Aunt Aggie left me all her money when she died, didn't you know?'

Ashleigh was taken aback. 'No,' she confessed. 'I didn't.'

'Neither did I!' Kate pronounced, sounding affronted that a piece of interesting gossip had somehow eluded her.

'I wrote to her when I got out of prison, telling her the whole truth. The old dear must have felt sorry for me and what I'd been through, and made me her heir. Six months later she was gone, and suddenly all my financial worries were over. Not only that, but I was also recently paid a packet for the film rights to a book of mine that's about to go on the stands in America. I'm loaded, my girl. Do you honestly think I'd expect you to rough it out in the wild somewhere? Not that I'm not flattered that you were prepared to.'

'Rhys told me that he was going to make a movie in Thailand,' Kate said with a frown. 'But I didn't make any connection with you, Jake.'

'Just as well,' Jake returned with feeling. 'As it is, I told Rhys not to talk about Thailand, but that man can't stop gabbling on about his damned movies.'

'You know he said if I ever wanted a job with his company as a hairdresser on set he'd be only too happy to oblige. You know what? I think I'll take him up on it.'

'What kind of book, Jake?' Ashleigh asked, a well of emotion filling her heart. He'd always said he'd be a great author one day. How proud of him she felt!

'A fictionalised version of my experiences in Thailand. Not all bad, either. It's a great country, you know, despite everything it put me through. Not that I can really blame the authorities. The man responsible for my imprisonment was damnably clever.'

'Yes, I'd like to know more about that,' his mother joined in. 'How *could* heroin get to be in your luggage without your knowing?'

If there was still a truculent note in her voice Jake was man enough to ignore it. He gave a nonchalant shrug. 'It was a simple yet clever ruse,' he explained. 'There was this fellow Australian named Doug, staying in the same hotel in Bangkok. He was always reading, great, thick tomes in hardback. He'd been wading through one on the day before our flight home, raving on about how great it was, even to showing me a particular passage he found very moving. I politely read it, not thinking much of it myself, but not saying so.'

Jake's laugh was rueful. 'Little did I know that this was just to reassure me it was a real book with real contents. When he complained the next day that he couldn't fit it into his luggage, and that he really wanted to read the rest when he got back to Australia, I let him stash it in mine; unbeknown to me the middle section was hollowed out and stuffed with heroin. Just enough, unfortunately, to upgrade my crime from possession to trafficking. Naturally, when I was picked up at the airport he conveniently disappeared, with my not even knowing his full name.'

'But didn't your lawyers try to trace him?' Ashleigh asked.

'They said there was little point, since I had no independent witness to any of this. It would just be my word against his.'

Nancy was beginning to look guilty. 'That still sounds negligent to me,' she muttered. 'They should have tried, the same as your father and I should have tried to find better lawyers for you, Jake. I. . .I'm sorry, son. We. . .we let you down. . .'

'It's all right, Mother. We all make mistakes in life, and we all have expectations of people that cannot sometimes be met. I was a difficult, selfish, rebellious young man back then. I can see that now. But I have matured and mellowed, I hope, even to trying to understand and forgive James. He only did what he did where Leigh was concerned because he was trying to live up to other people's expectations of him. Tell him when you see him, Mother, that you will love him, no matter what he is or does. That's very important. If you don't there's no hope for him. No hope at all.'

Nancy was not about to concede she had failed her favourite son in any way whatsoever. She stiffened, then stood up, proud and straight. 'I have a very good relationship with James. We love and trust each other. He. . .he didn't tell me about his. . .problem, because he knew it was just a phase he was going through. I'm sure he'll be fine once I can get him away from that wicked man.'

She turned to face Ashleigh. 'I will try to explain all this to your father in the morning. Leave your letter here, on the table, and I'll give it to him. But, for now, I. . .I must go to bed. I'm very, very tired.'

Ashleigh also got to her feet. 'I'll walk up with you, Nancy. Jake. . .perhaps you could ring Rhys while I'm gone.'

'Right away.'

The two women did not speak as they walked side by side up the stairs. They stopped outside Nancy's bedroom door. 'Don't worry about Jake and me, Nancy,' she said in parting. 'We'll be fine. . .'

Nancy gave her a rueful look. 'Oh, I can see that. You and Jake were somehow meant to be, Ashleigh. He was your destiny.'

'Maybe, Nancy. Maybe. . .'

Ashleigh turned away with an ironic expression on her face. Destiny had nothing to do with it, she still firmly believed. One made choices in life. Tonight she had *chosen* to spend the rest of her life with Jake.

She walked briskly along the corridor and turned into the bedroom at the top of the stairs, where she retrieved the locket from under the bed and the chain from the chest of drawers. Clutching it tightly in her hand, she made her way downstairs, where Jake was just hanging up the telephone in the foyer.

'Rhys is on his way,' he said, his eyes searching her face as she joined him. 'Are you sure, Leigh? I'm not rushing you, am I?'

'Of course you're rushing me,' she laughed. 'But no matter.' She moved into his arms and raised her face for him to kiss her.

He did so, gently and reverently. 'I really love you. You must know that. It's not just sex.'

'I know,' she admitted at last, and, taking his hand, pressed the locket back in it.

'What's this?'

'I'm giving you my heart again,' she said softly. 'But not on loan this time. This is for keeps.'

He stared down at the delicate locket and thought of all the long, lonely nights he had held it to his own heart and cried for the girl who'd once given it to him. Well, there would be no more lonely nights, no more despair. He would gather this lovely, loving woman to his heart and treasure her till his dying days.

'I'll give it to our first daughter,' he said in a thickened tone. 'And when she's old enough I'll tell her the story behind it.'

Ashleigh linked arms with him and they started walking slowly back to the kitchen, where Kate was sure to be waiting impatiently for them. 'How many children would you like, Jake?' she asked softly.

'Lots.'

'That's good. Because if I've done my sums right expect the first in about nine months' time.'

When she looked up at him, expecting a measure of shock, Jake was smiling wryly down at her.

'Jake Hargraves!' she gasped. 'You *knew* I might get pregnant tonight, didn't you?'

'Aye,' he agreed with mock contrition. 'That I did. James let the cat out of the bag when I—er—questioned him about how far things had gone between you two.'

'But why. . .I mean. . .why didn't you say something?'

'I thought I'd best keep an ace up my sleeve, in case

you decided we weren't quite right for each other. I rather thought a wee babe might change your mind.'

'Why, you sneaky, rotten. . .'

'My God, you two aren't fighting already, are you?' Kate groaned from the kitchen doorway.

'Who? Us?' Jake scooped an arm around Ashleigh's waist and pulled her close to his side. 'Never!'

'Certainly not,' Ashleigh giggled, seeing the funny side of it.

Kate eyed them both suspiciously. 'I hope not. People make their own luck in life, isn't that what you always say, Ashleigh?'

'Oh, definitely.'

'In that case,' she rushed forward, an anxious look on her face, 'would you have a spare room for me in Thailand if I came over for a while after I find a buyer for my salon? I think I'll take Rhys up on his offer.'

The front doorbell rang, and Jake stepped over to open it.

Rhys stood there, an equally anxious look on his face. 'All right, give me the bad news. She sent you packing once she found out, didn't she? I did tell you, Jake, this wasn't the way to handle it. Women don't like to be deceived, you know. They. . .'

He gaped into silence when Ashleigh walked forward and slipped a loving arm through Jake's. 'Now, Rhys, don't be so melodramatic. I'm not angry with Jake at all. I adore him and we're going to Thailand together to live and have babies while Jake writes and I doctor. We have only one further favour to ask of you.'

His mouth flapped open, but no words came out.

'Of both of you, actually,' she went on, her glance encompassing Kate as well. 'Would you two be our witnesses again when we really, truly get married, *legally* next time?'

'Well, of course,' Rhys agreed, still rather bemused by the turn of events.

'But only if you uphold all the traditions,' Kate inserted sternly. 'White dress and all the trimmings. I don't believe in any of those register office jobs.'

Ashleigh grinned. 'All right, Miss Tradition. But you'll have to come up with a different "something borrowed" for me. That locket just won't do any more. It's been "returned to sender".' And she looked lovingly up at Jake.

'Returned to. . .' Kate frowned. 'But I thought Nancy had. . .I mean. . . Ashleigh O'Neil!' she wailed. 'You've been keeping secrets from me!'

'I wonder why,' she laughed, and, smiling, went up on tiptoe to kiss the man she loved.

Vendetta

by
Susan Napier

SUSAN NAPIER was born on St Valentine's Day, so it's not surprising she has developed an enduring love of romantic stories. She started her writing career as a journalist in Auckland, New Zealand trying her hand at romantic fiction only after she had married her handsome boss! Numerous books later she still lives with her most enduring hero, two future heroes—her sons!—two cats and a computer. When she's not writing she likes to read and cook, often simultaneously!

Look out this autumn for Susan Napier's new book
MISTRESS FOR A WEEKEND in
Modern Romance™!

To my father, Ted Hedge, the Intrepid Traveller

CHAPTER ONE

THE time had come.

Ten years. . .

For ten years he had looked forward to this moment with a savage anticipation that had blotted out all lesser ambitions. He had forced himself to watch, to wait, to plan, to carry on with the rest of his life as if revenge had not become the pivot of his existence.

Of course, outside the waiting, the plotting, he had gone through all the right motions, maintaining the fiction of Christian forgiveness. . .smiling, talking, moving, interacting with those around him, accepting their praise for his achievements, cultivating their admiration and envy, consolidating his wealth. But none of it had had any meaning, any reality for him.

The admiration, the envy, the wealth were necessary only as a source of power. The power to see justice done. The power to punish . . .

He pressed his right hand on the hard, highly polished surface of his desk, watching the faint mist of heat from his skin bloom across the cool, dark surface between his splayed fingers. A heavy gold ring engraved with an entwined briar and snake on the flat shield flashed in the firelight, the only source of light in the coldly elegant room, as he turned his hand over and stared at the bold tracery of life-lines on his palm. They mocked him with their energy. He had had such grand hopes of life until *she* had come along and casually crushed them.

But now the long, bitter years of waiting were over. He finally had her exactly where he wanted her. . .in the palm of his powerful hand. And the timing was perfect. She thought that she was safe. She thought that she had got away with it, that everyone had forgotten her crime. Soon, very soon, she would learn differently. There was no statute of limitations on murder.

He curled his fingers inward to form a brutal fist. All he had to do now was close the trap and watch her futile struggles to free herself. She would probably weep and cry innocence, or bluster and threaten, or, better still, cringe and beg for his entertainment. Then he would strip away her pride and her self-respect and stand witness to the death, one by one, of all her hopes and dreams. It was an image that he treasured in the depths of his embittered soul.

He picked up the squat crystal glass next to his hand and took a long swallow of potent, twelve-year-old Scotch. The raw, smoky bite at the back of his throat was pleasurable, but it was no match for the intoxicating taste of revenge that was flooding his senses. For the first time in a decade, he felt almost whole again.

The time had come. . .

CHAPTER TWO

VIVIAN took the last two steps in one grateful stride and then paused for breath, forcing herself to look back down the narrow staircase that was chipped out of the rocky face of the cliff.

In spite of the fact it was a cold and blustery day, typical of New Zealand's autumn, sweat was trickling down her torso inside her cream blouse and her palm had felt appallingly slippery on the single, stout wooden rail that had been the only barrier between her and the rock-strewn, sea-green oblivion below.

She shuddered faintly as she watched the two men far below, unloading the cargo from the hold of the squat little ferry-boat.

Reaction hit and Vivian swallowed, her dry mouth suddenly thick with moisture. Her legs felt like jelly and she swayed, fighting the urge to sink weakly to the ground.

She pressed a hand to her abdomen, trying to control the unpleasant churning feeling as she turned away and followed the sharply rising, stony path up through the low, scrubby trees. She had to get a grip on herself before she reached her destination. She smoothed down her neat dark green skirt and adjusted the matching blazer as she went, nervously switching the soft-sided leather satchel from one sweaty hand to the other as she tried to calm herself by projecting a mental aura of professionalism.

She had a reputation to uphold. She was here as a

representative of Marvel-Mitchell Realties to close a vital property deal. A lot was depending on her. It wasn't just the money, but the future happiness of people that she loved that was at stake.

It hadn't helped that what she had been told was a forty-minute journey from the north-east coast of the Coromandel Peninsula to the island had actually taken over an hour and a half in very choppy seas. After a rushed three-hour drive from Auckland last evening, and an anxious, wakeful night in an uncomfortable motel bed, her close encounter with the Pacific Ocean had not been pleasant.

Since her destination was the private island of a millionaire, Vivian had naïvely expected a luxury launch or hydrofoil to be her mode of transport, not the ugly old tub that she had been directed to at Port Charles. She had also expected the island to be a lush private sanctuary, with beautiful white-sand beaches and flourishing vegetation, rather than a wind-swept, surf-lashed rock in the middle of nowhere. Although the name should have given her a clue, she thought wryly.

Nowhere. She had thought it quaint; now she realised it had been highly descriptive!

What kind of man would drag someone out all this way to conclude a business deal that would have been better, and more safely handled in a city office? Unfortunately, she thought she knew exactly: a man bent on causing trouble. A machiavellian man who would not be appeased by an easy victory. If she was to thwart any of his aims she would have to play his game first.

Vivian came through a small, wind-mutilated grove of low-growing trees and halted, her mouth falling open in shock.

Across a small ridge, perched on a flat tongue of land at the end of a rocky promontory, was a lighthouse. If she hadn't been so busy hanging miserably over the rail of the boat, wondering whether to cast up her rushed motel breakfast into the sea, she would have seen the tall white tower as they approached the island.

She lifted bleak eyes from the wide concrete base, up, up past the vertical line of four tiny windows to stare at the open balcony just below the diamond-shaped glass panes that housed the light. How many stairs to get to the top of *that*?

Her appalled gaze sank back down again and settled with overpowering relief on the low, white-painted concrete building that adjoined the towering structure. A keeper's cottage.

She got a grip on herself. No need to let your imagination run wild, Vivian. All New Zealand lighthouses were now automated. It might even have been decommissioned. She had no business with lighthouses. It was the man in the nice, ordinary, *low* building beside it that she had come to see!

The narrow pathway across the short ridge was fenced on both sides with white pickets, offering her at least a notion of security as the wind swept up one side of the steep, rocky face and wrenched at her hair and clothes with berserk glee. She touched each picket with her free hand as she passed, counting to take her mind off what lay at either side, aware that her neat bun was unravelling more with every step.

By the time she reached the stout, weathered timber door, she was resigned to looking like a freak. A quick glance at her reflection in the curtained window beside the door confirmed the worst. Her shoulder-length hair, inclined to be wild and woolly at the best of times, was making the most of its partial freedom in the moisture-laden air, and there was no time to try and torture the tight ginger curls back into businesslike obedience. Hurriedly Vivian pulled out the few remaining pins. Now, instead of resembling a lop-sided hedgehog, she merely looked like a frightened lion.

She took a deep breath, straightened the side-seams of her skirt, and knocked loudly.

After several moments she knocked again, then again. Finally she tried the door-handle and found to her surprise that it opened easily. She tentatively edged across the threshold.

'Hello, is anybody there? Mr Rose? Mr Rose!' The door closed behind her with a weighty clunk, sounding unpleasantly like the door to a cell.

She walked warily down the short narrow hall and into a large room, sparsely furnished in everything except books—walls of them.

A long, well-used, brown leather couch was drawn up in front of a coal-blackened fireplace and there was a big roll-top desk and chair beside a window overlooking the sea. Another small port-hole window among the books showed the smooth white rise of the adjoining lighthouse tower. There were a few rugs on the polished hardwood floor and a large, smooth-sided antique chest that obviously doubled as a coffee-table, but there were no ornaments or plants, paintings or photographs. Nothing that betrayed the excessive wealth of the owner. Nothing but the books to give the room character. . .and a rather daunting one at that, thought Vivian, eyeing some of the esoteric titles.

Like the adjacent lighthouse, the house was obviously

designed to withstand the constant buffeting of sea-storms, the interior walls made of the same thick, roughcast cement as the outer shell. She wondered nervously whether perhaps it was also designed to endure buffetings from within. The mysterious and formerly benignly eccentric Mr Rose, with whom Marvel-Mitchell Realties had dealt quietly and successfully for years via lawyer, letter and fax, was shaping up to be a chillingly ruthless manipulator. She didn't doubt for one minute that this wait was designed to make her sweat.

Unless he had never intended to turn up at all.

Vivian shivered. She put her briefcase down by the desk and began to pace, trying to burn off her increasing tension. There were no clocks in the room and she checked her watch frequently as ten minutes ticked slowly past. The captain had said the boat would be leaving again in an hour. If Mr Rose hadn't arrived by then she would simply leave.

To pass the time, she re-applied her lipstick and brushed her hair, cursing herself for not tucking extra hairpins into her bag, when suddenly her restless thoughts were drowned out by a loud, rhythmic beating that seemed to vibrate through the walls. Vivian turned towards the window to see a sleek white helicopter descending towards a flat circle of tussock just below the cottage.

She felt her temper fizzle bracingly as the craft settled to rest and the door opened and two men got out, heads ducked low as they battled the whirlwind created by the slowing blades.

Nicolas Rose had a helicopter! Instead of her spending an eternity on a heaving boat, he could have had her *flown* out to the island in minutes! For that matter, he could probably have got to Auckland and back in the time it had taken her to cross the angry patch of water.

She watched as the first passenger, a huge, blond bear of a man in jeans and a sheepskin jacket, stood back and respectfully allowed the man in the dark blue suit to pass him.

Vivian studied the man whom she had travelled all this way to see. Even bowed over, he was tall, and he looked lean and fit, with dark hair and a face that, as he glanced up towards the house, was hard and rugged. He grinned at something that was said behind him and her heart leapt with hope as the grimness dropped away from him and he looked comfortingly sane and civilised. The other one, the beefy blond who shadowed his footsteps with a cat-like alertness, had bodyguard written all over him. They disappeared around the back of the cottage. Vivian was facing the door, her hands clasped nervously behind her, when finally, after another agonised age, it opened.

She bit off a frustrated groan when the jeans-clad figure stepped into the room. Another carefully orchestrated delay, no doubt designed to undermine further her dwindling confidence. Or was the bodyguard here to check her for concealed weapons?

Her eyes darted to his face and the breath caught with a shock in her throat. There was a black patch over his left eye, a thin scar running vertically from his hairline to the top of the concealing inverted triangle and from beneath it down over his high cheekbone to the slanting plane of his cheek. The other eye was light brown, and Vivian's gaze hastily skidded down, afraid he would think she was staring.

His mouth was thin and his face uncompromisingly

square and deeply tanned, his thick, straight hair——wheat-gold at the ends and several shades darker at the roots—raked carelessly back from the scarred forehead by fingers and the wind, the shaggy ends brushing the upturned collar of his jacket. Darker gold glinted on the angles of the jutting jaw as his head shifted, revealing at least a day's growth of beard. Even with the eye-patch and the scar he was good-looking, in a reckless, lived-in, don't-give-a-damn kind of way.

Without speaking, he shouldered out of the hip-length jacket and she could see that its bulk had given her a deceptive impression of the man. He wasn't really the behemoth he had first appeared. Although his wine-red roll-necked sweater moulded a fairly impressive pair of shoulders, and was stretched to accommodate a deep chest, his body narrowed to a lean waist and hips that indicated not an ounce of unnecessary fat. His legs were very long, the muscles of his thighs thick enough to strain the faded denim. His hands, as he tossed the discarded jacket effortlessly halfway across the room to land over the back of the couch, were strong and weathered. Big, capable hands. Capable of hurting. . .or healing, she thought, startled at the unlikely notion that came floating up through her sluggish brain.

He leaned back against the door, snicking it closed with a shift of his weight, bending his knee to brace the sole of a scuffed leather boot on the wood behind him, crossing his arms over his chest. Vivian forced her gaze to rise again, to discover that she wasn't the only person who appeared to be shocked into a momentary trance. The single, brown eye was unblinkingly studying her, seemingly transfixed by the vivid aureole of hair surrounding her tense face.

Another man with conventional ideas about feminine beauty! She knew her own myriad imperfections well enough; she didn't need his startled stare to remind her. As if the scalding brightness of her hair wasn't enough, her green eyes had the garish brilliance of cheap glass, hardly muted by the lenses of her round spectacles, and a mass of ginger freckles almost blotted out her creamy skin.

Vivian's left hand lifted to smooth down the springy ginger mane around her shoulders, and she smiled tentatively at him, flushing when he didn't respond. A small freckled pleat appeared just above the gold wire bridge of her glasses, and she adjusted them unnecessarily on her straight nose, giving him the 'tough' look that she had practised in the motel mirror the previous night.

'Well, well, well. . .the Marvel-lous Miss Mitchell, I presume?'

His voice was like silk drawn over rough gravel, sarcastically smooth with a rustling hint of hard, underlying crunch.

A voice used to giving orders. To being obeyed. No polite deference or preening arrogance here. Just utter authority.

Vivian clenched her hands behind her back as the unpalatable truth burst upon her.

She would have far preferred to deal with the civilised Suit! A Suit might be persuaded to sacrifice a small victory for an immediate, larger gain.

This man looked too unconventional, too raw-edged, too primitive ever to have heard of the words 'negotiated surrender'. He looked like a man who enjoyed a fight—and had had plenty of them.

Looking defeat in the face, Vivian knew there was

no going back. She *had* to try and beat him at his own game. But no one said she had to play it solely by his rules.

CHAPTER THREE

'THE elusive Mr Rose, I presume?' Vivian echoed his mocking drawl, hoping that she sounded a lot more in control of herself than she felt.

There was a small, challenging silence. He inclined his head, still studying her with the arrested fascination of a scientist confronting a new form of life.

Vivian smoothed her hands nervously down the side-seams of her skirt, and to her horror her fingers encountered the crumpled tail of her blouse trailing from beneath the back of her unbuttoned jacket. Somehow it must have worked free on that nerve-racking climb. Trying to maintain her dignity, she continued to meet his dissecting stare coolly, while surreptitiously tucking her blouse back into the waistband of her skirt.

He noticed, of course, and a curious flicker lightened his expression before it settled back into brooding aggression.

'So. . .do we now blithely proceed from our mutual presumptions, or do we observe strict propriety and introduce ourselves properly?'

His murmur was rife with hidden meanings, and Vivian hesitated, wondering whether she was reading her own guilt into his words.

'Uh—well, I think we know who we are. . .' She closed her eyes briefly, cursing herself for her faltering of courage at the critical moment.

When she opened them again, he was metaphorically crouched in waiting.

'I think, therefore I am?' he said softly. 'Very profound, my dear, but I'm sure Descartes intended his philosophy to be applied to something more meaningful than social introductions. However, far be it from me to contradict a lady, particularly such a highly qualified one as yourself. So, we have an agreement that I'm Nicholas Rose of Nowhere and you are Miss Mitchell of Marvel-Mitchell Realties. Welcome to my world, Miss Mitchell.'

He kicked himself away from the door and walked swiftly towards her, hand outstretched. Without looking down, she was aware that he limped. She was also aware of the savage pride in the single, glittering eye which effortlessly dominated her attention. It seemed to flame with a strange inner light, until the almond-brown iris was shot with blazing spears of gold as he came to a stop in front of her, closer than was comfortable or courteous, towering over her by at least six inches as he insolently invaded her personal space.

She accepted his proffered hand with a wariness that proved wise when the strength of his grip turned out to be even greater than she had anticipated. His hand wrapped almost completely around hers, trapping it as he extended the moment of contact beyond politeness into the realm of pure intimidation.

The calluses on his palm as he eased the pressure created a friction against her softer skin which felt disturbingly familiar. It was like the faint warning buzz she had experienced when touching a faulty electrical socket. Indeed, the very air around him seemed to crackle and carry a whiff of burning. It was as if there was a huge energy source humming inside him, barely restrained by flesh and blood.

He released her slightly maimed fingers, the gold flecks in his eye glowing with a strange satisfaction as she stayed stubbornly where she was, lifting her firm chin, refusing to be daunted by his superior size and strength, or by the unsettling reciprocal hum in her own bones.

Surprisingly, he was first to disengage from the silent duel, turning away to sling himself down in the chair at the desk, stretching his long legs out in front of him. He didn't offer her a seat, just leaned back and regarded her in a way that seemed indefinably possessive. Vivian's blood tingled in her cheeks and she adjusted her spectacles again.

His thin mouth curved cruelly. 'Shall we proceed to the business in hand, then, Miss Mitchell? I take it you followed all the instructions in the fax?'

She thought of the tense drive down, the nerve-racking hours alone in the motel, the wallowing boat. . .and his helicopter. She set her teeth and nodded.

'Truly a Marvel—an obedient woman,' he punned goadingly, and Vivian's flush deepened with the effort of controlling her temper. 'And, knowing that your company's successful purchase of my land depends on your pandering to my every annoying little whim, of course you followed those instructions *to the letter*, did you not, Miss Mitchell?'

This time she wasn't going to chicken out. She squared her shoulders. 'No. That is, not exactly——'

'Not *exactly*? You do surprise me, Miss Marvel-lous.'

Nerves slipped their leash. 'Will you stop calling me that?'

'Perhaps I should call you Miss Marmalade instead. That would be a more descriptive nickname—your hair being the colour it is. . . That wouldn't offend you, would it? After all, what's in a name? "That which we call a rose by any other name would smell as sweet". . .'

His frivolity was definitely a trap, the quotation from *Romeo and Juliet* containing a baited message that Vivian could not afford to acknowledge without betraying her tiny but infinitely precious advantage.

'As a matter of fact, there's an awful *lot* in a name,' she said, ignoring the lure. 'Mine, for example, is *Vivian* Mitchell——'

Instead of leaping to his feet in justifiable outrage, he rocked his chair on to its back legs with his booted heels, his expression one of veiled malice as he interrupted her confession. 'Vivian. Mmm, yes, you're right,' he mused, in that low, gratingly attractive voice. 'Vivian. . . It does have a certain aptness to your colouring, a kind of phonetic and visual rhythm to it. . .razor-sharp edges springing up around singing vowels. I do have your permission to call you Vivian, don't I, Miss Mitchell?'

'Yes, of course,' she bit off, his feigned innocence making her feel like a mouse between the paws of a lion. 'But you requested that *Janna* Mitchell bring you the documents and co-sign the settlement. Unfortunately my sister couldn't come, so I brought them instead. Otherwise, everything is exactly as you asked. . .'

'She couldn't come?' he asked mildly. 'Why not?'

Having expected a savage explosion of that banked energy, Vivian was once more disconcerted by his apparent serenity.

She moistened her lower lip nervously, unconsciously emphasising its fullness. 'She has flu.'

Janna was also sick with guilt and remorse, and the combination had made her pathetically easy to deceive. As far as her sister or anyone else knew, Vivian's prime motive for taking her place on this trip was her desperate desire to get away from everyone for a while.

'Convenient.'

She winced at the flick of the whip. Not so serene, after all.

'Not for her. Janna hates being ill.' Her younger sister was ambitious. As a newly qualified lawyer, working in Marvel-Mitchell Realties' legal department, she had a rosy future ahead of her, one that Vivian intended to protect.

'Messes up those gorgeous ice-blonde looks, I suppose,' he said, casting a sardonic look at her wild ginger mane.

Vivian froze.

'You knew,' she whispered, feeling momentarily faint. Thank God the masquerade had only been intended to get her inside the door.

'The moment I saw you.'

'But you've never met Janna—or anyone from Marvel-Mitchell,' she said hollowly. 'Until now you've always insisted on dealing through an intermediary——'

'So you decided to be honest, in spite of the fact I might be none the wiser for the deception. I'm impressed. Or was I supposed to be?' he added cynically. 'Are you always so honest, I wonder?'

'I try to be.' Her tartness reproved his cynicism.

'A neat piece of sophistry. You try but you don't necessarily always succeed, mmm?' His voice hardened. 'You can't have been so naïve as to think I wouldn't investigate the people I do business with? I'm not a fool.'

'I never thought you were.' But she had seriously underestimated his thoroughness.

'I'm sure that Marvel, too, conducted its own investigations into my integrity. . .?'

It was a question rather than a comment, and Vivian answered it as such.

'Other than maintaining a current credit check, Peter felt there was no need, since we've been buying and selling properties on your behalf for several years without any problems,' she replied curtly. 'In spite of never having met you, Peter considers you a trusted ally. So your personal integrity was naturally taken for granted, Mr Rose.' Her green eyes were wide and innocent as she made the final, pointed statement.

'Call me Nick, Vivian.' His reaction was equal bland innocence. 'Of course, one man's integrity is another man's poison. I don't do business with cheats and liars.'

'Very wise,' she agreed distractedly, unnerved by his mention of poison. Was that supposed to be significant?

'Are you patronising me, Miss Mitchell?' he asked silkily, planting his feet back on the floor and leaning his torso threateningly towards her.

She was jolted out of her unsettling ruminations. 'I prefer to think of it as pandering to your every annoying little whim,' she said sweetly.

There was another small, dangerous silence. He seemed to specialise in them.

He rose, unfolding himself to his full height with sinister slowness.

'Brave, aren't you?' he murmured.

The thin, menacing smile and the burning gold splinters in his eye told her it was not a compliment. 'So. . .' Instead of the lawyer I requested, Marvel-Mitchell

Realties sends me a mere receptionist. A suspicious man might take that as an insult. . .'

'But then, from your investigations you must know I'm not *just* a receptionist,' Vivian defended herself. 'I'm also Peter Marvel's secretary/PA, and for the last eighteen months a full financial partner in the firm. I'm fully authorised to sign cheques and contracts on behalf of Marvel-Mitchell Realties.'

Not that she ever had. Up until now she had been quite happy to be Peter's sleeping partner—well, lightly dozing at any rate. She enjoyed her work and hadn't looked on the investment of her unexpected inheritance in Peter's firm as an excuse to throw her weight around the office, but rather as an investment in their shared future. . .

Brooding on that sadly faded dream, she didn't notice him moving until a large hand was suddenly in front of her face. For an awful moment she thought his repressed hostility had finally erupted, but instead of the impact of his palm against her cheek, she felt him pull off her spectacles so that his image immediately dissolved into an indistinct blur.

'Oh, please. . .' She snatched vaguely, but he was too quick for her.

'Salt build-up from all that sea-spray on the boat trip,' he said blandly, retreating out of her reach. She squinted to see him produce a white square from his pocket and carefully rub the lenses with it. 'They need a good clean.'

He held them up to the light and inspected them before breathing on the glass and polishing some more. 'Pretty strong lenses. You must be extremely short-sighted.'

'I am,' she admitted truculently. She could have pointed out with brutal honesty that he had a few glaring

imperfections of his own, but she was too soft-hearted
for her own good—everyone said so. Even Peter, who
was supposed to be madly in love with her, had always
been exasperated by her ability to empathise with the
opposing point of view in an argument.

'You must be rather helpless without them.'

Was that a hint of gloating in his voice? She squinted
harder. 'Not helpless, just short-sighted,' she said flatly.

Unexpectedly he laughed. It was a disturbingly rich
sound, unfavoured by bitterness. 'How long have you
worn them?'

'Since I was thirteen.'

And never had she been more grateful, for once there
were spectacles firmly perched on her nose she found
the boys less inclined to stare endlessly at her ever-
burgeoning breasts. From a potential sex-pot she had
become an egg-head, and even though her marks had
been barely average she had managed to cling to the
image until the other girls in her class had also started
acquiring ogle-worthy figures.

'May I have them back, please?' she asked the blurry
male outline, holding out her hand.

There was a pause. All he had to do was clench those
strong fingers and the fragile frames would be crushed,
leaving her more vulnerable than ever.

'Of course.'

Instead of handing them to her, he replaced them himself, taking his time as he set them straight across the
bridge of her nose, his face jumping back into disturbingly sharp focus, a close-up study in concentration as
he tucked the ear-pieces carefully into place, his rough
finger-pads sliding around on the ultra-sensitive skin
behind her ears for long enough to make her shiver.

'Th-thank you,' she said reluctantly, edging back.

He followed her, his fingers still cradling the sides of her skull. 'You have very speaking eyes.' God, she hoped not! She blinked to clear her gaze of all expression and shuddered again at the intensity of his inspection. What was he searching for?

'Are you cold?'

'No.' To her dismay it came out as a breathy squeak.

His hands dropped to her taut shoulders, then lightly drifted down the outsides of her arms to her tense fists.

'You must be, after being out in that draughty old boat,' he contradicted. 'Your hands are as cold as ice and you're trembling. You need some food inside you to warm you up.'

She cleared her throat. 'I assure you, I'm perfectly warm,' she said, pulling her hands away. 'And I'm not hungry.'

'Your stomach still feeling the effects of the trip?' he murmured with annoying perception, his dark brown eyebrows lifted, the one above the eye-patch made raggedly uneven by the indent of the scar. 'It's a mistake to think the ride back will be easier on an empty stomach. You'll feel much better with something inside you.'

Like you? The wayward thought popped into her head and Vivian went scarlet.

He stilled, looking curiously at her bright face and the horrified green eyes that danced away from his in guilty confusion. What in the world was the matter with her?

His eyebrows settled back down and his eyelid drooped, disguising his expression as he took her silence as assent. 'Good, then you'll join me for lunch. . .'

'Thank you, but the boat leaves again in——' Vivian

looked at her watch '——twenty minutes, and I still have to get back down to the wharf——'

'The captain won't leave until he's checked with me first.' He effortlessly cut the ground from under her feet.

'I'm really not hungry——'

'And if I said that I hadn't eaten since lunch yesterday and was far too ravenous to concentrate on anything but feeding my appetite?'

Your appetite for what? thought Vivian as she silently weighed up her options. . .which proved to be extremely limited.

'I'd say *bon appétit*,' she sighed. Maybe he'd be easier to handle on a full stomach.

'On the principle that it's better I take bites out of food than out of you?' he guessed wolfishly, coming a little too close to her earlier, forbidden meanderings.

'Something like that,' she said primly.

'While I arrange something suitably light for you and filling for me, why don't you get those papers out so I can look them over?'

Looking them over was a long way from signing, but Vivian hastened to do as he instructed while he was gone. He had shut the door behind him, and opened it so quietly on his return that she wasn't aware of him until he loomed over her at the desk. The first she knew of him was the hot, predatory breath on the back of her neck.

'You move very quietly——' she began, in breathless protest at his consistent ability to surprise her.

'For a cripple?' he finished with biting swiftness.

'That wasn't what I was going to say!' she protested, sensing that sympathy was the last thing he would ever want from her.

'You were going to use a more diplomatic term, perhaps?' he sneered. 'Disabled? Physically challenged?'

She was suddenly blindly furious with him. How dared he think that she would be so callous, let alone so stupid, as to taunt him, no matter what the provocation!

'You move quietly for such a *big* man is what I was going to say before you rudely interrupted,' she snapped. 'And an over-sensitive one, too, I might add. *I* didn't leap down *your* throat when you drew attention to the fact I was blind as a bat, did I? And I have two supposedly undamaged legs and yet I never seem to be able to co-ordinate them properly. I dreamed of being a ballerina when I was a girl. . .' She trailed off wistfully, suddenly remembering who it was she was confiding in.

'A ballerina?' He looked at her incredulously, his sceptical eye running over her five-feet-ten frame and the generous curves that rumpled the professional smoothness of her suit.

'It was just a childish thing,' she said dismissively, inexplicably hurt by his barely concealed amusement.

He tilted his head. 'So you dreamed of becoming a perfect secretary instead?'

'I wasn't qualified for much else,' she said coldly. Academically she had been a dud, but she was responsible and willing and got on well with people, her final-year form-teacher had kindly pointed out to her concerned parents, and weren't those things far more important in attaining happiness in the wider world than the mere possession of a brilliant brain?

Of course some people—like Janna and their younger brother, Luke, who was a musical prodigy; and her mother and father, an artist and a mathematician respectively—managed to have it all. . .good looks included.

Not that her family ever consciously made her feel inadequate. Quite the reverse—they sometimes went overboard in their efforts to convince her that she belonged, that she was the much-loved special one of the family. The Chosen One—because she had been adopted as a toddler, and had proved the unexpected catalyst for the rapid arrival of a natural daughter and then a son.

'No other thwarted ambitions?'

'No.' She didn't doubt he would laugh like a drain if she told him that her greatest desire was to be a wife and mother. It was her one outstanding talent: loving people—even when they made it very difficult for her. Sometimes almost impossible.

She looked down at the documents on the desk, concentrating on squaring them off neatly, aware of a nasty blurring of her eyesight that had nothing to do with foggy glasses.

The papers were suddenly snatched out of her fingers. 'This is what you want *me* to sign?'

'Mmm?' Distracted by her thoughts, she took no notice of the faint emphasis. 'Oh, yes.' She pulled herself together, certain that her ugly suspicions were correct and that he was now going to announce dramatically that he had no intention of doing so.

Four months ago, when Nicholas Rose had signed a conditional agreement to sell his Auckland property, his lawyer had cited tax reasons for his client wishing to retain legal title until the end of April. Peter had been happy with the extended settlement date, for it had given him time to chase up the other parcels of land that had been part of the lucrative contract Marvel-Mitchell had entered into with a commercial property development company. Nicholas's property had been the most critical, being a corner lot at the front of the planned shopping mall development, providing the only street access to the larger site. With that in his pocket, Peter had felt free to bid up on one or two other lots, whose owners had demanded much more than current market price.

Then Nicholas Rose had suddenly cancelled his appointment to sign the settlement in Auckland, citing a clause in the conditional agreement that gave the vendor the right to choose the time and place, and Janna had got sick, and Vivian had tried to be helpful and discovered two appalling truths: one, that Nicholas Rose was potentially an implacable enemy, and two, that her cosy dream of love and babies with Peter was shattered beyond redemption.

For long minutes there was no sound but the quiet swish of paper turning, and Vivian's heart thundered in her ears as she waited for her enemy to reveal himself.

'Where do I sign?' He flicked cursorily back through the pages. 'Here? Here? And here?'

'Uh. . .yes.' He bent and she watched disbelievingly as he uncapped a fountain pen and scrawled his initials in the right places, ending with a full, flourishing signature. The solid gold band on his ring-finger caught her eye as his hand paused, and she stared at the etching of snake and rose, the same crest that she had seen on the letterhead in his lawyer's office.

'Now you.'

She numbly took his place as he stood aside. The shaft of the expensive pen was heavy and smooth, warm from his touch, and she was so nervous that she left a large blob after her name. He blotted it without comment.

'We'll need this properly witnessed, won't we?'

He didn't wait for an answer but went to the door and bellowed for 'Frank'.

The man in the dark suit came in. He gave Vivian a single, hostile, sharply assessing look, then took the proffered pen and co-signed the document with a tight-lipped frown.

'Satisfied?' he asked gratingly as he straightened up, throwing the pen down on to the desk.

'Thank you, Frank.'

Frank grunted.

'Lunch ready?' Nicholas Rose asked, seemingly undismayed by his employee's surly air of disapproval.

'In the kitchen. Just as you ordered, *sir*. Just don't expect me to serve it!'

'We'll serve ourselves.' He turned to Vivian, who was watching the by-play with slightly dazed green eyes, still stunned by the inexplicable reprieve. Could she have been wrong about him, after all? 'Frank heats up a mean soup. Frank is my right-hand man, by the way. Frank, this is Vivian.'

Another grunt and a bare acknowledgement.

'I think Vivian has something to give you before you go, Frank.'

'I do?' She looked at them both blankly.

'The money, Vivian,' Nicholas reminded her helpfully. 'If you haven't brought the cash and the bank-cheque, then this contract of sale isn't worth the paper it's written on.'

'Oh!' She blushed. How unprofessional. She was surprised he hadn't asked to see the money earlier. 'Oh, yes, of course. It's right here.'

She unfastened a locked compartment of her satchel, drawing out the thousand-dollar bundle of notes from a cloth bank-bag, and the crisp slip of paper that made up the balance. She was about to put them down on the desk when she hesitated, eyeing the settlement papers still splayed out in front of him, her fears blossoming anew. Her colour drained away as she nibbled her lip.

With a sardonic look, Nicholas Rose silently gathered up the papers and handed them to her. She tucked them hastily into the satchel before she gave him the bundles. She couldn't quite hide her relief at getting rid of the oppressive responsibility and was chagrined when he tossed the money casually to Frank, who stuffed it in his suit pockets and stumped out, muttering something about the pilot.

'This is all very unorthodox,' she said disapprovingly.

'I'm a very unorthodox man.' If that was a warning, it had come far too late to be of any protection. 'Did it make you nervous travelling with such a large sum of cash?'

She thought of her sweaty drive and the almost sleepless night in the motel with a chair propped under the doorknob. 'Very.'

'Poor Vivian, no wonder you look so pale and tense.' He casually brushed her cheek with his thumb and she nearly went through the roof at the bolt of electricity that sizzled her senses.

They looked at each other, startled. His gaze dropped to her soft naked mouth, open in shock, then to the sliver of thickly freckled skin revealed by the modest cleavage of her blouse and the faint suggestion of lace hinted at by the trembling rise and fall of her lush breasts against the cream silk. In that single, brief glance he stripped her naked and possessed her.

'Come into the kitchen,' he said quietly. 'I know just what to give you to relax.'

He ushered her before him and she moved awkwardly, shaken by the most profoundly erotic experience of her life. And yet he had scarcely touched her! She felt confused, fearful and yet achingly alive, aware as never before of the feminine sway of her full hips and the brush of her thighs beneath her skirt. Her spine tingled in delicious terror. Was he stroking her again with that spiky look of hunger? Imagining how she would look moving in front of him without her clothes? She blushed in the dimness of the hall and chastised herself for her dangerous fantasies. Either it was all in her own mind, or Nicholas Rose had decided to set her up for a very personal form of humiliation. He couldn't possibly be genuinely attracted to her, not a man who, despite his physical flaws, possessed a raw magnetism that probably gave him his pick of beautiful women, not a man who showed every sign of being bent on vengeance.

The kitchen was small and compact and clearly the preserve of someone who enjoyed cooking. The benchtop was wooden, slicked with the patina of age, in contrast to the microwave and modern appliances, and in the small dining-alcove was a well-scrubbed kauri table and three chairs. Evidently Nowhere Island was not normally used for business entertaining.

The table was set with rush place-mats and solid silver cutlery, and the steaming bowl of thick, creamy, fragrant soup that was set before her made Vivian's tense stomach-muscles uncoil. There were bread rolls, too, which Nicholas got from the microwave, cursing as he burnt his fingers on the hot crusts.

The relaxant turned out to be a glass of champagne.

And not just any old bubbly, but Dom Perignon. Vivian watched as he deftly opened the wickedly expensive bottle over her murmured protests that wine in the middle of the day made her sleepy, and turned his back to pour it into two narrow, cut-crystal flutes he had set on the bench.

Vivian drank some more soup, and when she was handed the chilled flute with a charming flourish accepted it fatalistically. What would be would doubtless be, whether she drank it or not.

'Have you ever tasted Dom Perignon before?' he asked, seating himself again, and this time applying himself to his soup with an appetite that definitely wasn't feigned.

'Why, yes, I have it every morning for breakfast, poured on my cornflakes,' she said drily.

'You must be a lively breakfast companion. . .albeit a more expensive one than most men could hope to afford,' he said, with a provocative smile that was calculated to distract.

But not you. It was on the tip of her tongue to say it, but she manfully refrained. 'I pay my own way.'

His eyes dropped to her hand, nervously tracing the grain of the table, and the smile was congealed.

'Yes, that's right, you do, don't you. Even to the extent of bank-rolling your fiancé's grand property schemes. I suppose you could say he gained a sleeping partner in more than one sense of the word. . .'

As she gasped in outrage, he lunged forward and trapped her left hand flat on the table-top, his palm pressing the winking diamond ring painfully into her finger.

'You've been working for him since you left school,

haven't you? What took him so long to realise you were the woman of his dreams? It was around about the time you got that little windfall, wasn't it? Did he make it a condition of his proposal that you invest your inheritance in his business, or did you do it all for love?'

'How dare you imply it had anything to do with money?' she said fiercely, fighting the sudden urge to burst into pathetic tears and throw herself on his mercy. 'Peter asked me to marry him before he ever knew about the trust!' The release, on her twenty-third birthday, of funds from a trust set up by her natural parents had been a surprise to everyone, including her adoptive parents, who had refused to accept a cent of it. It was for Vivian to use how she wished, they had said—so she had.

'The wedding's this Saturday isn't it? Your twenty-fifth birthday?'

Her eyes lowered, her hand curling into a white-knuckled fist as she pulled it violently from under his and thrust it down into her lap. His investigations must have been appallingly extensive. How much more did he know? Please God, not enough!

'Yes.'

Her curt response didn't stop his probing as he leaned back again in his chair. 'You must be looking forward to it after such a very long engagement? And only four days to go until death do you part. No wonder you look slightly. . .emotionally ragged. It's going to be a big church wedding, I understand. I'm amazed you could spare the time to dash down here. . .or was this a welcome distraction from the bridal jitters?'

Vivian lifted her chin and gave him a look of blazing dislike. At the same time she lifted her champagne glass and took a defiant sip.

He watched her with a thin smile, and suddenly she had had enough of his subtle tormenting. Any moment now she was going to lose her temper and give the game away. Thinking, In for a penny, in for a pound, she closed her eyes and recklessly quaffed the whole lot. It really was glorious, like drinking sunshine, she decided, drenched in a fizzy warmth that seemed to invade every body-cell.

She was still feeling dazzled inside when she re-opened her eyes and found him regarding her with serious consternation.

'You shouldn't knock Dom Perignon back like water!'

Well, she had certainly succeeded in changing the subject! She gave him a smile that was almost as blinding as her hair. 'I thought that was the way you were supposed to drink champagne. It gives such a delicious rush! I think I'll have some more.' She held out her glass.

His jaw tightened. 'One glass is more than sufficient for someone who claims not to drink very much.'

'But I like it. I want another one,' she insisted imperiously. 'A few minutes ago you were trying to ply me with wine, and now you're sitting there like an outraged vicar. More champagne, *garçon*!' she carolled, waving the glass above her head, suddenly feeling marvellously irresponsible. She might as well get thoroughly drunk before she met her fate.

'Vivian, put the glass down before you break it!' he ordered sharply.

'Only if you promise to fill it,' she bargained, crinkling her eyes with delight at her own cunning.

He looked at her silently for a moment, during which her body began to take on a slow lean in the chair. 'All right.'

She chuckled at him. 'You promise?'

'I promise.'

'Cross your heart and hope to die?'

'Vivian——'

'Stick a needle in your eye——!' She broke off the childish chant, putting her free hand to her open mouth, her face blanching under the freckles. 'Oh, God, Nicholas, I'm sorry.'

'The glass, Vivian——'

She was too shocked at her thoughtlessness to register anything but her own remorse. 'Oh, Nicholas, I didn't mean it, I was just being silly. You mustn't think I meant——'

'I know what you didn't mean, Vivian,' he ground out, as she regarded him owlishly from behind her spectacles.

'I would never tease you about your eye,' she whispered wretchedly.

'I know,' he said grimly, lunging to his feet and reaching for her glass just as her limp fingers let it go. It slid past his hand and shattered on the stone-flagged floor into hundreds of glittering shards.

'And now I've smashed your lovely crystal,' she said mournfully, her eyes brimming with more tears at the knowledge of the beauty she had carelessly destroyed. 'You must let me buy you another one.'

'By all means pay for the glass. You've smashed a hell of a lot worse in your time. Perhaps it's time you were made to pay for that, too,' he growled, and caught her just as she toppled off the chair, bumping her cheek-bone on the edge of the table.

'Oh!' Her back was arched across his knee, her head drooping over his powerful arm, hands flopping uselessly to the floor. 'You've gone all wavy and soft,' she murmured dizzily.

'Your glasses have fallen off.' His voice came from such a long way away that she had to strain to hear it. Her thoughts seemed to flow stickily through her head, oozing aimlessly like melted honey and slurring off her tongue.

'Why won't my arms move? What's happening to me?'

'Perhaps you're drunk.'

She felt a warm weight slide under her knees and then the whole world went around and she gave a little cry as she seemed to float up towards the heavy-beamed ceiling.

'I don't think so. I never get drunk.' The rocking feeling didn't make her feel sick, as the boat had. She was being carried, she realised muzzily, struggling against the dragging desire to melt into the arms that held her against a hard chest.

'What's happening, where am I going?' she slurred weakly.

'Wherever I care to take you,' came the terse reply. 'Don't you know what you've done, Vivian?'

She had used to know, but somehow the knowledge was now wispily elusive. 'No, what have I done?' she mumbled.

'You've pricked yourself on a thorn, a very dangerous kind of thorn. . .'

'Poison.' The word floated up through her subconscious without fear. 'Was it poisonous? Am I dying now. . .?' It was much nicer than she expected, she decided woozily, aware of a strange, shining whiteness all around.

'No, damn it, you're just going to sleep. You're only drugged, not poisoned.'

'Must've been a rose-thorn, then,' she said, having trouble getting her silly tongue around the words. There was a flat, echoing, metallic rhythm coming from somewhere close by, keeping time with the rhythmic rocking that was making her float higher and higher away from reality. Confusing images clouded in her wandering brain. 'Was a rose, wasn' it. . .tha' caused all th' tr'ble? In B-Beauty an' the Beast. . .'

'You're getting your fairytales mixed up, Sleeping Beauty.' The bitter steel of his voice cut into her fading consciousness. 'I may be a beast but my name's not Rose—it's Thorne, Nicholas Thorne.' His grip tightened and he shook her until her bewildered green eyes opened, staring fiercely down at her.

'You do remember my name, don't you, Vivian?' he burst out harshly. 'Even if you never saw my face. Nicholas Thorne. The man you almost destroyed ten years ago. The Olympic athlete whose future you smashed to bits with your car?'

She stirred weakly in his arms. 'No. . .!'

'The man whose wife and son died while you walked away with hardly a scratch,' he went on relentlessly. 'Do you believe in the Bible, Vivian? That justice is an eye for an eye. . .?'

She rejected the horror of what he was implying, the black eye-patch suddenly dominating her hazy vision. Perhaps he intended that it was the last thing she would ever see! Frantically she tried to bring her hands up to hide her face, to protect her eyes from his avowed revenge, but they, like the rest of her body, refused to respond to orders.

'*No!*' She was falling now, with nothing to save her. He had thrown her from the high place into a pit of horror. She was falling down, down, down and he was falling with her, his breath hot on her face, his unmasked hatred and the formidable weight of his hard body pressing her deep into the soft white oblivion that was waiting to receive them.

'Ssh, I've got you.'

Her body twitched feebly. '*No. . .*'

'Fight it all you like, Vivian, it's too late,' he murmured in her ear, with the cruel tenderness of a murderer for his victim. 'All you're doing is hastening the drug's absorption into your system.' His hand was heavy across her throat, his thumb pressing against the sluggish pulse under her jaw as his voice deepened and roughened. 'You may as well accept that for the next few hours I can do whatever the hell I like with this voluptuous young body and you won't be able to lift a finger to stop me. Would Marvel want you back, I wonder, if he knew that someone else had grazed in these lush pastures?'

Strangely, the lurid threat with its menacingly sexual undertones didn't terrify her as it should have. To be ravished by a man who could make her tingle all over with just a look didn't seem such a bad thing. She was sorry she would miss it. She might even have said as much, for as her eyelids seeped closed for the last time she heard a soft, incredulous laugh.

Her last conscious awareness was of his mouth warm on hers, his tongue sliding intimately into her moist depths, a leisured tasting of her helplessness as large hands began smoothing off her clothes.

And the sound of someone wishing her sweet dreams.

CHAPTER FOUR

When Vivian opened her eyes she was still trapped in the fuzzy white wilderness.

She blinked, and discovered that she was lying in an incredibly soft, warm bed and the whiteness was the curving surface of a wall a few inches from her nose. She reached out to touch the rough plaster surface, using the contact with reality to push herself upright, meaning to peer out of the narrow window which broke the curve of the wall at the end of the bed. Instead she sank back on her heels with a smothered moan as her head swam horribly.

'Poor Vivian. Head thumping like a drum?'

She opened herself mindlessly to the warm sympathy in the sugar-coated voice. 'Umm. . .' she groaned in inarticulate agreement.

The sugar melted to sickly syrup. 'Hangovers are a bitch, aren't they? I had no idea you were such a reckless drinker. I told you champagne shouldn't be knocked back like water. . .'

Vivian swung around on her knees and froze, uttering a gasp of shock as she discovered why the bed was so blissfully warm.

'*You*!'

'Who did you expect? The faithful fiancé?'

Nicholas Thorne was sprawled beside her, his solid outline under the covers blocking the only escape-route from the narrow single bed. His tanned shoulders were

dark against the stark white pillows and his chest above
the folded sheet bare, apart from a thick dusting of gold-
flecked body-hair that didn't soften the impact of the
powerful slabs of raw muscle. Even lounging indolently
in bed he managed to exude an aura of barely leashed
strength. His head was propped against the stout slats of
the wooden bed-head and, with his tousled blond hair
and scarred beauty, and a mockingly cynical smile on
his lips, he looked to Vivian like the epitome of sin—
a fallen angel begging for the redemption of a good
woman. . .

It was a shockingly seductive thought and she
wrenched her eyes away from their forbidden fascination
with his body, all too aware that his expression of sleepy
amusement was belied by the tension in the muscles of
his arms innocently resting on top of the bed-clothes,
ready to thwart any foolish lunge to freedom across his
body. Not that she was in any condition to make one.
She could hardly think, over the riot in her head. She
rubbed a hand across her aching eyes and gasped, suddenly realising what was so different about him. He
wasn't wearing his eye-patch.

'You have two eyes!' she blurted out.

'Most people do,' he said drily. 'But, in my case, one
is strictly non-functional.' He angled his head so that she
could see the immobility beneath the distorted left eyelid,
the clouded iris.

'H-how did it happen?' she whispered shakily.

'You have to ask?'

She closed her own eyes briefly. 'Yes, it seems I do.
They told me at the time that your injuries weren't
serious——'

'I find that hard to believe.'

Her eyes flew open at his harsh scepticism. 'I was only fifteen! Still a minor as far as the law was concerned—nobody told me very much of anything. The police dealt mostly through my parents——' She broke off, realising the dangers of her impulsive self-defence. 'But you can't blame Mum and Dad for wanting to protect me,' she protested quickly. 'They were just doing what any parents would have done in the circumstances. . .'

In fact, they had been so anxious that she should not be traumatised by the tragedy that they had shielded her from all publicity surrounding the accident, and most of her concrete information had come from that dreadful night at the hospital where, still in a state of shock, she had been gently questioned by a Police Youth Aid officer. She was told that the pregnant front-seat passenger of the other car, Mrs Barbara Thorne, had been thrown out and killed instantly when it rolled down a steep bank. The driver, Nicholas Thorne, had suffered concussion and leg injuries. His son, who had been belted into a back seat, had also miraculously escaped without life-threatening injury.

The car-load of boisterous teenage party-goers, including fourteen-year-old Janna, that Vivian had been driving home along the gravelled country road had suffered only shock and bruises.

To her relief he didn't pursue the point. Instead he stroked a finger across his scarred lid and said simply, 'Fragments of flying glass. This was slashed to ribbons, although fortunately my sight seemed to have suffered only temporary damage. But an infection set in a few months later. A microscopic sliver of glass had worked its way through to the back of the eye. . .'

And here she was moaning in self-pity over a mere headache! 'And. . .your leg?'

'Not as bad as the limp might suggest. I can do pretty well everything on it that I used to.'

'Except run.'

Several days after the tragedy she had overheard part of a low-voiced conversation between her parents in which her father had said it had been a twin celebration for the Thornes that night—Nicholas's twenty-fifth birthday and the announcement that his sprinting had earned him selection to the New Zealand Olympic team.

'Oh, I can still run. Just not like a world-class sprinter,' he said, in a voice as dry as dust.

'I see. . .' She might as well plough on and remind him of *all* the dreams that meeting her on a rainy road that night had crushed. 'And. . .you never married again?'

'No.'

The clipped reply said more than all the rest. 'I'm so sorry,' she said, her voice crushed with guilt and compassion.

His expression tightened dangerously, then relaxed as he studied her gravity, the sincerity of the pain-glazed green eyes and tragic freckled nose. His gaze flickered over her kneeling figure, and he smiled with sinister intent that curled her toes.

'How sorry, I wonder?'

'Wh-what do you mean?' She put a hand up to her pounding head, overwhelmed by the impossibility of dealing with his unpredictability in her debilitated state. One moment he seemed charming, almost gentle, the next he was brimming with black-hearted villainy.

Maybe she wasn't even awake yet at all. Maybe this

whole ghastly week was just one, ultra-long, insanely bad dream. . .

'Having trouble concentrating, Vivian?'

'My head. . .' she muttered, hating herself for showing such weakness in front of him.

'Perhaps you'd like some hair of the dog? Champagne seems to do wonders for your mood. Makes you very. . .co-operative.'

Vivian stiffened. 'It wasn't the champagne, it was whatever vile stuff you put in it,' she growled raggedly.

'You mean the chloral hydrate?' He met her accusing glare without a flicker of remorse. 'I assure you, it's a very respectable sedative—the drug of choice for a whole generation of spy novels. Hackneyed, perhaps, but very effective: tasteless, odourless, highly soluble and fast-acting. You might feel a little hung-over for a while, but there won't be any lasting physical effects—at least, not from the *drug*. . .'

She wasn't up to interpreting any cryptic remarks. She was having enough trouble trying to establish the most obvious facts.

'Where am I, anyway?' she croaked, looking around the small, cheese-wedge-shaped room.

'The lighthouse. I'm in the process of having it converted into living-space. In fact, you might say this is the penthouse suite.'

Vivian winced as his words reverberated like a knell of doom inside her fragile skull. She lifted her other hand and massaged her painfully throbbing temples, desperately trying to remember how she had ended up in bed with her worst enemy—a man who ten years ago had accused her of murder and Janna of complicity, in words that had burned the paper on which they were written with their vitriolic spite.

Her fingers pressed harder against the distracting pain as she asked the question that should have been the first thing out of her mouth.

'What are you doing here?'

'If you mean physically, rather than existentially, at the moment I'm just enjoying the view.'

He wasn't referring to the window behind her, Vivian realised, as his gaze slid several points south of her pale face, where it settled with a sultry satisfaction that made her belatedly aware of a growing coolness around her upper body.

She looked down, and gave a mortified shriek as she saw that her chest was as bare as his—more so, since she didn't have a furry pelt to cloak her firm breasts, thrust into lavish prominence by her unconsciously provocative pose. All she had to hide behind were her freckles, which were scant protection from his mocking appraisal. In the split second before Vivian whipped her arms down, she was shamefully aware of a tightening of her pointed nipples that had nothing to do with the invisible caress of chilled air.

Flushed with humiliation, she snatched at the bedclothes, tugging the sheet up to her face as she cringed against the rough wall behind her. Outrage burned away her drug-induced lethargy as her blush mounted. All the time that they had been talking, Nicholas Thorne had *known* that Vivian was unaware of her semi-nudity. While she had been seriously struggling to communicate, he had been encouraging her to flaunt herself like a floozie, savouring the anticipation of her inevitable embarrassment!

She skimmed an exploring hand down under the covers and found to her deep dismay that all she had on were her tiny bikini panties.

'What happened to my clothes?' she demanded furiously, sweeping a blurred look around the room. The bed, a small bedside cabinet and a strange, triangular clothes-horse in the centre of the room appeared to be the only furniture. No closet or clothes, masculine or feminine, appeared in evidence.

'Don't you remember taking them off?' he asked, shifting to fold his arms casually behind his head, his leg brushing her knee under the covers and making her jump.

'No, I do not!' she gritted back fiercely. 'I remember *you* taking them off.'

Her fingers tightened their grip on the sheet, her eyes blazing green fury above the white veil of cotton as it all came rushing back in vivid detail. He had been kissing her, gloating over her helplessness, and it was only because of his insidious drug that she hadn't fought him tooth and claw!

But she wasn't helpless now, she thought grimly. He wanted a run for his money and that was what he was going to get!

After all, that was the reason that she had knowingly walked right into the jaws of his meticulously baited trap.

Her plan was beautifully simple: by presenting Nicholas Thorne with his prime target at point-blank range, she would draw his fire long enough to exhaust or at least appease the machiavellian lust for vengeance that was compelling him to treat anyone and anything that Vivian loved as a pawn to be used against her.

'Did I?' His surprise was patently mocking. 'Goodness, how shocking of me. Are you sure it wasn't just a wishful fantasy?'

'The last person I would want to fantasise about is *you*!' She whipped the sheet down to her chin, raking him with a look of furious contempt. She was prepared to take anything he dished out, as long as he left her family alone. The success of her whole mission hinged on his never finding out that she was a willing self-sacrifice.

'You lured me here under false pretences. You drugged me and took off my clothes!' she hissed at him goadingly.

'Only the ones that were superfluous to requirements,' he replied blandly.

'What in the hell do you mean by that?' She bristled like a spitting ginger kitten, all kinds of wild scenarios exploding through her scandalised imagination.

'What do you think I mean?' He stretched the arms behind his head languidly, expanding the impressive structure of his chest as he murmured tauntingly, 'Are you wondering whether those sexy emerald-green panties are a tribute to my gentlemanly honour. . .or to my sexual ingenuity?'

Since it happened to be exactly what she was thinking, Vivian reacted furiously. 'In the circumstances, I hardly think the question of *honour* arises,' she said scathingly.

'You may be right,' he stunned her by replying. He came up on one elbow and Vivian reflexively jerked the covers more securely around her.

Unfortunately, her hasty movement tugged the coverings away from the other side of the bed, exposing Nicholas's long, muscled left flank, lean hip and rippling abdomen. The skin was slightly darker on his half-raised leg and thick torso than on his hip, the naked swimsuit line jolting her with the knowledge that, while she might be semi-nude, he was totally naked!

Thankfully his modesty was preserved by a vital fold of sheet, for Vivian's wide-eyed attention lingered for a startled moment before being hurriedly transferred to his face.

'Some parts of me are fortunately still *extremely* functional,' he purred, his undamaged eye glinting with a predatory amusement. 'Especially in the mornings. . .'

'*Mornings*?' Vivian's hot face swivelled gratefully away from him towards the soft yellow-pink glow at the window. 'But. . .it's sunset,' she protested in weak confusion. 'It's just getting dark. . .'

'Actually, it's getting light,' he corrected. 'That window faces east, not west.'

Vivian sucked in a sharp breath as the full implication of what he was saying hit her. She hadn't just lost a mere hour or two. She had already spend half a day and a whole night entirely at his mercy!

'Quite so,' he said softly. 'This is the morning after, Vivian. Which, given the fact that we're in bed together, naturally poses the deeply intriguing question: the morning after *what*?'

Vivian stared at the thin, sardonic curl of his mouth that hinted at depths of degradation she hadn't even considered.

'Oh, my God, what have you done?' she whispered fearfully, her body shivering with the disgraceful echo of a half-remembered thrill.

'More to the point, what *haven't* I done?' he murmured wickedly, pivoting on his elbow in a fluid flow of muscle to retrieve something from the bedside cabinet behind him.

He offered it to her and, when she refused to let go of her flimsy shield of bedclothes, let a cascade of coloured rectangles spill on to the rumpled fabric between them. Her back glued protectively against the wall, Vivian frowned stiffly down, afraid to move, and frustrated that the surface of the bed was just beyond the range of her near-sighted focus.

'Here, perhaps these will help.' He sat up in a flurry of bedclothes, ignoring her automatic cringe as, moments later, he pushed her spectacles on to her wrinkled nose. 'Better?'

It was a hundred times worse! Vivian stared, appalled, at the photographs scattered like indecent confetti over the bed.

'Oh, my *God*. . .!'

'It's a little too late for prayers, Vivian. Your sins have already found you out. Quite graphically, too, wouldn't you say?'

'How. . .? I. . .You——'

He interrupted her incoherent stammering smoothly. 'I would have thought that the *how* was self-evident. There's this clever modern invention called photography, you see. . .'

The sarcastic flourish of his hand made Vivian utter a soundless moan as she saw that what she had myopically mistaken for a clothes-horse was in fact a tripod, topped with a fearfully sophisticated-looking camera, its lens pointing malevolently at the bed.

'And as for the I and you, well—we appear to be pretty brazenly self-evident, too, don't we? Here, for instance. . .'

Vivian's hypnotised gaze followed his pointing finger. 'See the way you're arched across the bed under me, your arms thrown over your head in abandoned pleasure. . .'

Vivian clamped the blankets rigidly under her arms, freeing her trembling hands to try frantically to push his away as he sorted through the collection and selected another.

'But this one is my own personal favourite, I think. So artistic. . .so erotic. . .so expressive. Don't you agree that we make a sensuous contrast of textures and patterns? With your ginger-dappled skin and my deep tan, and the way our bodies seem to flow over and around each other. . .'

Vivian tuned out his honeyed taunts, transfixed by the searing image suspended from his fingers.

She had seen raunchy advertisements for perfume in glossy women's magazines that were more physically revealing, but it was impossible to be objective now. The couple in this photograph weren't anonymous models posing for public display. That was *her* caught in an attitude of utter abandon, that was *his* nude body aggressively crushing her to the bed. She went hot and cold at the idea that he had somehow tapped into her forbidden desires.

Even as a tiny, clinical voice of reason was pointing out that the alignment of Nicholas's fingers on her hip conveniently covered the precise area where the thin strip of her bikini panties would be, Vivian was shattered by a sickening sense of betrayal. The pictures lied; they depicted an act of violation, not of love!

She tried to grab the photographs out of his hand and, when he laughed jeeringly and held it out of her reach, she fell desperately on the others, tearing them into meticulously tiny pieces, all the while trying to protect her threadbare modesty with the slipping covers.

He laughed again, making no attempt to stop her wild orgy of destruction beyond retaining safe possession of his avowed favourite. 'There are plenty more where those came from, Vivian. It was a very long, exhausting night. . .'

'I was unconscious,' she panted, rejecting his sly insinuation. 'Nothing happened——' She stopped, stricken. 'My God, you were going to do this to *Janna*?'

'Actually, the original plan was for someone else to play your sister's partner in sin,' he drawled. 'And when they supposedly disappeared together, with the payment for the land, I would send you photos of the lovers and evidence that they had planned the fraud together. You were supposed to come dashing to her defence on the eve of your own wedding, sadly too late to rescue the contract that your company was depending on, but in plenty of time to negotiate the salvage of Janna's personal and professional reputation—at the price of your own, of course. . .

'Your arriving in Janna's place sabotaged the exquisite complexity of the plan, but I'm nothing if not flexible. As soon as I saw you, I knew I wanted the privilege of handling you to be purely mine. . .'

She had already guessed much of it, but the callous detachment with which he outlined the bare bones of the plot was chilling.

She gasped, as an even more horrible thought smacked her in the face. 'Who took the photos? Who else was in here, watching us——?' She broke off, shuddering with humiliation at the thought that Frank had been a flint-eyed witness to her degradation. . .

'I can promise you, Vivian, you weren't seen or touched by anyone but me.' He took a small black wafer of plastic from the table by the bed and pointed it towards the tripod, pressing a button so that she could hear the electronic whirr as the flash momentarily dazzled her eyes. 'Remote control. It's a state-of-the-art instant camera—the photos only take a few minutes to develop.'

He rolled off the bed and Vivian uttered a choking cry, closing her eyes a fraction of a second too late to deny herself a glimpse of taut male buttocks and hard, hair-roughened flanks.

'Prude.' His mockery singed her burning ears. 'Here.'

She peeped warily through her lashes and relaxed a trifle when she saw that he had pulled on his jeans. He was holding out the thin red sweater he had worn the previous day.

He shook it impatiently at her immobility. 'Come on.' He threw it on the bed. 'Put that on.'

'I want *my* clothes,' she said stubbornly, as she watched him apply his eye-patch, raking his thick, blond-streaked hair over the thin band of elastic that held it in place.

'Then want must be your master.' He put his hands on his hips, legs aggressively astride, a bare-chested pirate. 'Or rather, *I* shall—and as your master I'm quite happy for you to remain without clothes indefinitely. In fact, yes, I rather like the idea of keeping you here naked. . .' He invited her to consider the notion in a dark, seductive voice, watching her defiance waver. 'Nude, you'd be so deliciously vulnerable, so much easier for me to control. . .'

With a muttered curse, Vivian snatched the sweater and hastily pulled it over her blushing head, contorting herself to arrange it carefully over the top of the bed-clothes before she let them go. Thankfully, the sweater came to mid-thigh, although she still felt horribly exposed as she crabbed to the edge of the bed and swung her feet tentatively to the floor.

'That colour makes you look like a fire-cracker with a lit fuse.'

The faint suggestion of approval confused her. She was acutely conscious of the scent of him clinging to the sweater, mingling with her own, and of the soft brush of the thin fabric against her bare breasts. She licked her lower lip, and then fingered it nervously. It felt fuller than usual.

'What are you going to do—with the photographs, I mean?'

'Why, there's only one honourable thing *to* do with them.'

Hope flared briefly. 'What's that?'

He plucked her hand from her mouth and mockingly kissed the backs of her fingers.

'Have them delivered to the church on Saturday, of course. Your poor fiancé must be given some reason for being left stranded at the altar!'

His tongue flicked against her knuckles, stroking her with a brief sting of moist fire that distracted her from his bombshell. She jerked her hand away, but not before he had caught her wrist and with a savage twist removed Peter's ring from her finger.

'We'll send this bauble along with the pretty pictures, just to make sure he gets the message that he can't have you.'

He tossed it in the air and caught it, flaunting his possession before thrusting it casually into his pocket.

'You can't do that. . .' Vivian whispered, her first thought of the havoc he could wreak on an already tense situation, that was, if the wedding hadn't already been cancelled. Had Janna and Peter taken her advice seriously and gone ahead with the arrangements, or were they still stubbornly wallowing in joint guilt and remorse?

'Marvel will never marry you now, Vivian. Learn to accept it.'

'No, Peter loves me!' she declared desperately, jumping to her feet. On one level, at least, it was still true. It was because of his deep affection and respect for Vivian that he and Janna had put themselves through such torture over the past few weeks. Vivian hadn't even been able to maintain a righteous fury over the betrayal, for it was obvious that the guilt-stricken pair had suffered agonies trying to ignore and then deny their love, in order not to hurt sweet, gentle, defenceless Vivian.

She had bluntly told them to stop being so nobly self-sacrificing. The practical thing to do would be to forget the huge hassle of calling off the elaborate wedding-arrangements and returning all the presents, and just switch brides. Janna and Peter had looked so appalled that Vivian had burst out laughing. It had been the laughter more than anything that made her realise that perhaps she wasn't as heartbroken as a jilted woman should be.

So, when the first opportunity had presented itself for her to prove that she wasn't the sweet, gentle, defenceless creature everyone was going to feel sorry for, she had grabbed at it defiantly with both hands.

'Marvel's going to take one look at those pictures and know it's all over between you.' Nicholas continued his ruthless attack. 'He'll never be able to forget the sight of you burning in your lover's arms——'

'We're not lovers!' Vivian shrieked. 'Those pictures—

they're all fakes. You just. . . You posed me, like a *mannequin*——'

'Did I really, Vivian?' he taunted softly. 'You were very willing. Don't you remember telling me how I made you feel all soft and hot and buttery inside, and grumbling that it wasn't fair you had to miss out on the thrill of being ravished by a sexy villain. . .?'

'That was the drug talking, not me! There's a big difference between being barely conscious and being *willing*,' she pointed out with smouldering force. 'And— and, anyway—if I. . . If we *had* done anything. . . I'd *know*. . .'

'How?' He seemed sincerely curious.

She practically melted her spectacles with the glare she gave him. 'I just would, that's all,' she said stubbornly.

'Not if I was *very* skilful and very tender, and you were very, very receptive. . . Not if you were all soft and buttery inside,' he said, in a satin murmur that slithered over her skin.

'Stop it! I won't listen!' she cried childishly, covering her burning ears with her hands. His eyes dropped to the sharp rise of the hem of his sweater as it flirted against her upper thighs, and she hurriedly lowered her arms. 'No one else will listen to your lies, either. They'll believe *me*. . .'

'But you won't be there to tell them the truth,' he said smoothly. 'You'll be here with me. You don't think I'm going to let you go so easily, do you?'

'But you have to let me leave eventually.' She tried to sound confident.

'*Eventually*, you may find that you don't *want* to leave. . .'

His insinuating murmur filled her with alarm. What

was he suggesting—that he intended to turn her into some kind of. . .*sex*-slave, addicted to the forbidden pleasure that he could provide?

'You can't keep me imprisoned here forever. . .' she protested faintly.

He shrugged. 'Who's keeping you prisoner? You came here of your own free will. In fact, you've already sent a fax to your office saying that everything is fine and that you'll be back with the contract the day before the wedding. So don't think anyone's going to come flying to your rescue.'

That much was true. She had been too secretive, too determined to solve the problem herself.

When she had gone to visit Nicholas Rose's lawyer, to plead that her sister's illness made it impossible for her to deliver the settlement papers personally, as arranged, Vivian had been still reeling from what she had discovered on her visit to Janna's flat.

Then she had bumped into a secretary over-loaded with files, and glimpsed among the scattered papers a letter addressed to Nowhere Island—but to Nicholas Thorne, not Nicholas Rose.

Some fast and furious digging for information had brought answers that had shocked her out of her self-pitying depression and sent her charging off in a spirit of reckless bravado.

Only now was she realising how ill-prepared she was for her mission. Nicholas Thorne had shown no sign so far of being open either to intimidation or to reason.

Vivian swallowed. Damn it, she couldn't afford to let negative feelings undermine the determination that had brought her here!

'Look, I realise that you genuinely feel that you have

some justification for hating me, but don't you see that what you're doing is *wrong*. That car crash was an *accident*. The police investigated it thoroughly at the time——'

'Your sister claimed that our car skidded as we came around the corner,' he said neutrally.

'Yes, but Janna wasn't *accusing* you of anything,' Vivian explained eagerly. 'She was just describing what she saw. The police said the skid-marks confirmed that neither of us was speeding. . .it was just the way the gravel had been shifted by the rain, making the road unstable—an act of God. . .'

Then she added gently, because she knew the tortuous ways that guilt could haunt the innocent, 'Neither of us was to blame for that night. Not me and not you. We'll never know if we could have prevented it by doing something slightly faster or reacting differently, but being human isn't a *crime*. . .'

She broke off because he was looking at her extremely oddly. 'You think I blame *myself*?'

She hurriedly changed her tack. 'When I wrote to you back then, I just wanted you to know that I was sorry for the accident. . .I didn't mean to taunt you with your grief, if that was what you thought. I—I never showed your reply to anyone else. I didn't think you meant those terrible threats. I thought it was just your grief lashing out. I can't believe you've nursed that mistaken grudge all these years. Surely, for the sake of your son, you should have put the tragedy behind you——'

'My *son*?'

The floor suddenly seemed to heave beneath her feet as Vivian realised what his arrested expression could mean. 'I—I know he was injured, and it's all a bit hazy now, but at the hospital I remember the doctor saying he was a very lucky boy to be in the back seat... H-he *is* still alive, isn't he?'

He nodded slowly. 'Very much so.'

'Oh. *Oh*! That's great!' Vivian's eyes were starry with brilliant relief. 'And...in good health?' she asked, with more restrained caution.

'Excellent.'

She beamed at him. 'I'm so glad for you!'

He cocked his head with an ironic smile. 'So am I.'

'It must have been a terrible experience for a child,' she said, her emotions swinging wildly back to deep compassion.

'At fifteen, you were little more than a child yourself.'

She drew herself up to her full height, once more unsettlingly conscious that the top of her head barely reached his unshaven chin. 'I've always been mature for my age.'

'You like children?' he asked inconsequentially.

'Of course I like children,' she said, bewildered.

'Some women don't.'

'Well, I *love* them,' she said firmly. She lifted her chin defiantly. 'Peter thinks I'll make a great mother.'

His eye narrowed. 'From what you know of me, you should be on your knees begging for mercy, not deliberately going out of your way to annoy me,' he warned with silky menace, and she gasped as his big hand suddenly curled around her throat, applying an uncomfortable pressure to draw her towards him until her breasts rested against his chest.

'Take your own advice, Vivian, and forget the past. You're not going home to marry Marvel; you're not going to have his children or share any kind of future with him. . .'

His hand tightened under her jaw, lifting her up on to her toes, so that she had to clutch at his thick shoulders for balance, her fingers sliding against his smooth skin.

'I'm your future now. I'm the one who controls your destiny.' She gave a little yip as his free hand slipped under the hem of his sweater to splay warmly across her quivering, tautly stretched belly. 'And I'm the one who controls your fertility. The first child you'll ever carry in your womb will be *mine*. The first baby to suckle at your breast will belong to *me*, as you will. . .'

Vivian trembled in shock at the starkly primitive statement of possession and her equally primitive response. Her lips parted soundlessly as his fingertips skimmed under the lacy band of her panties and pressed gently into the fringes of the downy thicket between her thighs.

'Such a fiery little nest. . . Is it as hot and spicy as its colour suggests? I'll bet it is. . .' She gave a faint whimper that was stifled by the nip of his teeth against her tender lower lip and his purred praise vibrating over her tongue. 'I bet you're hot and spicy all over when you're in sexual heat, peppered with those delicious freckles and salted with the sweat of your arousal. I look forward to dining on your splendour. . .' His hand moved up to brush briefly across the silky undersides of her heavy breasts, pausing to discover the betraying tightness of her nipples.

He made a deep sound of male gratification and suddenly released her, stepping back to study with ferocious pleasure her swaying body and her dazed look of sensual confusion.

His chest rose and fell rapidly, his body rippling with

arrogant satisfaction as he straightened her glasses, which were fogged and slightly askew.

'You do see the exquisite justice of it, don't you, Vivian? An eye for an eye is such a paltry vengeance for a man of my sensual nature. I prefer a much more intimate, pleasurable and *fruitful* form of revenge. . .'

CHAPTER FIVE

'LOST something, Ginger?'

Stomping out of the dilapidated old boat-house, which it had taken her half an hour to break into, Vivian stopped dead.

Yes, my sanity, she wanted to say. She must be mad to allow him to play these games with her; crazier still to be enjoying it.

Nicholas Thorne had threatened her in the most elemental way a man could threaten a woman, and yet it wasn't fear that made her heart race and her stomach churn whenever he was near. . .

She looked up, squinting against the slanting rays of the setting sun.

He was leaning against the corner of the salt-encrusted wooden building, a familiar, infuriating smile of mockery twisting his narrow mouth, an oilskin jacket flapping open over his grey fisherman's sweater and the usual pair of jeans. Somehow she had difficulty picturing him in a conventional suit, yet he must wear one all the time in his role as ruthless head of a sprawling business empire.

'A boat, perhaps?'

'You have to have one somewhere,' she growled, disturbed as ever by his wicked humour. 'You can't live on an island without owning *some* kind of boat.'

'Feel free to look around,' he replied with another quirk of his lips.

'Thank you, I will,' she said cuttingly.

She was glad she was muffled up in the bulky knitted jumper and her green woollen trousers for around Nicholas she was uncomfortably aware of her body. It was the way he looked at her—complacent, possessive, *knowing*. . .

At least she had clothes to cloak her self-consciousness. After staking his nerve-shattering claim on her womb, Nicholas had calmly directed her to her suit, blouse and bra lying crumpled under the bed and led her, clutching them in a bundle, down the iron stairs to the room below, where she had found her empty brief-case and the small suitcase she had left back at the motel at Port Charles. It held only toiletries, her nightdress and a single change of clothes, but it was enough to give her a slight sense of false security.

The sweater she was wearing, however, was his, reluctantly accepted as a necessity if she was to tramp around the island in the blustery weather and not die of exposure. It had amused him to lend it to her, just as it amused him to follow her around so that she couldn't just sneak off and *pretend* to search for an escape, she had *actually* to do it, thoroughly exhausting herself in the process. He was always hovering, offering irritatingly helpful suggestions and teasing her with intriguing little titbits of information about himself that increased her curiosity about him to a dangerous craving.

The more that she found out about him, the more Vivian's compassionate heart whispered that Nicholas was basically a good man whose fixation with brutal revenge was a cry from the wilderness of his frozen emotional landscape. He had found the loss of his beloved wife and unborn child unacceptable, so, in the nature of a competitive man used to winning, he *hadn't* accepted it, and the long years of denial had formed a barrier against natural healing.

In order to save herself, Vivian had realised that she would first have to save him. . .

'Poor Vivian,' he commiserated. 'Three whole days of scouring every nook and cranny and you still haven't succeeded in finding a way off the island. When are you going to give up?'

'Never!' She pushed past him and began stalking back up the uneven path from the rocky cove.

'Stubborn wench.' He was close on her heels. 'Maybe you should try offering bigger bribes. Frank was quite offended by the low price you put on his loyalty.'

She snorted. His number-one henchman had proved to be predictably incorruptible, but Vivian had known she was expected to go through the motions. She put her nose in the air, and promptly stumbled and teetered on the edge of a sharp, jagged incline.

At powerful arm whipped round her waist, dragging her back against him. Instinctively she reached behind her to clutch at the sides of his coat, her shocked breath rasping in her throat.

'Don't worry, I won't let you go,' he said, wrapping his other arm around her. 'You're safe.'

She felt his face nuzzling into the side of her neck, the stubble of his jaw pleasurably rough against her skin, and for a moment she leaned weakly against him, tempted by his gentleness.

'Safe? That's a laugh! I won't be safe until I get home!'

'Oh, yes, I bet you feel boringly safe with Marvel,' he said mockingly. 'Two years engaged to the man and your dossier says you never stay overnight at his flat.

I'd say that indicates a pretty huge lack of excitement on both sides——'

'Just because I'm not promiscuous it doesn't mean I'm sexless!' she flashed from the depths of her insecurity, deeply resenting his familiarity with the private details of her life.

'I don't think you're sexless, just surprisingly unawakened,' he told her smoothly. 'But I wake you up, don't I? You rise so beautifully to the slightest hint of bait. No wonder you're so gullible—you're tough on the outside and marshmallow within. A delicious bundle of contradictions. . .'

'*You* can talk,' she said, bristling at the gullible label.

'Oh, do you find me delicious, Vivian? I'm so glad it's mutual.' He smiled archly. 'Would you like another sample?'

'No, thank you!' she lied tightly. That searing, sensuous first kiss in his room had also been his last. His dark threats of sexual domination had made her lightning-swift response to his touch all the more shaming, and yet he hadn't pressed his advantage.

Braced for further brutally expert assaults on her deplorably shaky defences, Vivian had instead been left at the mercy of her own fevered imagination. This subtle form of self-inflicted torture had been refined with an added sadistic twist by Nicholas—she was still forced to share his bed every night.

The first night Vivian had searched everywhere, and been forced to accept that he was telling the truth when he said there were no extra beds. When she had tried to curl up fully-clothed on the couch in the living-room of the keeper's cottage, Nicholas had simply slung her over his shoulder and borne her off to his room in the tower, coolly telling her that she could change into her night-dress in privacy, or he would strip her himself and she could sleep with him naked. She had chosen dignity over humiliation and then lain on her side facing the wall, stiff with mingled rage and agonised apprehension as she felt him get in behind her.

Then—nothing!

He had whispered goodnight, tucked his arm comfort-ably around her middle, yawned and gone to sleep. She had tried to wriggle out from under his arm, but in sleep he was just as possessive, his hand sinking more securely under her waist, a thick, hair-roughened thigh pushing between her knees to drape over her leg, anchoring her firmly against the bed. Even through her blessedly mod-est nightgown she could feel the warm shudder of his heartbeat against her back and the firm definition of his manhood pressed against her soft bottom.

Each succeeding night it had taken her longer to fall asleep, and each morning when she woke up in a con-fusion of blushes it was to find that some time in the night she had turned over and mingled with him in a trusting sprawl of limbs.

To her chagrin he accepted her rejection with a careless shrug. 'I came to tell you that Frank almost has dinner ready,' he said. 'And I've already warned you it's not a good idea for you to be stumbling around out here alone when it starts to get dark. Look what nearly happened just now——'

'That was because you were distracting me. Maybe you did it on purpose,' she goaded, inexplicably angry at him for caring. 'Or maybe you'd like to see me go over a cliff, to be killed by an "accident". That would be rough justice for you, wouldn't it?'

In the waning light his features were blurred into softness, his eye deeply shadowed by his fierce brow. 'Do you really think I brought you here to kill you?'

'I. . . No,' she admitted truthfully. His declared intent had been to cause her maximum mental suffering and she couldn't suffer if she was dead. 'But we both know there are worse things than dying. . .'

He moved closer. 'Like bearing my child, you mean? Would that really be a fate worse than death, Vivian? To make love with me and create a new life. . .?'

The wind snatched her breath away. 'You only said that to frighten me, she choked. 'I know you weren't really serious——'

'Do you? Just because I haven't mentioned it again?' He captured her gaze with the bold assurance of his glittering brown eye. 'I knew I didn't have to. I knew you were thinking about it every time you looked at me—wondering what it would be like to accept me as your lover. Wondering if I would make love with the same passionate intensity with which I seem able to hate. I was giving you time to get used to the idea. After all, there's no real urgency now that you're here, living, eating, sleeping with me. I've waited this long for you. . .I can wait a little longer. . .'

A *little* longer? Heat suffused her body at his arrogant sexual confidence. She fought to cool her instinctive response. How could she feel anything but revulsion at his depraved suggestion?

She shivered. 'Surely you wouldn't use force to—to——'

'Not force—seduction,' he said smoulderingly. 'We both know that there's been some very volatile physical chemistry brewing between us since the moment we met.

Why don't you just accept that we were always fated to become lovers?'

Fate again. Wasn't that the very thing she had come here to defy boldly? Vivian shivered once more.

'You're cold—why didn't you say so?' Nicholas scolded her, shrugging impatiently out of his jacket and wrapping her in the heavy oilskin, tucking her chilled hand firmly through his elbow as he escorted her back along the stony path towards the cottage. 'You should have worn the parka I offered you. No sense in cutting off your nose to spite your face. And if you're going to go storming around in a temper, watch out for the wildlife—they have first priority. Nowhere Island is a wildlife sanctuary and part of a maritime park. All these outlying islands are really the tops of drowned hills, and the eroded volcanic tubes that riddle the shore and sea-floor make very rich habitats for marine life.'

'You sound like an environmental tour-guide,' she said grumpily, trying not to respond to the enthusiasm in his voice.

'I should hope my learning is a little more useful than that,' he said drily as he opened the back door. 'As a marine biologist, I don't approve of environmental tourism.'

'What!'

He pushed her stunned figure over the threshold of the kitchen, where Frank was cursing over a sizzling pan.

'You're a property developer!' she accused, as he whipped his jacket from around her shoulders and hung it on the back of the door.

'I'm also a marine biologist. It *is* possible to do more than one thing with your life, Vivian. One doesn't have to limit oneself to living down to other people's expectations,' he said softly. Was that a dig at her?

He pressed a finger against her jaw, pushing it closed with a slight snap. 'What's the matter, Ginger? Aren't I fitting into your stereotype of a grief-crazed vengeance-seeker?' He stepped away. 'I'm going to have a quick shower before dinner.' The dark gleam of light reflecting off his eye-patch managed to give the startling impression of a wink. 'Feel free to join me if you want to help conserve the tank-water.'

As soon as he was out of the room, Vivian turned to Frank.

'Does he really have a degree in marine biology?'

'Yep. An athletic scholarship in the States.'

She waited but, as usual, further information was not forthcoming.

'You don't talk much, do you?'

'Don't have much to say.'

She would have been offended if she hadn't discovered that he was almost as taciturn in his communications with Nicholas. She hadn't quite worked out Frank's job description yet; he seemed to be a combination of assistant, valet, bodyguard, mechanic—he had already fixed the faulty back-up generator—and chief cook and bottle-washer.

'Where's Nicholas's son?'

He shrugged. 'Ask Nick.'

'He won't tell me. He won't talk about his son at all. Or his wife.' She gave a little huff of frustration. 'How long have you worked for Nicholas? Did you ever meet his wife? Do you know what she was like?'

That brought the hawkish face around, bearing a hard stare.

'Six years. No. Beautiful.'

It took her a moment to realise he had actually replied to all her questions. She sighed. 'I thought she must have been.'

Astonishingly Frank's dour expression broke up in a grin.

'Nothing like you.'

She scowled. 'OK, OK, you don't have to rub it in. She was so perfect he's never met another woman to match up to her.'

'Is that what he told you?' His grin widened and she studied him with suspicious green eyes.

'What's that supposed to mean?'

He shrugged. 'It's your life—you figure it out.'

And, with that irritating observation, he crouched down to open the oven and stir something inside.

Vivian was about to demand a proper answer when her eyes fell on a bulge in the front pocket of the jacket hanging against the door. She remembered the weight of something bumping against the side of her knee with a vaguely familiar chink as Nicholas had hurried her along. His keys! She had searched all over the light-house, but there was one place she hadn't been able to look.

She darted silently over and boldly plunged her hand into the pocket. Fisting the key-ring, she just had time to nip back to the other side of the room before Frank closed the oven and turned around.

'Uh, I think I'd better go and change for dinner,' Vivian said uncomfortably, edging out of the door.

Her heart was in her mouth as she crept down the hall. The plumbing in the lighthouse was still incomplete, so Nicholas would be showering in the cottage bathroom and probably had his fresh clothes with him, which meant he wouldn't need to go back to his room before dinner. Even if he did, the locked room was on the fourth landing, and she would have plenty of time to hear him on the stairs and whip up to the next level to fossick innocently in her suitcase.

The locked door hid exactly what she had suspected: an office. A businessman with Nicholas Thorne's autocratic reputation would never trust anyone enough to relinquish control of his business, even temporarily. She pulled the door softly to, and switched on the light.

There was a computer work-station and various unidentifiable pieces of electronic equipment, and a big desk strewn with papers.

Vivian ignored the wall of shelves lined with jars and tubes of dubious-looking specimens, her heart sinking at the sight of the heavy steel combination-safe on the floor.

She went over to the desk. Only the top drawer was locked and she rifled quickly through the others, finding mostly stationery and files of scientific papers and journals. Nothing that might tell her more about Nicholas the *man*. No stray photographs of his wife or son. No photos of any other kind either. . .

Adrenalin spurted through her veins and her sweaty hands shook as she unlocked the top drawer and sat down on the big swivel chair behind the desk to reach inside.

The first thing she touched was a small medicine bottle, and her fingers tightened around the amber glass as she picked it up and read the typed label: chloral hydrate. Her soft mouth tightened and she pushed the half-full bottle into her trouser pocket, intending to dump the contents at the first opportunity.

Her heart gave a nervous convulsion when she saw what the drug had been sitting on—the settlement contract, signed, witnessed, dated—intact and still viable. . .

She lifted it out and weighed it in her hands. But no. . .even if she took it, where could she hide it? The fact that Nicholas hadn't already destroyed it was surely a hopeful sign. As long as it lay here undisturbed, Marvel-Mitchell Realties still had a future.

She put the contract back, her breath fluttering as she slid it to one side and saw her forlorn dis-engagement ring crowning one very distinctive, disturbingly erotic photograph. She tried not to look at the haunting image, afraid to touch it lest she become further victim to her depraved fascination with Nicholas Thorne.

But where were the others Nicholas had taunted her with? The wedding was supposed to be the day after tomorrow. If only she could continue to stave off disaster until the ceremony was over! She didn't want her wedding-present to Peter and Janna to be a bunch of pornographic photographs and a threat of financial ruin. She could just imagine the poor vicar's face if he caught a glimpse of any of those pictures. She would never be able to hold up her head in church again!

However much she longed to believe that her brief presence here had taken the edge off Nicholas's bitterness, had softened and changed him, she didn't dare take the risk of relying on her increasingly biased judgement where he was concerned. Only when Janna and Peter were safely and securely married would Vivian let herself take the gamble of trusting Nicholas, telling him the truth and hoping that he would justify her faith in his basic humanity.

She scrabbled frantically through the drawer, reaching deep into the back where she found something firmly wedged. She pulled it out.

A cellphone. She flicked a switch. A *working* cellphone.

Civilisation was only a single telephone call away.

The alternatives bolted through her brain in the space of a split second. She didn't have to go through with it. She could call Peter—call the cops. She could cause a scandal. Make a great deal of misery for everyone concerned, but save herself.

And perhaps drive Nicholas out of her life forever. . .

She let the telephone clatter back into the drawer at the same instant that she became aware of another presence in the room.

She hadn't heard him on the stairs and now she saw why. His feet were bare as he crossed the uneven wooden floor, not making a sound. He wore only a white towelling robe and his hair drifted in damp clumps across his brow.

He was breathing hard. And he was angry.

'Careless of me.' Nicholas leant over and slammed the drawer viciously shut, nearly catching her guilty fingers in the process.

'And even more careless of you to be caught.' He locked it and wrenched the keys out with a violent movement. Vivian slid out of the chair and nervously backed away.

'What were you doing, Vivian?' he demanded harshly, stalking her every move. 'Snooping? Or were you frantic to get to a phone so you could warn Lover-boy?'

The back of her thighs hit the computer table and she pulled her scrambled wits together as he halted, his whole body bunched with furious aggression.

'*No!*' His appearance had rendered her split-second decision redundant, but she wanted him to know what it would have been. 'No. I—I didn't even know there was a phone in here. I was just looking for the photos—the other ones you said you had——'

'I also said you were gullible,' he sneered. 'The only photos I had, you tore up—except for my personal favourite, of course. . .' He wasn't wearing his eye-patch and even his sightless eye seemed to blaze with sparks of angry golden life as he smiled savagely at her bitter chagrin.

'I was thinking of having it blown up and framed before I send it to Marvel,' he taunted. 'It'll have so much more impact that way. Perhaps I should even call him myself, give him a blow-by-blow account of how much pleasure I got from having his chaste bride-to-be *mounted*. . .'

She flinched at the crudely insulting *double entendre*. His volcanic rage seemed wildly out of proportion to the condescending amusement, even wry admiration, with which he had greeted her other failed attempts to thwart him.

'OK, OK, so I took the keys because I wanted to steal from you and snoop among your secrets,' she flared, fighting back with her own fortifying anger. 'I thought I might find something I could use to help persuade you to let me go. What's so terrible about that? *You* snooped through *my* life——'

He stiffened, his expression hardening to granite.

'And, tell me—if I suddenly agreed with everything you said? If I handed you your precious settlement contract and said all debts were cancelled—what then? Would you be able to walk away and forget that any of this ever happened? Would you still marry Marvel on Saturday?'

For a heartbeat Vivian ached to be selfish and trust to his sincerity. 'Why don't you let me go, and find out?' she said warily.

She knew instantly that she had made a serious mistake. His jaw tensed and colour stung his cheekbones as if she had delivered him a sharp slap across the face. Oh, God, had the offer been genuine?

'I wouldn't tell anyone, if that's what you mean,' she said quickly, hoping to repair the damage. 'Nobody back home has to know about any of this. It's still not too late——'

'The hell it isn't!' Turning away from her, he jerked his head towards the door and grated, 'Get out!'

Was he ordering her out of the room, or his life? She moved hesitantly past him. 'Nicholas, I——'

He sliced her a sideways glance of fury that stopped the words in her mouth. 'Frank said you were changing for dinner. Don't make a liar out of him.'

Then his voice gentled insidiously. 'And, Vivian. . .?' Her fingernails bit into her palms as he continued with dangerously caressing menace, 'If I ever catch you here again, you won't find me so lenient. Be very careful how much further you provoke me tonight. I'm in the mood for violence. . .'

'If I ever catch you here again. . .' He wasn't sending her away! Vivian was shocked by the turbulence of her relief as she shakily made her way up to the room where she kept her meagre selection of clothes.

Deciding it might be deemed further provocation not to obey his thinly veiled command, she quickly put on a fresh blouse, the cream one she had worn the day of her arrival, and changed her sneakers for her low-heeled shoes. The trousers, she decided with the dregs of defiance, could stay—she could do with their warmth around her woefully trembly knees.

The kitchen had been transformed in her absence. It was no longer a bright, practical workplace; it was a shadowy corner of a private universe, lit only by twin flickering candles set on a table laid for two. A casserole dish sat in the centre, flanked by a bottle of red wine and two glasses. Nicholas, she discovered with an upsurge of her heartbeat, was still wearing his white robe—a spectral white phantom floating at her out of the darkness.

'What happened to the lights?' she asked sharply. 'Where's Frank?'

There was a brief gleam of teeth from the phantom and a movement of his head so that she could see that the dark triangle of his eye-patch was back in place, his vulnerability well-masked. 'I'm conserving generating power,' he said, in a tranquil tone of reason that sent a frisson down her spine. His silky calm was like the eye of a hurricane—she could feel the energy swirling around it. 'And Frank's already eaten. He's in his bedroom. Why? Did you want him for something?'

The innocent enquiry made her seethe. He knew damned well why she wanted a third person present! Frank was no use as a buffer tucked away in his little concrete bunker down the hall.

It was pure nerves that made her blurt out as she sat down, 'I'm not sleeping with you tonight!'

He sat across from her, leaning his chin on his hand so that his face moved forward into the flickering pool of light, his eye gleaming, a tiny candle-flame dancing like a devil in the hot, black centre. 'What's so different about tonight?'

She was hypnotised by the devil. 'It just is, that's all.'

'Do you mean that you're more aware of me as a man than you were last night?' he murmured.

She didn't think that was possible! 'An *angry* man,' she qualified stiffly.

'I've been angry with you before. Usually you just fling my temper back in my teeth.'

'Usually you behave with more self-control.'

His smile was darkly knowing. 'Maybe it's not *my* lack of control that you're worried about. Don't you trust yourself in bed with me any more, little fire-cracker? Afraid I might have lit your fuse?'

Her soft mouth tightened and he laughed softly, reaching across the table towards her. Vivian stiffened, but he was only removing the lid from the casserole.

'You dish up the food. I'll pour the wine.'

'Oh, but I don't know if I like red wine——'

'You'll like this one. It's a gold-medal winner from a vineyard I part-own in Gisborne,' he said, brushing aside her diffidence as he filled her glass. He poured himself a glass, drank half and refilled it, all in the time it took her to ladle some of the steaming casserole on to their plates.

She waited until she had eaten several mouthfuls of food before she took her first sip. In spite of her determination not to react, she was unable to prevent a murmur of surprised pleasure as the full-bodied flavour exploded against her palate, drenching her senses in its heady bouquet.

'You see, you never know whether you're going to like something until you try it. You need to be more adventurous, Vivian, experiment more. . .'

She didn't like the strange tension in him. . .nor the dangerous ease with which he broached the bottle as they both pretended to eat. She noticed he had shaved since their confrontation in his office. It had been necessary for him to shave but not to *dress?* She felt a strange thrill of fear.

'Weren't you afraid?' he said disconcertingly, his deep, hushed tone seeming to weave itself into the darkness. 'The only locked room in Bluebeard's castle. . . Weren't you afraid of the horrors you might find in there when you stole the key?'

'This isn't a castle and you're not Bluebeard,' she said, resisting the powerful vision he was slyly conjuring out of her imagination. 'You've only ever had one wife,' she said deliberately. 'And I'm certainly in a position to know that you didn't murder her.'

He looked at her broodingly over the rim of his glass. 'Ah, yes, my beloved wife. Frank tells me you're curious about her. . .' Vivian was suddenly certain that Nicholas was building up towards some kind of critical release of the tension that raged in his face, seethed in his restless eye.

'I'm in the mood for violence. . .'

She rubbed her damp palms surreptitiously against her thighs and felt the forgotten bulge in her trouser pocket.

The idea sprang into her mind full-blown. Her fingers closed around the glass bottle warmed by her thigh.

'I wouldn't mind a drink of water, please.'

He got up, moving with his usual swiftness and precision, and Vivian knew that in spite of the wine he had consumed he was still dangerously alert. It was only his inhibitions that had been relaxed, and thus the bonds that chained his savage inner demons.

The moment he turned away to the sink, she pulled out the chloral hydrate, wrenched off the lid and tried to shake a few drops into his full wine glass, horrified when the clear liquid came out in a little gush.

She didn't have time to get the bottle capped and back into her pocket, and had to thrust it down on her lap as she accepted her glass of water, feeling the remainder of the drug soak into the fabric over her hip as her heart threshed wildly in her chest.

'You wanted to know about Barbara. . .'

She watched, her green eyes wide with fascinated horror, as he re-seated himself and took a long swallow of his wine before he spoke again. Oh, God, what madness had possessed her? What if she had given him too much and he died?

'The biggest mistake of my arrogant young life. . .'

Mistake? Vivian was jolted out of her frantic abstraction.

His mouth twisted at her expression. 'You thought it was the love-match of the century? Mis-match, more like. It was my father's idea. He's an extremely dominating man and I'm his only son, his greatest pride—and his greatest disappointment. We clashed on just about everything. When I came back from university overseas, he was very ill and used some very clever emotional blackmail to pressure me into marriage with his god-daughter. Needless to say, he then miraculously recovered.'

'Then. . .you fell in love with each other after the marriage?' Vivian said, her thoughts falling into chaos.

'Love was never part of the equation. Like my father, Barbara saw our marriage in terms of status and control. We lived separate lives from the start. She politely endured me in her bed because it was necessary in order to secure her permanent place in the Thorne dynasty—

part of her bargain with my father, I gather—and I politely endured for reasons just as selfish, because I wanted nothing to disturb my build-up for the Olympic trials. . .'

He paused and Vivian held her breath, hoping the fascinating revelations were going to continue.

'Then Barbara told me she was pregnant and I realised just how permanent was the trap my father had planned for me. Except it wasn't—the next day she and the baby were killed. . .'

He reached for his wine-glass again and Vivian couldn't stop a darting gesture of involuntary protest.

'Oh, no, please don't drink that!' She clumsily tried to knock it out of his hand.

'Why not? Are you afraid I'll pass out on you before I finish baring my soul?' He stopped, his face sharpening as he looked from her stark expression of appalled guilt to his glass, his shrewd brain making the impossible leap in perception.

'My God, is there something wrong with this? *What have you put in my wine?*'

He lunged across the table with a roar, scattering the burning candles, and Vivian's chair crashed over as she jumped to her feet, sending the empty bottle in her lap spinning to the floor.

She didn't wait to see him recognise it. She fled.

She flew down the hall and crashed through the door into the lighthouse in a blind panic, triggering the sensor lights in the stairwell. She was thundering up the stairs before she remembered there were no locks on the doors, nowhere to hide. It was too late now; she could feel the pounding vibration of his mysteriously delayed pursuit through the steel under her flying feet.

He caught her just below the fourth level, not even attempting to stop her but merely gathering her up in his furious momentum, driving her onwards and upwards with the bulldozing threat of his body. Only when they reached the landing of his room did he actually lay a hand on her, catching her right wrist and using their combined speed to swing her away from the stairs and through the doorway, shoving her back against the wall, anchoring her there with the full thrust of his body, slamming his other hand on to the light-switch so that she was exposed to the full glare of his rage.

'How much did you give me?' he snarled, his breath fogging up her glasses, his lips brushing hers in an angry parody of a kiss. 'The whole damn bottle? How *much*, damn you?' He rattled her against the wall.

'I don't know—a little, a teaspoon, I don't *know*!' she panted desperately. 'I spilled the rest of it, that's why the bottle was empty. I'm sorry, Nicholas, I panicked, you were frightening me. . .' She was begging now, but she was beyond caring. 'Please, I'm sorry——'

'*Sorry*!' he ground out. He shook his head violently, as if the drug was already beginning to affect him.

'Maybe you should sit down before you fall down,' she said, feeling wretchedly weak herself.

'Maybe I should,' he said thickly. He pulled her away from the wall and dragged her over to the bed, pulling her between his spread legs as he sat down, fumbling in his bath-robe pocket. She felt a cold metallic clasp replace the heat of his hand on her wrist, and looked down just in time to see him snapping the other handcuff around his own wrist.

'My God, what are you doing?' she asked numbly, staring at their shackled limbs. So this was why she had got such a head start on his superior strength and speed. He had gone to get *chains*!

'Making sure you'll be here when I wake up,' he said grimly. '*If* I wake up.'

She shuddered. 'Don't say that! Please, Nicholas, where's the key? You don't need to do this. I promise I'll stay. . .'

For an answer he fell diagonally back on the bed, throwing his shackled right wrist forcefully out to his side so that she was brought tumbling down on top of him with a soft scream of terror. He pulled off her glasses and tossed them on the floor in a careless gesture that she found paradoxically even more threatening than his violence.

'Nicholas, no. . .' She struggled to find purchase with her knees against the mattress, conscious that she was straddling him, and the towelling robe was parting over his powerful thighs.

'Nicholas, *yes*!' He pulled her head down, crushing her mouth against his, wrapping his right arm across her back so that her captive arm was forced behind her. He kissed her until she tried to bite him, and then he nudged her face aside with his jaw and sank his teeth into her vulnerable throat. She cried out, struggling weakly as he began to suckle at the bite, murmuring words against her skin that sapped her will and created tiny shocks of pleasure deep in her feminine core. He began to kiss her again, and this time she didn't fight him and the forceful thrust of his tongue gentled to a slow, seductive glide that made her tremble with yearning.

'I may pass out, but not before I've had a taste of you. . .not before you've given me everything I want. . .' His mouth moved to the other side of her throat, nibbling and sucking with tender savagery as his hips and thighs began to undulate beneath her. 'I'm going to devour every lovely inch of you. . .use my lips and teeth and tongue on you in ways that you've never even imagined. . .brand you all over with my mark so that anyone who looks at you will know you've come from my bed. . .'

Vivian knew he was talking about Peter. Briely surfacing from her passion-drugged state, she tried to arch away, but Nicholas shifted his hand from the back of her neck to the front of her silk blouse, slipping his fingers into the prim neckline and ripping it open with a single downward stroke that scattered the pearl buttons like lustrous tears across his chest.

'Nicholas!'

Her gasp was lost in a spasm of violent sensation as he flicked open the tiny plastic catch between her breasts and allowed them to tumble free of the confining lace. The ginger freckles were stretched over their swollen fullness, the soft pink tips swaying against the hard contours of his chest, contracting instantly into tight points that scraped and caught on his own peaked masculine nipples.

His chest heaved and he uttered a harsh sound, violently tilting his hips to roll her on to her side and then her back, hefting her up against the pillows, rising up and over her on his braced hands. In almost the same motion he loosened the belt of his robe so that it fell open around her, baring the full length of his body to her restless gaze. He was hugely aroused and shuddering with a fierce tension, for all the world as if she had given him an aphrodisiac instead of a sedative.

He looked triumphantly down at the lavish bounty he

had exposed, his nostrils flaring as he caught the enticing
scent of her body, and recognised the subtle signals of
her arousal.

'Yes—*Nicholas*,' he ground out. 'Not Peter, *Nicholas*.
Admit it. You couldn't give a damn about him when
you're with me!'

He cupped her breast with a possessive movement of
his manacled hand, the narrow chain connecting their
wrists dragging in a cold caress against the skin of her
ribs as he moved deliberately, his fingers contracting and
relaxing, his thumb rubbing against the rigid nipple.

He bent his head and his tongue darted out to curl
around the tip he was cherishing, dragging it up into his
mouth, moistening it with tender care then releasing it
to the cool night air.

'You don't love him; you don't want to marry him.'
The words were muffled by her flesh. 'You don't want
to cling to your safe, unadventurous past. . .you want
the fierce excitement only I can give you. . .you want
this. . .and this. . .' He held her pleasure-drenched gaze as
his mouth closed over her, slanted softly, sucked lightly,
twisted, lifted and lowered again. . .

'I'm. . .not. . .the one who won't let. . .the past go,' she
panted, biting her lip as he repeated the voluptuously
unsatisfying action over and over, clenching her chained
hand helplessly against her side, groaning with sweet
agony as he finally used his teeth and suckled her with
the rough urgency that she needed, marking her as he
had promised with his erotic brand of possession. Her
extravagant response made him explode into action,
pushing heavily between her thighs, moving jerkily on
her as if the fabric between them didn't exist, as if he

was already buried deep inside her, pleasuring them both beyond imagining. . .

'Say it, Vivian. . .stop holding yourself back. . .stop pushing me away.' She was suddenly aware of a settling heaviness in his body as his head sank down on her shoulder. 'Don't let me go down into this damned darkness without a prayer. . .'

'Stop talking about dying!' she cried frantically, tugging at his hair to try and keep him awake.

'I'm not talking about dying, I'm talking about living. I can't let him get you. . . Gotta keep you with me,' he said with a blurred illogicality that Vivian knew from experience was the drug tightening its grip on his mind, but she sought to drag him back to her with desperate words of truth.

'Peter won't ever get me because he doesn't *want* me, damn you. Do you hear me, Nicholas Thorne? You were right. I don't love Peter and Peter doesn't love me. He loves my *sister*. It's *Janna* he's going to marry on Saturday, you big, gullible oaf, not me!'

For a moment he remained still, a dead weight, and she thought he had lapsed into unconsciousness, but then he suddenly rolled off her in a tangle of white towelling.

'What did you say?'

The face beside hers on the pillow suddenly looked completely wide awake. But no, his pupil was almost a pinpoint. He was conscious through sheer force of will.

She moistened her lips and nervously tucked her blouse across her breasts one-handed as she said in a husky little voice, 'I cancelled our engagement last week. But not the wedding. You see, I found out Peter and Janna had fallen in love, and, well—they were sort of mired in the inertia of their guilt. They didn't deliberately set out to hurt me, and I realised I hadn't ever really been in love with Peter, not the way that Janna is. So I told her to go ahead and get married in my place and I'd dance at their wedding.'

She smiled to show how bravely she had accepted the crushing blow to her feminine pride, but the smile began to waver under his sombre stare and, to her horror, her eyes began to fill.

'I suppose now you're going to tell me I got what I deserved,' she whispered, and burst into a flood of tears.

But instead of gloating, as she had always dreaded that he would, Nicholas quietly gathered her shuddering body against his warm length and stroked her wild ginger mane, uttering soothing murmurs while she sobbed out all the wretched details against his chest.

It took a long time to expend her storm of stored-up tears, and repeated assurances from Nicholas that he had no interest in wreaking his savage revenge on her damned sister's damned wedding, before Vivian finally hiccupped herself into exhausted sleep. Only then did the man holding her allow his mind and body to go equally lax, finally relinquishing his formidable will to the powerful seduction of the drug in his veins.

CHAPTER SIX

VIVIAN took another frigid slap in the mouth and felt her throat burn with the salty abrasion as she coughed the sea-water out of her lungs.

She sluggishly instructed her head to turn and her arms to rise and fall, rise and fall, in the rhythmic stroke that had won several long-distance ocean swims at the surf-club she had belonged to in her late teens.

The wet-suit that she had taken from among the diving-gear in the lighthouse storeroom was providing her with extra buoyancy and some protection against the cold, but she knew that mental stamina would be her greatest asset in the gruelling swim.

She turned on her side, checking that she was still moving in the right direction, heading towards the uneven lurch against the horizon that Frank had let slip one day was the nearest inhabited island. Thank God the weather was good and the sea not too choppy, but even if there had been a cyclone Vivian wouldn't have cared.

She had woken just before dawn and looked at the man lying next to her in a deep, drugged sleep and acknowledged with a thrill of despair that she was in love with her capricious captor.

In the space of a few days the morals of a lifetime had been swept away. Instead of drawing Nicholas into the sunlight of reason, she had been drawn into the shadows. Something dark in herself was called forth by the darkness in him. She could protest all she liked, but all Nicholas had to do was touch her and she melted. And he knew it.

Last night he had admitted that he had never loved his wife. That called into question everything she had come to believe she knew about him. It made his motive for revenge not one of honest emotional torment, which could be appeased, but of cold-blooded, implacable malice.

The realisation that Nicholas must have uncuffed her before he fell asleep was merely confirmation of her bleak theory that he believed he had won their battle of wills. The empty steel bracelet dangling from his own still-manacled wrist was a mute testament to his confidence in her sexual subjugation.

Protest had exploded in her brain. *No*! She wouldn't let him distort her love into something that she was ashamed of. She had to be out of his reach before he woke up. Before he could touch her again. . .

Fool, fool, fool, Vivian chanted inside her head, in rhythm to her stroking through the water. To believe that you could play with fire and not be burnt. Fool, fool. . .

'Little fool! What in the hell do you think you're doing? Of all the ridiculous, theatrical stunts!'

She suddenly realised that the new voice was much deeper than the one in her head and far more insulting, and the loud slapping sound wasn't the rising waves hitting her face; it was the sound of oars striking the water.

Water sheeted down her face from her sopping hair, sticking her eyelashes together and getting in her swollen eyes as she stopped to tread water and was nearly run down by a small aluminium dinghy rowing furiously towards her.

Nicholas was shipping the oars, leaning over the side, yelling, cursing, trying to grab her slippery wet-suited arm.

Vivian swam away, coughing and spluttering as she briefly sank. When she struggled to the surface again, Nicholas was standing silhouetted against the crisp morning sky, the boat rocking dangerously. 'For God's sake, Vivian,' he cried bleakly. 'Where in the hell do you think you're going?'

Still choking on salt-water and shock, Vivian didn't bother to answer; she just pointed in the direction of the distant island.

Nicholas exploded in another series of explicit curses. 'Do you *want* to bloody drown? You can't swim that far! Get in this damned boat *now*!'

For an answer Vivian rolled over and began swimming with renewed energy. Each time she turned her head to breathe, she saw Nicholas pulling on the oars, keeping on a parallel course, his grim mouth opening and shutting on words she couldn't hear through her water-clogged ears.

Gradually Vivian's false burst of strength drained away and the next time that Nicholas veered close she didn't have the energy to pull away.

He leaned over and caught her by the zip-cord trailing from the back of her neck, forcing her to tread water as she clung to the side of the boat, gasping air into her burning lungs. 'That's enough! You've made your point, Vivian,' he said roughly. 'You want me to beg? I will: please get into the bloody boat. We'll talk, and then I'll take you anywhere you want me to. . .'

Her green eyes were enormous in her exhausted face. 'I'm not that gullible any more,' she choked, fighting her pathetic desire to trust him, even now. '*You're* the gullible one. You never fooled me at all. I knew even before I came here who you were!'

He looked thunderstruck. 'You *knew*?'

'That Nicholas Rose was Nicholas Thorne,' she threw into his haggard face. Her frigid lips and tongue shaped the words with increasing difficulty. 'But I came anyway, because I knew that if this was some kind of vicious v-vendetta, then the only way to stop you was to confront you face to face. . .so I let you d-drug me. . .I only *pretended* to w-want to escape. . . Everything you did to me you were only able to d-do because I *chose* to *let* you. . . Because I wanted t-time to b-be with you and c-convince you that r-revenge is n-not the way for y-you t-to find p-peace. . .'

Her teeth were chattering so much that she could hardly get the last defiant words out, and Nicholas made an abrupt growl and rammed his hands under her arms, hauling her over the gunwale and dumping her into the bottom of the boat.

'Thank you for *letting* me rescue you!' he said sardonically. 'I take it you weren't simply *pretending* this time.'

Vivian suddenly felt blessedly numb all over. Even her bleeding heart was cauterised by the cold. 'Why?' she whispered. 'Why did you b-bother to come and get me?'

'Why in the hell do you think? Because I love you, damn it!' he snarled savagely, not even bothering to look at her as he swivelled his torso to signal with his upraised arm. Automatically following his gaze, a stupefied Vivian saw the blurry image of a white launch that looked as big as an ocean liner foaming down on them.

'Coastguard?' Her mouth seemed to have split from her mind.

'No. Mine. The *Hero*. It's been out doing a marine survey for the last few days. As soon as I found your clothes on the beach, I called her up and used her radar to track you. Ahoy! Derek! Send down that sling, will you?'

She screwed her eyes shut as she was strapped and hauled and bundled, and passed from hand to hand like an unwanted package until she felt the familiar arms taking possession of her again.

Nicholas carried her down a brightly lit companionway and into a spacious white cabin, kicking the door shut before rapidly stripping the over-large wet-suit from her numb body.

His mouth quirked when he saw the emerald-green bra and panties she wore underneath. His smile thawed a tiny slice of heart. Maybe she wasn't hallucinating, after all. Maybe he really had said it.

'My favourites,' he murmured, fingering the saturated lace. 'Underwear that matches your eyes.' And then he peeled them off too, smothering her protests at his rough handling with a thick, blue towel, rubbing her vigorously until she cried out at the pain of the blood returning to the surface of her icy skin.

'Don't be such a baby!' he said, planting a kiss on her blue lips as he finished a strenuous scouring of her hair, which had turned the dripping tails to dark red frizz. 'We have to get you properly thawed out.'

He stripped off his own clothes and walked naked with her to the wide berth, lying down on it and mounding the patterned continental quilt over them both as the boat's powerful engines throttled to full power and the sky began to whip past the brass port-hole above their heads.

'Stop cringing, this is all very scientific. I'm a

scientist—I know what I'm talking about,' he said, cuddling her close, warming her with the sensual heat of his body, breast to breast, belly to belly, thigh to thigh. He shuddered and buried his face in her neck. 'Oh, *God*, that feels good.'

Vivian knew what he meant. Tears of exhaustion and confusion trembled on her still-damp lashes.

He lifted his head and kissed them away. 'I'm sorry, Ginger—first things first. If you had bothered to wait for me to wake up this morning, you would have known this already. . .in fact, you would have known last night if you hadn't sabotaged my good intentions. My name is Nicholas James Thorne. . .the Second.'

'The Second?' she whispered, bewildered. Was he suggesting they start all over again? A second chance?

'To distinguish me from my father—Nicholas James Thorne the *First*,' he said deliberately.

Her brow wrinkled soggily. 'Your father has the same name as you?'

'No *I* have the same name as *him*,' he corrected urgently, as if the fine distinction was important. 'Just before I was born he had an illness that rendered him sterile, which was why he was so obsessive about me marrying and perpetuating the name. There are two Nicholas Thornes, Vivian, but only one was driving the car that night—my father.'

Vivian's bleached face stormed with vivid emotion as she realised what he was telling her. 'But, your son——'

His fingers across her mouth hushed her confused protest, and the riot of blood in her veins became a visible tumult that bloomed across her skin. 'I have no son. Your "boy" in the back seat was me. To the doctor who patched me up, a twenty-five-year-old probably *did* seem like a boy—he certainly seemed old to me, although he was probably only in his late fifties.

'After Barbara was killed, my father said it didn't matter that I was crippled, as long as my genes were healthy. We had endless rows about my refusal to marry again. In the end I turned my back on it all—my father, his money, the business I was supposed to take over, the whole concept of Being A Thorne. I didn't realise that after the accident his dream had become a ruthless obsession, and the obsession had developed into a dangerous fixation with you. . .'

Vivian struggled to sit up, but Nicholas held her down with implacable gentleness. 'Are you saying this was all *his* idea?' she asked hoarsely through her salt-scored throat.

'I had no idea what he was planning,' he said emphatically. 'Not until I paid a long-overdue duty visit last week. As usual, our discussion turned into a furious row. He suddenly started shouting the most ridiculous things. . .about how it was all your fault his son had turned against him and how he was finally going to make you and Janna pay for murdering his grandson. How he had waited years for just the right moment to get you where he wanted you. . . He was boasting about how he was going to do it when he had a massive stroke——'

'Oh, God. . .' Vivian's fist came up to her mouth and Nicholas eased it away, unsurprised by her horrified compassion for the man who had tried to hurt her.

'No, he's not dead, but he's in an extremely bad way,' he said sombrely, wrapping her fist reassuringly in his. His body shifted against hers, enveloping her in a fresh wave of blissful warmth.

'As soon as he was taken to hospital, I scoured his

desk and files in case his incredible ravings were true. I found his dossier on you and a load of legal transactions with Marvel-Mitchell, and I got a shock to find it was actually on the verge of happening—and on Nowhere of all places—while I was scheduled to be away in Florida. Here!' His voice hardened and she felt the muscles of his chest tense as if against a blow to the heart. 'On *my* island. . .the place I used to come to get away from his insidious interference in my life. That was part of his sick delusion, you see' he added tiredly. 'That he was doing this for *my* sake. So I fired the sleazy hireling who was supposed to do all the dirty work, and flew down here myself to. . .'He hesitated uneasily.

'To take his place?' she challenged painfully.

He leaned up on one elbow and said ruefully, 'Actually, I came hot-foot to rescue you. To apologise and try to smooth things over and explain about my father's condition——'

'Rescue me? *Apologise?* By *drugging* me and photographing me naked in bed with you and threatening to make me have your *baby*?' Vivian squawked at him incredulously. 'You expect me to believe that was your idea of *smoothing things over*?'

To her fascination he flushed, adjusting his eye-patch in the first unconsciously nervous gesture she had ever seen him make. 'Yes, well, you weren't quite naked. And, anyway, that was partly your fault.'

'*My* fault?'

'I was expecting your sister. I had intended to be very civilised and restrained and then use my power of attorney to sign the settlement contract and wave Janna a grateful goodbye, but I took one look at you and went off like a rocket.' His voice roughened as he began to play with her damp ginger curls. 'I wanted you more than any woman I've wanted in my life. I can't explain it. I just saw you, touched you, and *knew* that we were made for each other, that you felt the same, powerful attraction that I did. . .

'But I knew from my father's file that you were due to get married in a week, so I didn't have much time. I decided to take some drastic short cuts, use every despicable tool conveniently placed at my disposal, to keep you here and break down your resistance to the notion of breaking up with Marvel. I thought that my pretending to be my father would buy me the time I needed to build on the potent physical chemistry between us. Of course, I didn't realise that you were also doing some bidding for the same reason. . .' he added slyly.

She placed her hands flat against his bare chest. 'Not quite the same reason,' she teased.

To her surprise he didn't smile. 'Are you trying to let me down lightly?' he asked quietly.

She suddenly realised that she hadn't told him. She traced his tight mouth with her forefinger. 'I woke up this morning horrified to admit I'd fallen in love with you,' she said softly. 'My heart skewered on the sword of an emotional pirate. You can't blame me for choosing the deep blue sea over the devil. You should have been more honest with me from the start. . .'

'Like you were, you mean,' he said drily, smiling at her rueful acknowledgement. 'It may not seem like it, but I do have *some* sense of honour, you know. I wasn't going to make love to you until you asked, and I wasn't going to ask you to marry me until you'd given Marvel his marching orders.'

'Marry!' He looked amused by her shock, and she

recovered quickly. 'I thought you wanted me to be your sex-slave,' she pouted huskily.

'That, too, of course,' he said, lambent flecks of gold sparkling wickedly in his eye at her sensual boldness.

He rolled over on top of her. 'And speaking of slavery. . .I had to be rescued from a very embarrassing state of captivity myself this morning. Handcuffed to my own bed! I had to drag it over to the door and spend fifteen minutes yelling down the stairwell before Frank heard and came up and jemmied the cuffs open for me. He'll never let me hear the end of it!'

'You should be more careful who you go to bed with,' said Vivian demurely.

His head lowered as his knee brushed between her legs. 'I will be. *Very* careful,' he murmured against her mouth. 'In future I'll only be going to bed with my fire-cracker wife.'

As she slid her arms around his satiny-hard waist and blossomed eagerly for his love, Vivian thought it sounded like a just fate for a retired pirate. . .

Some Kind of Hero

by
Leigh Michaels

LEIGH MICHAELS has always loved happy endings. Even when she was a child, if a book's conclusion didn't please her, she's make up her own. And, though she always wanted to write fiction, she very sensibly planned to earn her living as a newspaper reporter. That career didn't work out, however, and she found herself writing for Mills & Boon® instead—in the kind of happy ending only a romance novelist could dream up!

Don't miss THE BOSS'S DAUGHTER by
Leigh Michaels in March 2002 in
Tender Romance™!

CHAPTER ONE

LAUREN LEANED into the display window and pushed at the crumpled sheets of red tissue paper that lined it. If she flattened an area at the corner, there would be room for a small velvet box to nestle comfortably, almost against the plate glass, where no passer-by could miss the ruby-studded ring it held. And then. . .should she put out that sterling-silver bracelet with the heart-shaped links, or would the window look better with only gold?

She drew back to study the effect. It was hard to tell from her position inside the store what the finished window looked like from the outside. From this angle, it was impossible to tell if the glorious diamond in the necklace that was the centerpiece of her display caught the spotlight and fractured it into a dazzling rainbow, or if it looked as dull as a rock instead. She glanced out to the street, her head to one side, and then looked thoughtfully over her shoulder at the girl who was straightening the trays of diamond engagement rings in the display case across the store. 'Kim,' she began, 'could you give me a hand with this window?'

Kim didn't look up. 'If you're going to suggest that I stand on the street and tell you in sign language when you've got each piece of jewelry at the right angle, don't even think about it.'

Lauren laughed. 'I wasn't—not exactly.'

'Good. Because I'm not going out. Haven't you noticed? It's sleeting now.'

She was right. The January wind had shifted, too, and pellets of frozen rain were rattling against the plate glass. Lauren shivered. 'It's inside work,' she said. 'Just hand me things, will you? I can't keep crawling in and out, but I can't reach both the window and my supplies.'

Kim locked the engagement rings into the display case and crossed the room. 'Why can't you crawl in and out? It would certainly draw a crowd.'

Lauren made a face at her. 'Hand me that white leather glove. And the ruby dinner ring—No, not that one. The really exotic marquise with the baguette diamonds.'

Kim picked up the glove and the velvet box from the assortment scattered over the top of the display case and looked thoughtfully out at the storm. 'I may not go outside ever again. At least not till spring.'

From the back of the display area, the owner of the jewelry store sniffed. 'As long as you're not going anywhere,' he said, 'do you suppose you could manage to do some real work, instead of simply leaning on a display case looking decorative?'

Kim shrugged. 'I can't sell things if there are no customers, Mr. Baines,' she pointed out sweetly. The instant the man vanished into his office, she tugged hard at Lauren's sleeve. 'I thought he'd never leave,' she said in a rush, 'and he might be back any instant, and I've been choking myself to keep from asking since I came in the door this morning. Ward got the tickets for you, didn't he? How can you be so calm about it?'

Lauren's hand trembled just a little as she slid the ring onto the proper finger of the glove, so it looked like the languid white hand of a ghostly lady, draped across the red tissue. But her voice was perfectly calm. She had known, of course, that this would happen, and she had rehearsed the conversation in the mirror. 'No,' she said. 'He didn't.'

Kim's mouth dropped open. 'But he said—' It was practically a screech. 'Some birthday! I thought Ward told you it was going to be a special celebration.'

'He did. And it was. We had a very nice evening at his apartment, and he cooked steaks, and—'

'He didn't even take you out to *dinner?*'

'—gave me a book I've been longing to read, and—'

Kim dismissed the book with a gesture that verged on obscene. 'How perfectly romantic!' she said dryly. 'You were counting on those tickets, Lauren. What a horrible thing to do to you. Aren't you just furious at him?'

Lauren had to swallow hard to keep from agreeing, but admitting that to Kim would only encourage her to continue, and Lauren wasn't sure her pride could take much more.

If only Ward had not told her that he wanted to keep his plans for the 'very special celebration' of her birthday a surprise, she might not have let herself hope so much. She had been a fool, perhaps, but after that buildup, how could she help but be disappointed by an ordinary dinner and an ordinary book? Oh, the food had been wonderful, and she would genuinely enjoy the book, but how could things like that compare to the much-coveted tickets to the Hunter Dix concert?

The biggest trouble with Ward, she thought, was that there was not a single romantic bone in his body. If there had been, he would appreciate Hunter Dix's music—the most touching love songs anyone in the world was singing today—and he would not have to be told why his concert tonight was so important to Lauren.

'He knew how much you want to go,' Kim wailed. 'How could he *not* get you the tickets?'

Lauren had practiced the answer to that, and it came out sounding rather flat. 'The same way you and I missed out on getting them. There just weren't enough to go around, and they were snapped up by the members of the group that's sponsoring the whole event.'

'A bit selfish of them, I'd say,' Kim said unforgivingly. 'Just because we're not alumni of the college doesn't mean we're the dirt under their feet. They could have given us ordinary people a chance to buy them. But Ward knows enough of those people. Surely he could have talked a couple of tickets out of one of his doctor friends.'

'Apparently not. The few that aren't held by fans are in the hands of the scalpers, and they want a fortune. I can't blame Ward for not wanting to spend so much money on a single evening's entertainment.'

Kim didn't believe a word of it, and Lauren had to admit it sounded rather unconvincing. But how was she supposed to convince Kim when she wasn't convinced herself? she thought rebelliously. Kim was right; she was absolutely livid at Ward. She would walk on ground glass to be able to go to that concert, but just because Ward didn't happen to like Hunter Dix and his kind of music, he wouldn't ask his friends if they had extra tickets. He wouldn't do even that much for her. . ..

'Ward is a jerk,' Kim said, under her breath.

The comment startled Lauren back into sanity. 'No, he's not,' she said soberly. 'He's a very nice guy who just doesn't understand that this is the best chance I'll ever have to see Hunter Dix in person—' She stopped and bit her lip, and went on in a very small voice, 'The best chance I'll ever have to actually see and hear the best singer in the world.'

'Well, you'd better think twice before you marry him,' Kim said unsympathetically, 'or you'll never have a chance to go anywhere or see anybody.'

Lauren looked at her in surprise. 'Who said I was going to marry Ward?'

Kim shrugged. 'Everybody on the street thinks you're practically engaged. And you certainly act like it. You never date anyone else.'

That was true enough, and Lauren thought about it while she finished trimming the window, scattering pink marshmallow hearts and red silk roses among the jewelry. She had been dating Ward for months, and oh so slowly she'd stopped seeing anyone else. She almost hadn't noticed the change, for Ward had filled her time, and she liked him better than anyone else she had ever dated. So much better, in fact, that only yesterday it wouldn't have bothered her to know that everyone along the close-knit little street assumed that someday they would marry.

Whereas today. . .today it bothered her a lot.

BY MIDAFTERNOON it was almost dark, the wind had come up, and the sleet had turned to steady snow. The small flakes whipped against Lauren's face with cutting force as she walked slowly down Poplar Street toward the pharmacy. It wasn't that she really wanted to go there, but the pharmacy's snack counter was the only place in this small retail district to have lunch or get a cup of coffee. And she couldn't help the fact that Ward owned the pharmacy. She certainly wasn't trying to avoid him, was she?

Alma, the motherly woman behind the snack counter,

had a cup and saucer already out for her when Lauren sat down. 'Coffee or tea today, Lauren?' she asked. 'Or hot chocolate? I made it from scratch. Ward will be right down—I made sure he knew you were here.'

'Thanks,' Lauren said dryly. She remembered hearing much the same words on a dozen other occasions, but they had never grated on her quite this way before. 'Tea, please.'

She sat dunking her tea bag in the hot water and looking at nothing. Kim was right, then. Everybody on Poplar Street did assume that she and Ward had some sort of private understanding about their future—together.

But the fact was, they did not. Until today, it hadn't occurred to her to wonder about it, but now that she gave it some thought, the question made her feel almost queasy. Surely if Ward was serious he would have said something by now—not a proposal, perhaps, but something that indicated his intentions. And since he had not, in all these months, did that mean that he was contented to leave things just as they were? Birthday dinners, movies, pleasant Sunday afternoon drives—going on straight into the indefinite future?

A big hand brushed gently over her hair. It was typical of Ward's greetings; in public, there would be a restrained touch and a private smile, but never a kiss. Funny, she thought, that it had not occurred to her before. It wasn't that he had a distaste for physical contact, she knew, for last night, when she had arrived at his apartment, he had kissed her so long and thoroughly that she'd been practically smoldering by the time he'd finished. So what caused this hesitation now? Was it simply that he didn't want to commit himself in public?

'Sorry,' Ward said briskly as he sat down beside her.

'Everybody in the whole town has the blasted flu, and I'm an hour behind on filling prescriptions. I can't even stop for coffee.'

She didn't lift her eyes from the surface of her cup. 'That's certainly good for business.'

'Yes, but if I had my choice... Are you trying to drown that poor tea bag?' he asked, with a hint of laughter. 'Lauren...'

She looked up, then, into his face. His eyes were deep set and a wonderful shade of coffee brown, especially when they were lit by a smile, as now, and he had the world's longest lashes. It was a pleasant face, well put together, though not exactly handsome. His nose had character; his mouth was generous; his ears were a little large—or did they look that way only because of the sternly conservative cut of his dark hair?

She had teased him once about his haircut, and he had confided the advice he'd been given by the previous owner of the pharmacy, who had warned him that people found it hard to trust a man who looked too young, no matter how solid his qualifications. 'I can't exactly make myself look wrinkled and stooped,' Ward had finished, 'but I can be careful about my haircut and my clothes and the way I talk and act, so that I look solid and trustworthy and not like some harebrained kid.'

Lauren had listened, straight-faced, and then solemnly recommended that he have half of his hair surgically removed and the remainder dyed gray. That was when she first discovered the dimple lurking at the corner of his mouth, just waiting for him to laugh, and she had promptly forgotten haircut and all in her fascination with that improbable little dent in his cheek.

It was so fascinating, in fact, she told herself, that she

hadn't ever noticed how stubborn his chin was, and how unyielding the line of his jaw.

That wasn't fair, she told herself. After all, no two people can agree on everything, and if they did it would make life pretty boring.

But still. . .Ward didn't even seem to know how much she had been hoping for those tickets! He hadn't any idea, despite all her hints, how important it was to her. He obviously hadn't wanted to get the message. She wondered what he would have said if she had come straight out and told him how much she wanted to go to that concert?

He was watching her, too, and his eyes were twinkling. 'For an older woman,' he teased, 'you're holding up really well—'

'Ward,' she said abruptly, 'could you try once more to get just two tickets?'

He sighed. 'Are we back to what's-his-name again?'

'Don't worry,' she said grimly. 'I'm not asking you to come along. The tickets are for Kim and me.'

'Lauren, there just aren't any.'

'If the price is right, someone will sell. You certainly know enough people who have tickets, Ward. And you don't need to be concerned about what it costs. I'll pay you for them.'

He said quietly, 'It's that important to you.'

It was not a question, but she nodded, anyway. 'Ward, please.' It was a bare whisper.

'All right,' he said, his voice still quiet. 'I'll try. But—'

'Thank you.' It was cool.

Ward pushed himself off the stool. 'I'd better get back to work, or I'll be two hours behind.' His hand flicked over her hair again, and revealed the sparkle of diamonds on her earlobe. 'New earrings?' he asked casually.

Lauren nodded.

He tucked a windblown blond lock of hair behind her ear, and studied the inch-long curve of glittering stones, half a carat's worth in each ear. 'They're pretty. I'll let you know what I find out.'

'I'll be at the store until six.'

She didn't watch him go. Alma came to clear away the mess, and eyeing the earrings, said, 'I'd be afraid to wear that sort of thing myself. I'd be petrified of losing one.'

'No big deal. They're insured.' Lauren paid for her tea and went back to work. Her hopes were no better about the odds of getting a ticket, but at least she had done the best she could.

Mr. Baines was arranging a new shipment of pearls in the velvet-lined case. 'Did anybody notice the earrings?' he asked eagerly. At Lauren's nod, he beamed. 'I knew having you wear them would be a good idea—those perfect earlobes of yours make a great advertisement. Wear them for a week or so, all right?' He didn't wait for an answer, but went off toward his workroom, whistling.

'Perfect earlobes,' Kim muttered, on her way to the door for her own afternoon break. 'You've got perfect hands, too, long and slender and just right to show off dinner rings. And that throat. . . We should all be so lucky.'

Lauren grimaced at her. 'I thought you weren't ever going outside again.'

Kim let her coat slide off her shoulders and gave it a

backward kick into an out-of-sight corner. 'Not right now, I'm not.'

Lauren looked at the cast-aside wrap with concern; it wasn't like Kim, the clotheshorse, to mistreat her things like that. But Kim's face was rapt as she stared out the window, and instead of saying anything, Lauren followed her gaze and found herself looking at a long white car that had pulled up just in front of the jewelry store. 'What on earth?'

'You might as well ask,' Kim said. 'That, my friend, is a limousine. A Cadillac limousine.'

'I know a limousine when I...' Lauren's voice trailed off.

'But how many people do you know who might be riding around this city today in one?'

A man in a dark uniform and a gold-braided cap got out of the driver's seat and opened the limousine's rear door for his passengers.

'That's Hunter Dix,' Lauren whispered, as the famous profile came into view. 'And he's coming in here.'

THE UNIFORMED DRIVER climbed back into the car, and Hunter Dix turned toward the jewelry store. The two burly men with him wore very dark glasses.

What a hoot, Lauren thought. As if they needed protection from brilliant sunshine instead of the gray gloom of a winter storm.

One of the men came in, glanced around the store and then jerked his head to the other, who held the door for Hunter Dix and followed him in.

Of course, Lauren thought. They were bodyguards, and the dark glasses allowed them to look around without it being obvious what they were looking at. Bodyguards—she hadn't thought, before, about the need for them. Hunter Dix probably couldn't go anywhere without them, for fear of being mobbed by fans.

Across the store, Kim fiddled with her glasses and said nervously, 'Mr. Dix. . .can I help you find something?'

He glanced at the display of engagement rings and matching wedding bands in the glass case in front of her and said, with a wry smile, 'Not that sort of thing, I'm afraid.'

His voice was softer than Lauren had expected, but then she'd only heard it amplified and recorded; of course it would be different in person. It was more intimate, somehow, and it seemed to sweep around her in waves and tickle in her ears.

He turned toward Lauren. 'Now that's the kind of thing I'm looking for,' he murmured, and crossed the store, silent footed, looking straight into her face. His eyes were big and icy blue and magnetic, and he did not blink.

Lauren swallowed hard. He was not as tall as she had thought he would be—not even as tall as Ward—and that surprised her. The oversize trench coat he wore was belted but not buttoned, and its bulk made him look thinner than she had expected. His hair was longer than in most of his photographs; it rested, curling softly, on his collar. And his face—it, too, was subtly different, for no photograph could possibly capture the intensity of his eyes and the charm of his slightly crooked smile as he studied her face. . ..

'Now that's the kind of thing I'm looking for,' he repeated softly, and then added calmly, 'Gold chains, that is.'

Lauren turned to the case at her elbow and unlocked it. 'Of course,' she said. 'What else?'

He laughed delightedly. 'So you're not impressed with me, are you.' It was more a statement than a question.

'Impressed?' Kim had found not only her tongue, but her feet, for she appeared at Lauren's elbow. 'Of course she's impressed. You're her hero.'

Lauren ignored Kim and began laying out chains on a black velvet background. 'What sort of thing are you looking for, Mr. Dix? Do you prefer fine gold, or something that is a little less pure but more durable? And is it for yourself, or is it a gift?'

He stretched out a hand and picked up a diamond-cut rope. 'For myself,' he said.

'Is it true, then?' Both of Kim's elbows were propped on the case. 'What the tabloids said, that she left you? The actress, I mean.'

Seemingly undisturbed by such blatant curiosity, he smiled ruefully. 'Don't remind me. For once they got it right, yes.'

'And she broke your heart.' Kim sighed. 'I'm so awfully sorry that it almost breaks my heart, too.'

He looked startled, and then a light that was almost amusement sprang into his eyes. 'Does it? How lovely of you. And what about your modest friend, hmm?' He swung the chain and watched it catch the light, and then laid it down, leaned on the counter and looked into Lauren's eyes. 'So I'm your hero? What's your name? I'll sing a song for you tonight.'

She couldn't quite get a full breath. Just being so close to him was putting clamps around her chest, and the idea of a song, just for her. . .'I—I'm afraid I won't be at the concert. I couldn't get tickets.'

He frowned. Then he raised his hand from the gold chain he'd been caressing and snapped his fingers. 'Two passes,' he said, without even looking over his shoulder, and one of the bodyguards pulled an envelope from the inside breast pocket of his jacket.

Kim started to shriek, then clapped her hands over her mouth. Mr. Baines rushed out of the workroom, his mouth open in shock and his jeweler's eyepiece still firmly over one eye. The combination made him look vaguely like a trout. 'Is there a problem?' he said.

Lauren imagined Mr. Baines thought his tone sounded menacing; it came out with a waver, instead. 'It's all right,' she managed. 'I think Mr. Dix has found a chain he'd like, that's all.'

Hunter Dix snapped his fingers again at the bodyguard who had handed him the passes. 'Take care of this,' he said. 'I'll take this one. . .this one. . .and this one. . .and this one. . .' The guard picked up the selected chains with surprisingly delicate fingers until his hand was almost full.

'But the prices,' Lauren said helplessly as she watched her inventory being rapidly depleted. 'I didn't even tell you the prices.'

'I hate being bothered with things like that,' Hunter Dix murmured. 'I'd much rather hear your name.'

But it was Kim who obliged, and eagerly. The singer filled out the passes himself and signed them with a flourish. 'These will get you backstage, too, so do come and say hello. And there will be a song for each of you tonight,' he promised lavishly as he wrapped Kim's fingers around her pass. But when Lauren reached for hers, he caught her hand and raised it to his mouth, lingering over her fingertips, kissing each one.

Mr. Baines was writing up the bill, looking less distressed by the moment. The guard fingered one of the chains and said, 'Hey, it's an honor to you to have Mr. Dix wearing your product. How about giving him a break on the price since he's buying so many?'

'Alec,' Hunter Dix said between gritted teeth, 'you idiot, not *here*.' He smiled at Lauren and murmured, 'Brains so seldom go with size, you know.'

The bodyguard scowled and began peeling bills off a sizable roll into Mr. Baines's hand, and then Hunter Dix and his retinue were gone, a mere memory except for the two bits of cardboard that Kim was waving over her head as she did a joyful jig in the middle of the store.

It had really happened, Lauren told herself blankly. He had really been here. *And I'm really going to the concert.*

Well, she thought. That should put Ward in his place— but good.

The rest of the afternoon was a loss; every time one of them caught the other's eye, Lauren and Kim were off in a spasm of delighted giggles, and Mr. Baines would make a snide remark about their attitude toward work. Even he couldn't be too annoyed, however, considering Hunter Dix and the gold chains and the infusion of cash into the register that afternoon, and so he finally left them alone and retreated to his workroom.

Kim was leaning against a case, holding out the hand that the singer had caressed and studying it, when a longtime customer came in to have Mr. Baines check a loose stone in her diamond ring.

'I will never wash this hand again,' Kim was vowing

as Lauren came back from the workroom with the finished ring. 'Never. I swear.'

'You'll look pretty funny with one grubby hand,' the customer said. 'But it's more than most of the fans will have. Too bad about the concert, isn't it?'

There was nothing save good humor in her voice, but Lauren's throat closed up. 'What do you mean, the concert?'

'Hadn't you heard? It's been canceled. The wind is up to gale force now—so strong that the airport's had to close, and that means Hunter Dix's backup musicians are stranded in Chicago. Since they can't get here, he can't perform. That's that.'

Lauren thought for an instant that the floor had dropped out from under her.

'It's kind of funny, really,' the customer's relentlessly cheerful voice went on. 'All the talk about this exclusive concert, and now it'll never happen. All those uppity, educated people at the college, and they didn't have enough sense to schedule a thing like that for some other time than the last day of January. Ought to have known Mother Nature wouldn't cooperate. Thanks, Lauren.' She slid the ring back onto her age-spotted hand and gathered up her shopping bags.

Lauren peered out the window and watched her walk down the street. The woman hadn't been kidding about the wind, for she was bent almost double as she struggled against it.

'I think I am going to kill myself,' Kim said. 'Diamonds cut glass. I wonder if they'd cut my wrists.'

Lauren didn't even answer; the lump in her throat was far too large. She could live without going to the concert, she thought. But to have the damned pass in her hand—

not just a ticket, but a personal backstage pass!—and then to have the whole thing snatched away. . . It was too much to bear.

Mindlessly, automatically, she went through the routine of closing the store, putting the most valuable of the merchandise in the huge old double-locked safe, closing out the cash register, putting the afternoon's receipts in the bank bag to be dropped off on her way home. Only the familiarity of the routine saved her; if someone had asked whether she had done the work, she would not have known.

She was not surprised when Ward came up behind her at the night-deposit drop at the bank; the pharmacy closed at six, too, and she frequently saw him there. It was where they had met, actually. One evening last summer she'd forgotten to zip the bank bag and then had stumbled and dropped it at his feet, letting change bounce in the gutter and checks flutter off in the breeze, and he had helped her chase it all down. . ..

But she didn't want to think about that, tonight, and so she said, rather formally, 'I hope you didn't go to much trouble over the tickets this afternoon.'

He nodded. 'I heard you'd managed it yourself, after all. Poplar Street has been buzzing about the visit all afternoon.' There was an odd overtone to his voice. Was it a note of warning?

She knew it was foolish to be angry at Ward; it wasn't his fault that the weather had gone foul. But she heard herself saying, 'I suppose you're happy the concert has been canceled!'

'Of course I'm not happy. Lauren, I really did try my best. I just didn't realize, before, how strongly you felt about it.'

She didn't answer.

After a moment he said, 'It's too cold to stand here, that's for sure, and I have to go back to the store, anyway—I have another batch of prescriptions to get ready before the delivery van comes back. How about later? Would you like to go to a movie?'

She shook her head silently.

Ward's eyebrows shot up. 'I see,' he said quietly. 'You'd rather just go home and feel sorry for yourself.'

Lauren didn't feel cold anymore; the heat of anger started clear in her toes and swept over her like a wave. 'That is the most heartless thing anyone has ever said to me!'

He said quietly, 'I'm sorry, Lauren. You've got a right to be disappointed. Well, see you tomorrow, then.' He turned back toward the pharmacy, his long stride consuming the distance. Within three steps he had been nearly swallowed by the gloom. If it hadn't been for his height and his broad shoulders, he would have vanished altogether.

She almost called him back, but she swallowed the words and turned toward the parking lot instead. She didn't need any more lectures or sermons tonight, that was certain. And if she wanted to go home and sit by the fire and think of what could have been, what business was that of Ward's?

She didn't hear the limousine until it pulled up beside her and the darkened rear window slid down. 'Lauren Hodges,' said a voice that there could be no mistaking, and her heartbeat started to quicken. 'You've no idea how lucky I feel to see you. Will you take pity on a stranger in your town—an unemployed stranger, at that—and let me take you to dinner?'

She thought about it, for five endless seconds. Having dinner with Hunter Dix was the chance of a lifetime, but—as he'd said himself—he was a stranger; a wise woman did not get into a car and go off with a man she didn't know. Ward would be absolutely livid at the idea, she thought.

She stepped over the hump of snow at the edge of the street and into the limousine without another thought.

CHAPTER TWO

SHE WAS VAGUELY disappointed by the back of the limousine, but she couldn't have said just why. It was nicely lined with butter-soft black leather, and fitted out with a television, a tape player, a telephone and a refrigerator.

So what on earth more had she expected, Lauren asked herself with a jeer. A full-fledged bar, complete with bartender? A pint-size hot tub surrounded by bathing beauties? If that had been so, Hunter Dix wouldn't have been looking out the window!

'The people at the hotel recommended Marconi's,' he said. 'So unless you have a better suggestion. . .'

She sank down beside him; the bodyguards were occupying the facing seats. 'That's the best place in town.' Then, a bit too late, she saw the trendy rip in the knee of his jeans, and swallowed hard. Marconi's was the town's premier restaurant, and it had a dress code to match. But surely they wouldn't throw Hunter Dix out, no matter what. Would they?

The maître d' looked askance at his famous guest, but the ripped jeans and the lack of a jacket and tie seemed to fade as one of the bodyguards murmured in the man's ear and warmly pressed his hand. From the sudden smile that dawned on the maître d's face, Lauren judged it must have been a sizable banknote that had slipped from palm to palm.

The maître d' held her chair, and Hunter Dix seated

himself opposite her. Lauren glanced over at the bodyguards, three tables away, and raised her eyebrows.

'The poor guys get tired of looking at me,' the singer
said, and that engagingly crooked smile lit his face. It
seemed to light a candle in her heart, and she relaxed.
Why should she be so concerned about his clothes? There
was nothing really wrong with his appearance, now that
the rip had disappeared under the table. And what did
the rules matter, after all? Certainly they didn't seem to
trouble him.

Ward, now, would never have dreamed of walking
through the Marconi's front door in ripped jeans. He
didn't have the self-assurance that Hunter Dix had,
Lauren thought, and—she smiled a little to herself—he
probably didn't even own a pair of ripped jeans. Last
fall he had helped her clean up her lawn and get it ready
for winter, and even after a full day of digging up
flowerbeds and pushing the mower he had looked cool
and unsmudged and almost *neat,* for heaven's sake. She
had been tempted to push him into the compost pile just
to see what he'd look like with dirt all over him, except
that he'd probably have dragged her in, as well.

'You are a beautiful lady,' Hunter Dix whispered.

There were steel bands around her chest, keeping her
from breathing right. 'Mr. Dix—'

'I'm Hunter, to my friends.' He reached for her hand,
and held the curve of her fingers to his cheek. 'Your
hair looks as if it's been kissed by starlight—it has the
strangest silvery glow.'

Ward had told her once that her hair looked almost
dusty under certain lights—Dammit, Lauren told herself,
I am not going to think about Ward again!

'Tell me what that was all about this afternoon, when

the old guy came flying out of the back room,' her companion prompted.

The waiter arrived with champagne, somewhat to Lauren's surprise. Had it even been ordered? Hunter tasted it and shook his head, and the waiter retreated, silently, with the bottle.

'The old man,' Hunter prompted again. He was stroking the back of her hand with his fingertips, and it took an effort to pull her mind back to his question.

'Mr. Baines?' she said. 'Oh, well, just think about it. It's his store. He hears a shriek from one of his staff, and the first thing he sees is two big bruisers in dark glasses, looking as if they're ready to haul the safe away, to say nothing of everything in the display cases.'

Hunter was shifting his grip on her fingers from one hand to the other. He frowned a little, as if he was preoccupied.

'I just meant,' Lauren said hesitantly, 'that I wondered myself for a second if your bodyguards were getting ready to rob the place.'

He smiled then. 'I suppose I've gotten too used to having them around to think about what other people see,' he said, and she laughed.

The second bottle of champagne arrived; this one was satisfactory, and the waiter was filling their glasses when a teenage girl fluttered up to the table to ask for an autograph. Before she could get all the words out, a bodyguard materialized beside her and urged her gently away. Lauren would have liked to kick the bodyguard in the shin; the girl looked so disappointed, and it would have taken such a little time and effort to grant her request.

Hunter intercepted her glance and shrugged. 'If I start,'

he said rather sadly, 'they'll be standing in line, and I'll never have a minute to eat.'

'Oh. Of course.' She was faintly embarrassed. 'I hadn't thought about that.'

The singer snapped his fingers at the other bodyguard and murmured something to him, and then settled back in his chair with the stem of his champagne flute between two fingers. 'I'd be going on stage just about now,' he said thoughtfully.

'Are you sorry to miss the concert?'

His eyes narrowed a little as he studied her. 'And miss this? What do you think, Lauren Hodges?'

The bands around her chest tightened just a little. 'How did you happen to get separated from your backup band, anyway?'

He shrugged. 'I made a side trip. They stayed an extra day in Chicago. Damn charter jets, anyway. You can't ever count on them.'

'It's hardly the airplane's fault that the storm blew in.'

He looked at her for a long moment, and then laughed softly and reached over to turn her face up to his. 'You're an earnest little thing, aren't you? Tell me about yourself, sweet Lauren.'

She smiled and shook her head. 'There's nothing much you'd like to know, I'm sure.'

But it seemed there were a great many things he wanted to hear about, as many as she wanted to ask of him, and their leisurely dinner was gone before all the questions had been answered. It hardly seemed possible, she thought in astonishment, that they had talked the hours away so easily, that a man like Hunter Dix could have been so interested in the way she had lost her mother the year before, and in the question of whether she should

keep the house where she had grown up, or sell it for the freedom of an apartment, now that she was alone. . ..
She hadn't shared that particular concern with anyone before; indeed, she hadn't really thought it out completely for herself until she had started to tell Hunter about it. It was so natural, so perfectly effortless, to share things with him. It was unlike any first date she'd ever had—

Whoa, she told herself sternly. *First date?* Don't be an idiot, Lauren Hodges. Don't set yourself up for grief; just hold on to the treasure you already have. No one can take this night away, this special few hours all alone with your hero. For all you know, he was just politely listening to you babble, doing his best not to yawn, and not really hearing you at all!

She looked around when she heard the scrape of the bodyguard's chairs, and was surprised to see only empty tables around them. 'It's gotten so quiet,' she said a little nervously. 'Even with a storm I've never known Marconi's to be so empty.'

Hunter smiled a little. 'That's because I bought it out for eight o'clock on, so you wouldn't be disturbed by autograph hounds.'

The candle flame in her heart steadied, then grew. She'd known he was special, she thought. But she'd had no idea. . .

'I wouldn't say the food was worth it,' Hunter went on thoughtfully. 'But the company certainly was.'

She hastily picked up her coffee cup for a last sip.

'Don't rush,' he said. 'The boys will take care of the bill and get the car.' He leaned forward and, letting his fingertips rest along the line of her jaw, kissed her, very softly, his mouth warm and mobile against hers.

It was like a benediction, she thought. The perfect ending to a perfect evening.

He raised his head. 'I don't suppose you're the kind of girl who would accept an invitation back to my hotel?'

Her eyes must have dilated in shock.

He laughed a little. 'I'm sorry. I guess you just sort of overwhelmed me, Lauren. I've never felt this. . . . Well, just forget I said anything, all right?'

Never, Lauren thought humbly. *This supreme compliment I will never forget . . .*

The bodyguards discreetly turned their backs when Hunter walked her to her door. He touched her face, then kissed her hungrily, and Lauren fought a battle between her own desires and what little was left of her common sense.

You can't just go to bed with a man you've known such a short time, she thought.

But I feel I know him so well. . . .

He'll be gone tomorrow, and you'll never see him again!

Exactly. And it would be a night to celebrate the rest of my life. . . .

'Don't forget me, sweet Lauren,' he whispered.

'I couldn't,' she tried to say.

'I won't let you.' He grinned at her in the cold shadows. 'After all, I owe you a concert!'

And then he was gone, without another word. He might have called goodbye, but if he had the wind whipped it away. She watched the white limousine speed off, gleaming under the streetlights despite the falling snow.

When the car was out of sight and she went inside, the first thing Lauren did was to take the useless pass and slip it into the corner of the big gilt mirror in the front hall. Not that she needed a reminder. This evening had been so much better than any concert could have been. How could any detail of it ever fade from her memory?

I owe you a concert! What on earth had he meant by that?

The morning brought another cold gray sky; the wind had died, and the snow had stopped, but the day was even drearier for Lauren than yesterday had been, because she knew that the brilliance that was Hunter Dix was gone from the city. There were people waiting for him somewhere else—she hadn't had time to ask where he would be going next.

Business was slow, because the streets had not yet been thoroughly plowed. Even walking was difficult; most of the snow had been shoveled away, but the sleet had stuck stubbornly to the concrete walks, and now the surface was uneven, as well as slick. Lauren picked her way cautiously up Poplar Street to the pharmacy to get Mr. Baines's morning coffee. It looked to be a quiet day, he had said, and it would be the perfect time to bury himself in the delicate repair and finishing work that took so much time when it was constantly interrupted by customers. And since there was little to do in the front of the store, if Lauren would just bring his coffee. . .

She could hardly refuse. For months now she had eagerly seized any opportunity to run down the street, because she might see Ward. And now that she suddenly didn't care to see Ward. . .

But it wasn't that exactly, either, she told herself. There was no reason to avoid him. She certainly wasn't feeling guilty this morning; she hadn't violated any vows to

Ward by spending the evening with Hunter Dix, because she had never *made* any vows to him. She had no apologies to make.

And nothing had changed, when it came right down to it. She'd had a pleasant evening, that was all. Not even Ward could begrudge her that.

But she was uneasily aware, even as she said it, that it was not true. Something *had* changed—Lauren herself. She was no longer quite the same woman she had been just yesterday. For she had discovered that there were men in the world to whom romance was not a foreign concept; men to whom complimentary words came easily; men who knew the good things in life, and enjoyed them.

Well, one man at least, she told herself.

The pharmacy was busy, of course, despite the aftermath of the storm. It nearly always was; people were always getting sick, and though Ward had a part-time assistant, as well as several employees who took care of all the other departments, the largest part of the drug dispensing fell on him. Lauren supposed he must like it that way, for he even lived in the apartment above the store, as if he couldn't bear to be far from his business. If he'd wanted, he certainly could have hired another pharmacist so that he could be free more often—to take up a hobby, or have a day off, or just to go for a walk in the snow.

She wondered if Hunter liked to walk in the snow, and she was smiling softly, thinking about it, when she bumped into Ward in the aisle and had to juggle Mr. Baines's large foam cup to keep from spilling the contents down the front of Ward's immaculate long white lab coat.

'Take-out coffee this morning?' he mused. 'Am I supposed to read a message into that?'

That annoyed her. Was he so self-centered that he took her actions personally? 'No message,' she said tartly. 'I can't imagine why you'd think I need to play that sort of game, Ward.'

His eyes darkened, and the dimple that had been playing hide-and-seek at the corner of his mouth disappeared. He thrust his hands into the pockets of the lab coat. 'I begin to see,' he said levelly. 'One of my employees saw you getting into the limousine, you know.'

'What business is it of yours?' Lauren said tightly.

'And of course she noticed that your car was still in the lot this morning. . ..'

Lauren bit her lower lip and stared at the precise center of his tie, so that she didn't have to look up into his eyes. She had paid off the taxi at the end of Poplar Street this morning rather than in front of the jewelry store, thinking that there was no need to advertise the fact that she had never come back for her car. And now he was making it look sordid, when it had been so very innocent. So very beautiful. . .

'You know that you're playing with some rough customers, of course,' Ward went on quietly. 'A local photographer tried to get a picture of your hero yesterday, and his camera was smashed into the street by one of his goons.'

'Well, what do you think bodyguards are for? If he was threatening—'

'By taking a picture?' Ward scoffed. 'Come on. Lauren, you don't know what you're dealing with.'

She squared her shoulders. 'For your information, and certainly not because I owe you any explanations—'

'Hey,' Ward said. 'Lauren. If you'll stop a minute, you'll notice that I didn't ask for any explanations, either. I'm worried about you, that's all. I'm—'

'Well, you don't need to be. Hunter took me to dinner, and then home, and that's all. And we were chaperoned all the time by those "goons," as you call them, and nothing happened, and—and I wish it *had*, you miserable, suspicious creep! But it's all over, so you don't need to make it sound like a one-night-stand, which it wasn't, and I'm only telling you this so the rumor doesn't take over the whole street by the end of the day—'

'Are you going to stop for a breath, or keep right on for the rest of the morning?' Ward asked calmly.

She glared at him.

'All right,' he said hastily, 'I owe you an apology. I'll freely admit it—I suspected the worst, and I should have known better than to think you'd lose your head. You're too solid and sensible for that.'

Solid? *Sensible?* She was furious. Was that what Ward considered a compliment? And as for his apology, it was hardly the most gracious she had ever received, but she knew better than to hold her breath and wait for an improvement. Ward, she thought mockingly, was too solid and sensible to abase himself! So she nodded stiffly. There was nothing else she could do.

Ward's eyes softened a little, but she never found out what he might have said then, for there was a sort of scuffle at the back of the store, and a voice called his name. There was a note of urgency in it, almost of panic, and Ward moved off briskly without another word to her.

Lauren peered around the corner of the aisle. She could see a man stretched out on the floor with a frantic woman at his head; then Ward knelt beside him and her view was blocked.

'Has someone called an ambulance?' she asked.

The cashier who was standing beside her nodded. 'He's a sweet old man—he had a heart attack last year. This looks like another one. I hope he doesn't die. But Ward's there now, so it will be all right.'

'Oh, absolutely,' Lauren said dryly. 'Nothing bad can possibly happen as long as Ward's there.'

The woman nodded.

She didn't even hear the irony in what I said, Lauren marveled. What was there about the man, she wondered as she walked back to the jewelry store, that had inspired his staff to such worship?

She had been home barely a quarter of an hour that evening when the flowers came, two dozen glorious creamy-white roses, with Hunter's name on the card. He had thought of her this morning, even on his way out of town, she realized, and her heart nearly burst with quiet gladness.

She kicked the front door shut and stood there hugging the huge box, with almost the same enthusiasm as if he himself had returned to her. She was breathless with delight. Roses—what luxury! And these were the most beautiful ones she had ever seen, with enormous blossoms still studded with water droplets, the velvety petals just starting to unfold. . ..

She pulled a single rose out of the bundle and whirled around the room with it as if it were a dancing partner. Then she put it back with its fellows and buried her face in the green tissue that cushioned the blooms, taking long deep breaths of their fragrance until her head swam with the heavy, drugging scent.

She had forgotten all about dinner and was still arranging the flowers—trying out new combinations and filling vases for her bedroom, the kitchen, the mantel—when the telephone rang.

'Hello, sweet Lauren,' said the throaty, intimate voice, and she almost dropped the telephone.

'Hunter!' She twisted around to see the kitchen clock. 'But it's concert time!'

He laughed. 'Oh, my innocent, it's two hours earlier on the West Coast, so I'm supposed to be getting rested and ready. But I couldn't rest. I can't close my eyes without thinking of you. Did you get the roses? I hope you like white ones. I think red ones are prettier, but they just wouldn't have been right for you.'

'Oh, yes, I got them. Thank you! They're beautiful. I've never known such luxury.'

'You poor child! Does no one ever send you flowers?'

She stopped herself abruptly. Was he laughing at her? There had certainly been a hint of humor in his voice, and her words *had* been awfully naive. 'I mean, of course I get flowers,' she said primly. 'Just never two dozen roses at one time. I hardly know what to do with them all.'

Now he was certainly laughing. 'Oh, don't spoil it, darling! You're so preciously innocent and sincere, sweet Lauren, don't try to be sophisticated. That's why I sent white roses, you know—for your purity and innocence and earnestness. I've never met anyone like you.'

She clutched the telephone in a hand that was suddenly damp and shaking. With anticipation? With fear? With shock? Yes, last night he had implied that he had found her attractive—more than attractive. But. . .

'Most of the girls I meet are such a cynical lot,' he went on very quietly. 'They seem to think it's the only way to impress a man these days. No one would send them white roses, that's for sure—not with a straight face, at least. But you. . .I never thought I could feel this way again, sweet Lauren.'

She swallowed frantically, trying to get her heart back to its proper anatomical location. It seemed to be permanently lodged in her throat.

The husky, sexy murmur gave way to a more vibrant tone. 'I've shocked you, haven't I? Perhaps I'd better not pursue that any further—just now. We'll take it up on Valentine's Day.'

'Valentine's. . .' she said uncertainly. 'What. . .?'

'How could I have forgotten to tell you the good news? I've arranged it all with my manager, and we've rescheduled last night's concert.'

'For Valentine's Day?' *I will see him again,* her heart was singing. *I will see him soon. . .*'That's wonderful! But how is it you don't already have a concert then, Hunter? I mean, you sing love songs! Doesn't everyone in the world want a concert on Valentine's Day?'

She could hear the smile in his voice. 'The day for lovers? Plenty of them do, yes. I'd kept it free, you see, for. . . well, we won't talk about the woman who used to be in my life. That's all over now. And since now I have a new Valentine—' the husky twinge was back in his voice. '—I do, don't I, sweet Lauren? I can't be the only one who felt that instant attraction.'

'You're not the only one,' she whispered. It felt almost like a vow.

'Do you have one of those roses handy?' His voice was a little unsteady.

'Right here. Why?'

'Give it a kiss,' he whispered. 'And pretend it's me.'

The next morning when Lauren told Kim about the rescheduled concert, Kim dropped a tray of rings that she had just taken out of the safe. Gold and precious stones spilled and rolled and scattered across the floor.

Lauren stopped wiping glass cleaner off the top of a display case and plunged to her knees to help grab up the rings before Mr. Baines could see what had happened.

Once the rings were safely corralled, however, Kim began to look concerned. 'If I were you, Lauren, I don't think I'd say much about the concert until the newspaper announces it,' she advised. 'There's no reason to have everybody on Poplar Street asking how you were the first to know.'

'Oh, for heaven's sake. You can't mean you believe the nonsense that's running up and down the street, Kim!'

'Of course I don't think you spent the night with Hunter Dix. But I'm warning you, plenty of people do.'

A customer came in just then, and Kim began showing him earrings for his girlfriend's Valentine's Day gift.

Lauren caught herself chewing on a perfectly manicured nail, and took it out of her mouth. Glass cleaner tasted awful, she thought. Or was it the gossip on Poplar Street that had left such a bitter aftertaste on her tongue?

She hadn't finished the display cases yet, and Kim's customer was still working his way through every pair of earrings in the store and shaking his head over each one, when Ward came in. Lauren saw him coming down Poplar Street and watched as he tried to dodge between the random droplets of melting snow that fell from the awnings, and thought, *Just what I need this morning!*

'Spring is on the way,' he announced with a brilliant smile. 'At least it looks like it on a morning like this, with the sun out and the mess starting to melt.' He set a bag down on the case right in front of her. 'And here's a little bit of springtime for indoors.' He began to unbutton his wool topcoat.

'If it's so nice,' Lauren said, 'I'm amazed you bothered with a coat. It's only three doors down.'

'I didn't say it was warm, exactly, just that the groundhog saw his shadow this morning, so there are only six weeks of winter left.'

Lauren put her elbows down on the glass case and propped her chin in her hands. 'And do you know what happens if he didn't see it? It means we have a month and a half, instead.'

'You're certainly a pessimist this morning,' Ward said. 'Did somebody steal the hole out of your doughnut at breakfast, or something?'

Lauren couldn't help but laugh; she couldn't be gloomy, even about the certainty of more snow and cold to come, after last night's good news—the concert, the phone call, the roses. . .

A warm, almost mischievous gleam sprang into Ward's eyes. 'Besides,' he said, 'now you don't have to wait even another day for spring.' He waved an inviting hand at the bag.

Lauren unfolded the top and peeked in, a bit warily, at a shallow clay pot full of crocus bulbs. The leaves were already fully developed and brilliantly striped in grassy green and white, and tiny buds were just beginning to peek up from the base of the plants. She thought she saw a hint of purple on one of them. 'They look quite healthy,' she said.

He nodded. 'The shipment just came into the store this morning. And of course they can be transplanted to your garden after it warms up, and then they'll bloom every spring.'

He sounded very proud of himself. Wasn't that just like Ward, she thought. He was so efficient himself that even when he gave a girl flowers, he expected them to do double or triple duty!

That wasn't fair, she told herself. He knew she liked things like crocus—he saw that last fall when he'd helped clean up the flowerbeds in her back yard for winter. His gift might not be glamorous, but it was thoughtful.

She bit her lip. 'Look, Ward,' she said softly, 'I shouldn't have said those things yesterday. I can't even remember what I called you, but I know it wasn't very pleasant. . ..'

He winced a little. 'Let's not try too hard to recall it, shall we? And I'm sorry to have been so abrupt—walking away from you like that.'

She set the crocus next to the cash register and said carelessly, 'Oh, that's all right. You had other things to worry about. How is the patient?'

'He'll be fine.' He didn't enlarge on the topic. 'Lauren, that movie is still on. Would you like to go?'

She didn't want to refuse him, yet something inside her shivered away from accepting any invitation whatever; it wouldn't be fair to encourage him just now. And besides, what if Hunter called again and she wasn't there? 'Oh, here comes Mrs. Schuyler,' she said quickly. 'That will take care of the morning—you know what a talker she is.'

Ward seemed to accept her changing the subject as a refusal. 'I'd better get back to the store—no doubt there are people waiting in line for me already.' He patted her hand and, with one well-groomed fingertip, turned the sapphire ring she was wearing until it caught the light perfectly, then smiled and went out just in time to hold the door for Mrs. Schuyler. If he'd been wearing a hat, Lauren thought, he'd have tipped it.

It was almost noon before she and Kim were alone again. Lauren was counting the excess money out of the cash register so she could make a bank deposit on her lunch hour. Kim was studying the sturdy buds of the crocus. In the warmth, one of them was already pushing aggressively upward, as if it was eager to see its new surroundings.

'Poor Ward,' Lauren said, glancing at the crocus. 'He tries so hard, and it just never quite comes off.' Crocus, she was thinking. Ward would never dream of blowing money for two dozen roses. He would think so many all at once was a waste.

Kim didn't look at her. 'I was thinking it was awfully nice of him.'

Lauren stopped counting cash for a moment. 'Correct me if I'm wrong, but aren't you the one who called Ward a jerk?' Her fingers began to move again, efficiently rippling through the twenties.

'I didn't mean it exactly. I was just disappointed about the tickets, and you know how I say things sometimes without thinking.' Then Kim added, 'That guy's heart had stopped yesterday, at the pharmacy. Ward saved his life. The paramedics said so.'

'That's wonderful, but what does it have to do with the crocus?'

Kim shrugged. 'Nothing, I suppose. But give Ward some credit. He could be telling everyone what a hero he is.'

'Perhaps he realized that bragging about it wouldn't be the way to impress me.'

'I don't think he wants to impress you. Ward's trying to bail you out of trouble, Lauren. Why do you think he brought those flowers down here, anyway? He knows that everyone on the street is watching, and if he were to turn his back on you now. . .'

Lauren said with frost in her voice, 'Are you implying that he's trying to patch the tatters of my reputation back together? Well, isn't that thoughtful of him!'

Kim gave the clay pot a push. 'That's not what I meant, Lauren. Not exactly. I just, well, I'm confused. And I'm surprised at you, I suppose.'

'Because I'm too solid and sensible to lose my head like this? That's no compliment as far as I'm concerned.' Lauren slammed shut the cash drawer. 'Have some crocus, Kim,' she said on her way out the door. 'I certainly don't want them.'

CHAPTER THREE

THE DAYS THAT FOLLOWED would have been pure magic if it hadn't been for the head cold that attacked Lauren over the weekend. She must have picked it up from running to the bank without her coat on Groundhog Day; she'd been so furious at Ward, and at Kim, that she hadn't felt the need of a wrap to keep her warm, and now she was paying the price.

Hunter loved what the cold did to her voice; he teased her about her sexy little whisper, especially the night he called just after finishing a concert in Honolulu and woke her at three in the morning when she had only just managed to fall asleep. But she couldn't be annoyed for long, because he began to confide in her about the problems attacking his tour from all sides. An inept advance team had booked him into a series of inadequate concert halls and uncomfortable hotels. And it was impossible to get anything decent to eat. Only her soft voice and common sense could make things feel right again, he declared.

'If it wasn't for having you to talk to, sweet Lauren, I'd cancel the whole tour. It's a disaster. But of course,' he added, with self-deprecating humor, 'we performers have to make the little people happy.'

It made her feel sad; he was always on stage, in a sense, no matter where he went—always surrounded by fans, each wanting a piece of his attention, a piece of his heart.

Her cold gave her a good excuse to stay at home; she

231

played a lot of solitaire that weekend while she waited for the telephone to ring. Ward stopped by on Sunday afternoon with the newest issue of her favorite magazine and a jigsaw puzzle, and he stayed to help her put it together. She was glad of his company, even though every time she sniffled she was reminded of her annoyance at him. Trying to preserve her good name on Poplar Street, indeed, when she hadn't done a single thing to injure it in the first place! Still, his company was a lot better than being alone. Her thoughts strayed often to Hunter; she knew he was on his way to Tokyo that afternoon.

She was looking forward to getting back to work on Monday, but overnight her cold became worse. Her cough deepened into a bark that threatened to rip her ribs apart, and so she dragged herself to the doctor's office, instead, only to be told that she had developed bronchitis.

'Go home and go to bed,' the doctor ordered. 'And don't worry about your antibiotics. I'll have the pharmacy deliver them to you before the day is out.'

She went home, but she didn't have enough strength to get herself to bed; she collapsed in her living room and woke to early-evening darkness with a neck so stiff from being propped against the arm of the couch that she thought her head might never turn again.

When the doorbell rang, she groaned and actually thought about lying still and not bothering to answer it. But it pealed a second time, followed by a fist hammering against the door, and then she remembered the pharmacy's delivery van, and her promised medicine. It had certainly taken long enough.

It wasn't the delivery boy, however, but Ward himself who stood on the small front porch, with a white bag in his hand and huge snowflakes drifting down around his head, sticking in his dark hair and clinging to the shoulders of his coat. There was even one enormous crystal flake caught in his eyelashes, and he blinked and flicked it away with a gloved finger just as she opened the door.

It wasn't fair, Lauren was thinking. A mere man shouldn't be allowed to possess the world's longest, darkest and curliest eyelashes. Especially a man who didn't have the slightest idea how to use them to best advantage.

'Come in,' she started to say, and had to stop till her coughing spell relaxed. Ward almost pushed her back into the house, away from the cold sweep of outside air, and he supported her with an impersonal arm around her shoulders till the spasm had passed.

'Sit down,' he ordered, 'and I'll get your first dose. It should have been here hours ago, but my delivery boy got sick, too, and went home to bed.'

She sank onto the couch, weak from the coughing spell, and he brought her a glass of water and dropped a huge red-and-white capsule into her palm. Lauren swallowed it with difficulty—her throat was sore, too—and looked up at him with a grateful smile. 'Take your coat off,' she said.

Ward shook his head. 'I can't. I have a dozen more deliveries to make.'

Disappointment shot through her; she felt abandoned. But she couldn't blame Ward. He was busy, and why on earth would he want to hang around her, anyway— red-nosed, croaking, stringy-haired and laden with germs? She lay back on the couch with an achy little moan.

From her almost flat position, Ward looked incredibly

tall as he studied her, his forehead wrinkled with concern. 'You'll be all right, now? You'll be able to rest?'

'Sure. I'm in great shape.' Tears crept into her eyes; she couldn't even manage irony. Ward looked awfully tired, too, she thought. He needed a rest himself, from the sound of that sigh. Having to do all the deliveries himself, on top of everything else. . .

'Your cough syrup is in the bag,' he said, 'and I brought a decongestant, in case you need it. If your nose isn't stuffy tonight, it will be by morning. Don't get up— I'll let myself out.'

Then he was gone, and silence closed around her again. Lonely, chilly silence.

'You have two minutes to wallow in self-pity,' Lauren told herself aloud, 'and then you are going to get up and find something to eat. You're miserable because you've been by yourself all day, and it isn't very pleasant to be alone when you're ill, but feeling sorry for yourself certainly isn't going to make you less wretched. So you're going to get up and do something to help yourself feel better.'

But the pep talk didn't do much good. Thinking about a mug of hot soup was one thing, but actually getting up and making it was something else when every muscle in her entire body ached. So she dozed off instead, and she dreamed that Ward returned with something that smelled delightful—was it possible for anything to smell so good, even in a dream?—and stooped over to kiss her temple. Tears stung the corners of her eyes. . ..

'I brought chicken soup,' Ward said cheerfully. His fingertips brushed the rumpled hair back from her face.

'You did come back!' She turned her cheek into his palm. It was blessedly cold against her hot skin.

She saw his eyes darken, and she sat up hastily. 'I mean,' she croaked, 'you got your deliveries all finished?' It was stupid, she thought, to feel so grateful just because he was here.

He nodded. 'I'm done for the evening, thank God. Have you had anything at all to eat today?'

Lauren shook her head tiredly. 'I don't think so.'

He said something under his breath that she didn't quite catch, because her ears were plugged, too, and went out to the kitchen. Lauren put her head back down with a sigh of relief.

The first thing he brought her was a tall, frosty glass full of orange juice and tiny chips of ice that slid refreshingly down her burning throat, soothing as they went. Between sips she said, 'I don't know why you're taking a chance with my millions of germs.'

Ward shook his head. 'I think I must be immune to this one. I've obviously had a hundred chances to get it.'

'Well, I must say I'm awfully glad you're here. Sorry I'm not up to offering you a game of gin rummy or something—unless you'd like an awfully easy victory, that is.'

He smiled. 'I'll wait till you're mended enough to be a worthy opponent. I brought a movie, though, from the rental place, if you'd like some entertainment.'

'As long as it doesn't require me to think. But if it's something deep and foreign with subtitles. . .'

'Pure fluff.'

'I can handle that. Did you say something about chicken soup a while ago?'

'It's warming. I'm not promising that it's gourmet quality, but it was the last quart the deli had.' He brought in two bowls on a tray. 'They seemed to be doing a booming business in the stuff.'

'Chicken soup from the deli?' she teased. 'You mean it's not homemade?'

He smiled again. 'I see you're starting to feel human again.'

Lauren sat up experimentally and stirred her soup; it was steaming gently and smelled divine. So she hadn't been dreaming, after all. 'Almost human,' she decided. 'Except for my neck. I think my head's going to be at this angle permanently.'

He moved to the couch beside her, and his fingers moved gently over the vertebrae. 'Where does it hurt?'

'Right there. Ouch,' she muttered as his thumb dug with certainty into the protesting muscle. But it was a healing discomfort, one that brought warmth and relief to the painful spot, and within minutes the tightness had relaxed and her neck turned easily again. She tipped her head back and looked up at him through narrowed eyes.

'You're awfully good at this,' she said. 'Where did you learn it? Did you have a summer job as a masseur, or something?'

Ward laughed. 'Nothing that exotic, I'm afraid.'

Of course it hadn't been exotic, she thought. It was impossible to think of Ward and exotic summer jobs in the same breath.

His arm was lying about her shoulders now. It was warm and pleasant, and she was too comfortable to move. There was no point in moving, anyway; she could see that her soup was still too hot to eat.

His mother had probably liked to have her neck rubbed, that was all, she thought. 'Don't worry,' she said lazily. 'Your dusty little secret is safe with me.'

He smiled a little at that, and his arm tightened, just a fraction. His fingertips were drawing slow circles on the curve of her shoulder, still massaging the aching muscles even as he pulled her gradually closer.

She really should sit up this minute, Lauren thought. It really wasn't fair to Ward to let this go on. It wouldn't be very flattering to him for her to be in his arms, letting him kiss her while she was thinking of Hunter. Pretending he *was* Hunter. . ...

But there was something almost hypnotic about the motion of his fingers, and so she didn't move. Instead, she warned in a soft almost-whisper, 'You'll get my germs, Ward.'

He said huskily, 'It's worth it.'

And then it was too late to move, to sit up, to call a halt. His big hand came up to cup her face. His fingertips caressed her jaw and the soft hollow beneath her ear, and his palm rested warmly over her throat. His thumb brushed the point of her chin as softly as his mouth touched hers, like the kiss of a butterfly's wing.

But the caress did not remain tentative for long: The gentleness remained, of course—Ward could never be anything but gentle—but there was certainty in it now, and confidence, and sure knowledge.

I had almost forgotten, Lauren thought, *how very beautifully he does this.* His kisses were never smothering, never grinding or demanding, like so many men's were. Ward's kisses could go on forever, and a woman would never feel suffocated or assaulted, just elated and uplifted and practically delirious with delight. . ...

Her eyelids drooped as if her brain had ordered them to, closing out all other information so it could better concentrate on this supreme sensation. Her thoughts became nothing more than a senseless swirl.

No wonder he'd never kissed her—or anyone else, she'd bet—where other people could see. It wouldn't be fair not to give a woman a chance to recover a bit from this kind of sensual uproar before exposing her to curious bystanders. And Ward was, above all, a gentleman. Yes, a very decent sort of man. . ..

She knew, with a sort of detached sense, that his heart was pounding, and realized that her fingertips were resting on the pulse point just below his ear. She didn't even remember reaching up to hold him.

He raised his head and said almost hoarsely, 'Lauren. . .' and she waited, without anxiousness, to see what it was he wanted to say. She wasn't even curious—she was incapable of curiosity, for she was still floating on that seductive cloud he had so masterfully created.

The telephone rang beside her. It might be Hunter, she thought, and in a fraction of a second crashed off the cloud and back to cold, solid earth. She had lain here in Ward's arms and allowed him to kiss her, and had not even once thought of Hunter. How on earth had she allowed herself to lose control like that? It was a compliment to Ward's technique, that was all—but he certainly wouldn't hear about it from her!

Guiltily she pulled away from him and reached for the telephone.

'Dammit, Lauren, let it ring,' Ward said, his voice a little rough, but she had already picked it up.

The first thing she heard was muted swearing. 'I did it again, didn't I?' Hunter said ruefully. 'Woke you in the middle of the night? I couldn't remember how many blasted hours different Tokyo is, and I thought it was worth a chance. . ..'

Beside her, Ward abruptly got to his feet, picked up her orange-juice glass and vanished into the kitchen.

'No, of course you didn't wake me. It's only—' Lauren peered into the clock on the mantel '—half-past eight, that's all.' She tried to see around the corner in the kitchen. Ward couldn't be leaving, she thought; his coat was still draped over the back of a chair in plain view, and he certainly wouldn't walk off without it. Not Ward. Not when a snowstorm was going on outside.

'Well, you sound as if you just got out of bed,' Hunter said. He sounded a bit disgruntled.

She could feel the warm flush of embarrassment rise in her cheeks. 'Oh. . .that's only my cold. It's gotten worse, I'm afraid, and now I'm really croaking.'

'Aren't you over that yet?' Hunter asked. 'Your special concert is a week from tonight, and you have to be well by then.'

My special concert, she thought, with the lift it always gave her. *A Hunter Dix concert just for me.* 'Oh, I wouldn't miss the concert, no matter what!'

'Well, you'd better get over this disease of yours so you don't infect me with it.'

'Hunter!'

'I'm only teasing,' he said hastily. 'You know that, sweet Lauren. You wouldn't like it if I couldn't sing at all, would you?'

She relaxed. 'Of course I know you're teasing. And I'll be well by then, really I will. I'll probably be back at work tomorrow.' She reached out, half-consciously, and touched the rose in the vase on the coffee table. It was the last survivor of the two dozen, and it, too, was drooping now, its creamy-white petals withered and crumbly and slightly brown along the edges. It looked a little like she felt, Lauren thought ironically. As if she was on the verge of dying, and should be carried upstairs and put to rest between two heavy things, to be preserved forever... But this wouldn't last. She would be better tomorrow.

'I've been writing your song,' Hunter said. He sounded almost shy about it.

'My song? You're writing me a special song?'

'Well, you're a special girl, aren't you? And it's a special concert. And I promised you a song.'

'But one all my own—just for me?' She could hardly breathe, she was so deeply touched. 'Oh, Hunter—'

'I woke up at an ungodly hour this morning with it running through my head. It, and thoughts of you.'

'Sing me a bit of it now, please!'

'Oh, no. That wouldn't be fair to the song. I want you to hear it the first time in all its glory—not over a phone line sung by a worn-out old hack singer who's still hoarse from last night's concert.'

'A hack singer?' she said indignantly. 'Don't you dare run yourself down that way, Hunter Dix!'

There was a laugh in his voice. 'That's my sweet Lauren, keeping me on the straight and narrow. Don't you want to hear about the concert last night? Tokyo turned out in droves. I wish...' His tone dropped. 'I wish you could have been with me to see it.'

To share it with him, to experience the adulation of the crowd as he received his well-earned acclaim. How she would have loved being there. 'That would have been wonderful!' she said.

'I wish you'd been here with me last night after the

concert, too,' he went on huskily. 'I needed your warmth last night.'

'After all that adoration? Surely you didn't need one more fan.'

'Not just one more fan. I needed *you*, sweet Lauren. Adoration is fine until you come home alone,' he confessed, and there was a tremor in his voice that startled her.

'Hunter. . .' she began uncertainly.

The tremor gave way to urgency. 'And I need you right now, too, when I've got a long day on an airplane stretching out ahead of me, and only a band and a bunch of backup singers for company.'

'I miss you a lot, too—'

'Dammit, it's more than that, and you know it. How about it, sweet Lauren? You're coming with me next week, aren't you?' There was a sudden harsh note to his voice, as if he couldn't stand the waiting, the not knowing, any longer.

'Coming with you? I don't—'

'Yes. Coming with me. Sharing with me. Making it all worth doing. Surely you know that's what I want, what I've been wanting for a week. I was a fool to leave you there. A fool.'

What he was saying was too much for any heart to hold; Lauren thought hers would crack open from the strain of being overfull with happiness. The difficulties of a world tour that he had described to her—the less-than-perfect hotels, the long flights, the occasional troublesome fan, the arrangements that sometimes went wrong—would all be bearable if he had her beside him.

If he has me, she thought humbly. *Me—ordinary Lauren Hodges . . .*

'We'll be in New York next month,' he cajoled. 'And then London. And after that, Paris. . .'

The real world reasserted itself for a moment. 'It can't all be Paris,' she reminded him. 'I'm sure there will be plenty of boring little cities like this one in between the glamorous spots.'

She could almost see the careless wave of his hand as he dismissed the objection. 'Yes, there always are. But with you beside me, not even the little towns will be so bad. You'll see. It's settled, then.'

A tremor ran through her. 'I don't know,' she heard herself saying. 'This is so sudden.'

'Dammit, it's not sudden.' His voice had a hard edge to it. 'You know it as well as I do—and you knew it that first night, too. You don't have any more doubts than I do, so don't be coy about it!'

'Hunter, there are things here that I can't simply walk away from—'

'What things? A job? A house? You don't need them, Lauren.'

'I can't just leave—'

'Yes, you can. Maybe I shouldn't have asked you like this over the telephone. I should have waited till I could hold you, and kiss you, and convince you with all the right trappings, but I'm too impatient for that, sweet Lauren. You don't have to answer me now. You don't have to say anything at all. And I'm not going to bring it up again, because there's nothing more to discuss. Just be prepared to come with me on Valentine's Day— because that's what you want, just as much as I want it.'

And with that, he whispered a goodbye, and he was gone. Once more he was half a world away, unreachable.

Lauren replaced the receiver slowly. He was so sublimely sure of her, she thought, as if she would have no objections, as if there were no barriers standing in the way of their being together. But it wasn't fair. He could not dismiss her job and the question of the house so lightly—or could he? She certainly would not need employment if she went with him. And the house, well, she'd been thinking of selling it, anyway, and he knew it.

He was so superbly self-assured. . .but what woman in her right mind could turn down the promise of New York, London, Paris, with Hunter Dix at her side? And even if there were only the multitude of tiny nameless cities, well, the sophisticated cities weren't really what Lauren wanted, anyway. Nor was it Hunter Dix the famous singer, either. It was Hunter Dix the man, the lost little boy she had gotten to know that first night over dinner at Marconi's. As long as she was with Hunter, she would have the best of all the world, no matter where they were to go.

And if she didn't seize this chance now, it might never come again. When they were half a world apart like this, there were too many things to interfere, to pull them away from each other. They might never be able to recapture the perfect harmony they had known that night at Marconi's. Already the frustration of having only a telephone link between them was showing on him, and perhaps on her, as well.

'Your soup has gotten cold,' Ward pointed out.

'Oh.' She pulled herself back with an effort. She hadn't even heard him return. 'It doesn't matter. I wasn't really hungry, anyway.'

He looked down at her, his hands in his trouser pockets. She noticed—why hadn't she realized it before?—that he was still in his working garb—dark trousers, striped shirt, tie. He'd left the long lab coat at the store, of course, and he'd loosened his tie, but that was all. Didn't the man ever relax?

He looked as if there was a great deal he'd like to tell her, but instead he said mildly, 'I'll put it in the refrigerator, in case you want it later.'

'That's fine. Thank you.'

She put her head back against the couch cushions, and her eyes were closed a couple of minutes later when he returned. 'You look exhausted,' he said. 'It takes a lot of energy to put on a performance like that, doesn't it?'

She sat straight up. 'What is that supposed to mean? What performance?'

Ward shrugged. 'Just that you certainly came back to life when Hunter called, and now look at you. Worn to a thread.'

'If you'd think about what you just said, Ward, it's not at all hard to understand.' She curled up.

'Oh, I don't have any trouble understanding that you wanted to impress him. What I don't quite see is why. Does he think getting bronchitis is a moral weakness, or does he just disapprove in principle of anything that keeps you from giving him your full attention?'

She opened her eyes and glared at him. 'Hunter is a very sweet man who's absorbed right now in a draining world tour. It would be a miracle if he wasn't tired out and short-tempered sometimes, so I try not to weigh him down with my problems. And of course he tries to stay away from colds and things like that. His voice is his profession, and he can't afford to take chances with it.'

'Of course.' His tone was faintly mocking.

'I wouldn't expect you to sympathize, but he's a very lonely person, really,' Lauren said.

'Lonely? Perhaps. Also spoiled, selfish, cynical, rude, manipulative. . .'

She was getting annoyed. She wasn't surprised that Ward felt jealous, even though he had no real right to be. But this vindictiveness was completely unlike him. This was not the Ward she knew. Certainly he was no Pollyanna—he could see the shadowed side of things—but he usually didn't attack people without reason, and he didn't call them names. 'What's the matter with you?' she asked. 'You've got no right, just because I let you kiss me tonight, to carry on like this!'

There was no hint of a dimple now at the corner of Ward's mouth; instead a muscle twitched tensely. 'He's quite possibly abusive,' he went on levelly, 'and he's certainly—'

She got shakily to her feet. 'That's enough. I don't know where you got your ideas, but they're wrong, Ward. Dead wrong. Hunter is like a gentle, lonely little boy. Oh, you must know the kind I mean. They have a bigger allowance than most kids, and so the ones who don't have as much make up to them and use them, and they never know who their real friends are.'

Ward shook his head. 'The little boys with money that I knew were never like that. They were the users and the bullies, and they didn't care whether they had any friends at all.'

She stamped her foot. 'Would you stop twisting my words? You're taking something beautiful and making it sinister, and I won't let you do it! I don't have to listen to this!'

There was a long silence. Lauren sat down again, because her knees were trembling. And she was cold, all of a sudden, as if every nerve had suddenly been rubbed with ice.

Ward's voice softened. 'You think he loves you, don't you, Lauren?'

She said peevishly, 'I think I'm certainly a better judge of that than you are.'

'And you're actually thinking of going with him when he comes back?'

'Yes,' she said. Her voice was very low, as if saying it aloud made it somehow more real—even though it was only Ward, not Hunter, she was telling. 'Yes,' she repeated, more firmly. 'I am going with him.'

The silence in the house could not have been more complete.

'What's holding me here, anyway?' she said at last, like a child parroting what she had been told. 'I have no family. The house, well, it's only a place to live, after all. And as for my job, Mr. Baines won't mind all that much, because it's the start of the slow season. After the Valentine's Day rush, Kim can handle the store by herself most of the time. Mr. Baines will probably be happy to have one less on the payroll, to tell the truth, and he'll have plenty of time to train someone new before the store starts to get busy again next fall.'

'Who are you trying to convince, Lauren? Me? Mr. Baines? Or yourself?'

She turned her back. 'Please don't feel that you have to stay here and lecture me.' Her tone was icily polite. 'I'm certain you have more important things to do tonight.'

'You're a fool, Lauren.'

'You don't have any right to judge me.'

There was a rustle; when she looked over her shoulder

he was putting on his topcoat. 'I suppose that's so,' he said quietly. 'I don't have any rights at all, when it comes down to the bottom line. I'm terribly sorry I bothered you this evening.'

'Don't forget your movie,' she said childishly. 'I don't think I'll be watching it.'

He took the videotape box from her hand and shoved it into his pocket. 'You'll be too busy humming your song, I suppose—the one he's writing for you. If you want my advice—'

'I don't.'

'—you should learn it by heart, and substitute it for where you used to say your prayers. Perhaps you'll be lucky, and it will help to keep you warm at night after you realize what a terrible mistake you've made.'

She slammed the door behind him, then struggled up the stairs and almost fell into her bed, too drained even to straighten the crumpled sheets she had crawled out of that morning.

And she was not surprised when it was Ward who stalked her fevered, restless sleep. Ward, and the way he had behaved tonight, was the stuff of nightmares. When she began to feel better, then she would be able to dream once again of Hunter, and the lovely days to come.

CHAPTER FOUR

MORE ROSES ARRIVED the next day—another two dozen long-stemmed, creamy-white beauties. They must have been wired the moment Hunter set foot back on American soil, and Lauren buried her face in them and thought, *Six more days and I'll be with him. By the time these roses fade . . .*

Then she drew back and looked at the flowers a little sadly. Two dozen glorious roses, and she couldn't even enjoy their heavy, sultry fragrance, because she couldn't smell a thing. 'They'll last,' she whispered. 'I'll smell them later. It's all right. I can wait.' Her words sounded like a vow, made in the cathedral-like silence of her living room.

Six more days. . .

Each hour passed with infinite slowness. The time dragged even more because there was no one to share Lauren's excitement, her anticipation, her joy. For she had decided not to tell anyone of her plans.

She knew she ought to tell Mr. Baines, at least, but she just couldn't bring herself to do it. He hated having his neat time schedules upset, and Lauren knew that he simply wouldn't understand why she wasn't giving him the full month's notice she should. If she was going to leave him in the lurch, anyway, she might as well really be a rat, she told herself, and avoid the trouble that honesty would bring. For if she told him she was leaving in less than a week, things would be mighty unpleasant around the store, and the details would inevitably leak out to the rest of Poplar Street.

Ward's reaction to the news had made her wary of letting anyone else have a chance to comment. While she didn't think that many people would dare to say the things Ward had—at least to her face—she knew they would talk about it and shake their heads, up and down the length of Poplar Street. She would be the subject of gossip once she was gone, of course; that was inevitable. But to face it in person, to have to keep her chin up while people covertly pointed her out and discussed behind her back, to have to pretend calmness when guilty silence fell as she walked into a room or met a group on the street. . . No, she couldn't face that.

At least, she didn't have to bring it upon herself, she thought. Ward might not keep her secret, of course. All he had to do was to let a word drop, and it would unleash a firestorm of talk. But, she told herself with a mental shrug, that was completely out of her hands; she could not prevent him from talking. If Ward wanted to soothe his masculine pride by making her appear to be some sort of dreamy-eyed star-chaser, he could do it easily enough. The people on Poplar Street would be easily convinced that she was truly the dizzy blonde of legend, off on a mad whim. They simply wouldn't comprehend the sort of instant understanding that she and Hunter had found, and Lauren knew it would be senseless to try to explain to them that she wasn't acting on some crazy self-destructive impulse, but that this was a true and lasting love.

It still brought faint pink to her own cheeks, to think of the magic of loving Hunter, so how could she hope to explain it to these people, who didn't know the real man?

Only Kim seemed to understand at all, and even she wavered now and then—or perhaps it was just her habit of saying whatever she was thinking. One day a customer brought in the latest tabloid and, with a malicious smile at Lauren, murmured, 'I'm sure you've already seen this, since it has Hunter Dix on the front page. But I thought you'd like an extra copy.' And as soon as the customer had left, Kim buried her nose in the paper.

Lauren sighed and turned back to her sketches of a window display for St. Patrick's Day; it was a display she would certainly never be arranging herself, but to ignore the window would raise suspicion, and she supposed Kim would appreciate the suggestions when the time came. 'Enjoying yourself?' she asked finally.

Kim tossed the tabloid across the display case. 'You might like to see this.'

It sounded like a warning. Lauren glanced at the front page. HUNTER TAKES HONOLULU! the headline shrieked. SEXY SINGER SETS THE TOWN ON FIRE AFTER CONCERT. . .

The headlines went on, in banks of descending size, but Lauren stopped reading. 'What nonsense,' she said. 'I know perfectly well what he was doing after that concert. He was in his hotel room talking to me on the phone.'

Kim reached for the paper. 'There are pictures inside—'

'Haven't you ever heard of faked photographs? Oh, Kim, you know the press will go to any lengths to get a juicy new story. You even heard Hunter himself say that they just aren't ever right.'

Kim shook her head. 'What he said was, they were right about his actress friend leaving him.'

'Well, it would have been difficult for anyone to mess those facts up, don't you think?' Lauren held her sketch out at arm's length. 'Do we still have those ceramic leprechauns in the back room? I think with a little of that sticky wax they could each hold a ring, don't you?'

'Only if you promise to clean the wax off afterward,' Kim said.

Lauren almost smiled, and then stopped abruptly, as the realization sank in that she certainly would not have to worry about the wax. She had always enjoyed decorating the windows, coming up with new ideas as the season passed, refining and changing them each year. And now she wouldn't ever be doing this again. No more collecting unusual little objects at flea markets, just because they might fit into a display someday. No more gathering up odd trinkets from her friends' castoffs. There were boxes of things like that at the house; what on earth would she do with all of them?

Throw them away, she told herself firmly. She should go home and put them in the garbage tonight. She certainly wouldn't need that kind of junk anymore. She'd have much more important things to do than decorate windows, and just because she didn't know yet exactly what those things would be, certainly didn't mean that she wouldn't enjoy them just as much—even more, because they would involve Hunter. She'd always had sort of a knack for public relations. Maybe she could—

Kim was still studying the tabloid. 'Lauren, I think you should at least look at these pictures.'

'What? No, I won't, Kim. I won't dignify that rag by looking at it anymore. The pictures are bound to be retouched or airbrushed or whatever they do to make people look as if they're in compromising situations—'

'How did you know that they're compromising pictures?' Kim asked quietly. 'I didn't say they were.'

'Aren't they always? For all I know, they could even have used a double. I've heard of them doing that, when they can't get real dirt on someone.' She took the paper by the corner and dropped it into the nearest wastebasket.

'You're probably right,' Kim said. 'Doubles, hmm? Still—' But she stopped there, and she didn't say any more about the tabloid.

Neither of them said much at all, in fact, and Lauren was glad when the time came for her afternoon break. Not even the pharmacy snack counter could be worse than silence.

At least, it hadn't been yet. On the first day that her cold had allowed her to go back to work, she had taken her courage very firmly in hand when it was time for her break. What if Ward thought that her mere presence in his store was an invitation to take up his lecture again precisely where she had called a halt to it before?

He wouldn't do that, she told herself. Not in public. Not Ward, who always thought about appearances.

But it wasn't until her coffee was in front of her and she was aimlessly stirring it that she realized that an argument was not the only sort of conduct that would draw attention. If Ward simply ignored her, that would be equally curiosity-provoking. And, she realized, it would be far more soothing to his ego than would an embarrassing fight. It would look, if he simply paid no attention to her, as if she was pursuing him. As if he had jilted her and not the other way around.

But of course he hadn't done that. Not Ward, the perfect gentleman. On that first afternoon, he had simply come down from the glass-walled cubicle at the back of the store to have his cup refilled, as he always did when she came in. And if this day, he had perched for barely half a minute on the stool beside hers and talked only about the suddenly warmer weather, well, who would notice, really? He was obviously busy; that was enough to account for the brevity of their chat and the fact that he hadn't even touched her hair, or commented about the silver-dollar-sized opal in the new necklace she was wearing.

And so it had continued as the days dragged slowly by. Sometimes he came down and sat beside her briefly; sometimes he only waved when she came in and then turned back to his work. She was grateful to him for not making a scene.

Alma refilled Lauren's cup. 'Don't let it get you down,' she recommended.

Lauren was so startled that she burned her tongue on her coffee.

'Ward, I mean,' the woman went on. 'With this bug that's going around, he's so busy he doesn't know if he's coming or going these days. It's nothing for you to worry about, dear.'

'I'm sure it isn't,' Lauren managed to say.

Alma smiled a little. 'Trying to put a good face on it? I understand. He's a little impatient these days, himself. Just don't fret. As soon as the rush dies down he'll be the same old Ward. I understand you've had this bad cold, too?'

Lauren nodded, and got out of the pharmacy as soon as she could. The next day she didn't go back. There was no sense, she told herself, in making things more difficult for both of them.

The experience left her feeling a bit somber. For the

first time, she had gotten a glimpse of what it was going to be like for Ward after her Valentine's Day departure. If everyone on Poplar Street was as sympathetically understanding of his feelings as Alma was, well, it wouldn't be easy on him, once everyone knew that Lauren had tossed him aside for Hunter Dix. In fact, for a man like Ward, that sympathy would not only grate, it would be close to unbearable.

At least he knew the truth, she reminded herself, so it wouldn't come as a nasty shock to him at the same moment the rest of Poplar Street found out. But there was nothing much else she could do to lessen the blow, and she felt guilty about leaving him to face the inevitable gossip.

Ward didn't deserve this kind of pain, that was sure. But someday, she knew, this would all be behind him, and he'd be happy again. Someday Ward would make some woman a wonderful husband. All he had to do, Lauren thought, was find a purely practical woman, one who would be happy with the things he could give her. A woman who understood that Ward was frosty orange juice and chicken soup and crocus bulbs in a pot, and who would be content with that. A woman who didn't have a romantic streak, and so didn't long for champagne and caviar and white roses by the dozen.

She hoped it didn't take long, for she hated to see him hurt like this and know that she had been the cause of it.

VALENTINE'S DAY dawned clear and unseasonably warm, and Lauren greeted it with the boundless, breathless joy of the sort she could recall feeling as a child on Christmas mornings when her feet scarcely touched the stairs as she hurried down to see what Santa had brought.

Her heart was like a hot-air balloon, struggling to be free, and even doing the final things could not tug it back within earth's sober gravity again. The final things—cooking the last breakfast, cleaning out the few remaining perishables from the refrigerator, telephoning to stop the newspaper delivery, running across the street to drop off the extra key with the neighbors who always kept an eye on the house when she was gone—all those things she had done before, when she was leaving for a week or two. It would not truly sink in on her for days, perhaps, that this was the very final time.

She put the last few things in her suitcases, which lay stretched open on the bed in the guest room, but she did not close them up. Hunter hadn't been very clear about the exact schedule of the day, and so she thought they'd probably get her things after the concert. There was no sense in letting everything be mashed for longer than necessary; she could close the bags in a minute, when it was time.

And then there were the boxes to deal with—quite a pile of them, really, containing the sentimental things she simply could not let go. Family photo albums, her own baby book, her father's proudly framed law degree, that sort of thing. The boxes would have to go into storage for a while, she supposed; she certainly couldn't drag them around the world with her. The rest—the furniture, the dishes, the odds and ends of living—could be auctioned. That was the simplest way. The real-estate people could handle that, she supposed, before she actually put the house up for sale.

She felt a little disloyal for not having done so already; after all, she would not be coming back. But that news would have been very hard to keep quiet, so she had decided to wait till after Valentine's Day. The necessary papers could be mailed, and by that time, Poplar Street would have so much to talk about, the house wouldn't matter.

She made a last tour, pausing to rub a hand over her mother's oak hutch in the dining room with its precious Haviland china so carefully arranged on the shelves. She sat for a moment in the leather chair behind her father's walnut desk, and looked at the books that lined the shelves in his study.

'No,' she told herself. 'You must be reasonable, Lauren. You cannot take everything.'

But perhaps she could take some extra things later. She would have to talk to Hunter about that, of course. If he had a house, there would surely be room for the hutch and the desk, at least, and for the precious memories they represented. There simply hadn't been time to talk to him about details like that.

The bronze mantel clock that had been her grandmother's told her that she had to go now, or she would be late for work. She turned the thermostat down and drew the curtains in the living room, then paused in the front hall. It was silly, but she could have sworn that something—the house itself, perhaps—had whispered goodbye. It was an almost mournful sound.

She gathered up her things from the hall table—her gloves, her handbag and the sealed envelope that held her resignation letter. She would leave it in the safe tonight for Mr. Baines to find tomorrow morning, after she was gone. . ..

Tomorrow morning, when she would truly be beginning her new life, with Hunter.

'Oh, Hunter,' she whispered. 'To have you always! How did I deserve to be so lucky?'

The pot of crocus was still on the counter next to the cash register. Lauren hadn't touched them, but she knew that Kim had watered them faithfully, and she had been rewarded with a burst of cheerful, satiny, deep-purple blooms. This morning, even the prosaic crocus brought joy to Lauren's heart, and she was sniffing a particularly beautiful bloom when Kim came in. 'You're actually here?' Kim said in disbelief. 'I thought sure you'd be waiting for Hunter at the airport.'

'No.' Lauren tried to pull discreetly away from the crocus; she'd practically had her nose buried against the secret orange center of that flower! 'He asked me not to, because there will be fans all over the place. He said he'd rather see me privately, later.'

'Privately? I suppose that means he'll turn up at the store, white limousine, bodyguards and all?'

'Kim, what's happened to you? I thought you admired him!'

Kim shrugged. 'I don't know. It was different somehow, looking up to him when he was untouchable. He was so glamorous and so perfect, he wasn't like a real person at all. Then when it turned out he's human after all. . .'

'Then it's even more wonderful,' Lauren said.

Kim sighed. 'I guess I like my heroes to stay on their pedestals, that's all.'

Lauren shook her head sadly. 'It makes it very difficult on the heroes—trying to live up to all their admirers' illusions.'

'There's nothing wrong with illusions,' Kim said

flatly, 'unless you get confused about what's real.' Then she changed the subject firmly.

Lauren was glad. She knew that Kim must suspect what she was going to do, and it wasn't a thing she wanted to argue over—or even to talk about. She wanted only pleasant memories to take with her when she left tonight.

That was why she almost groaned when she saw Ward coming down Poplar Street late in the afternoon. She had deliberately avoided taking her coffee break, so she didn't have to go to the pharmacy and face him. And so he had come to her—to try one last persuasive argument? Or simply to say goodbye? Either would be less than comfortable, with Kim in the room and Mr. Baines within hearing.

Ward leaned on the counter and touched a fingertip to the satin petal of a crocus bloom. 'They've done well, haven't they? It's hard to believe that such beautiful blooms can come from such tiny bulbs.'

Lauren said a little stiffly, 'It was very thoughtful of you.'

'It's too bad. . .' he began, then turned a little pink, as if the words had slipped out despite his best intentions.

Lauren knew what he was thinking—that the crocus would have only a brief life, since they would never be planted in the garden he had intended them to grace. It hurt her, too, now that she thought about it. It was not the crocus' fault, after all. They shouldn't get a death sentence out of it.

'I suppose. . .' It was a bit awkward. 'Well, Kim's been taking care of them. It's up to her, really.'

Kim looked at her oddly and opened her mouth as if to ask why Lauren would be giving her credit—and, incidentally, telling Ward that she had given his flowers away to someone else!

Lauren hurried on. 'There's a little patch of dirt by the street lamp.' She waved a hand toward the front of the store. 'Maybe they could go there, and help make the street pretty next year, too.' She touched a glossy petal and bent over quickly to sniff the bloom. 'They *are* too beautiful to waste, and the fragrance. . .I'm only now beginning to be able to smell again, after my cold, so I hadn't noticed before.'

You're babbling, she told herself. Why can't you just shut up, and let Ward say whatever he came in for, and then he'll go away and leave you alone? It's almost the end of the day. . ..

And Hunter has not come, the demon in the back of her brain reminded. His plane landed hours ago, and you have not had a word.

As if in answer, the white limousine pulled up in front of the store and double-parked, blocking a traffic lane. The chauffeur did not appear, and the rear door opened from the inside. One of the bodyguards got out with a package in his hands.

Lauren's heart felt as if it had bounced on the floor. No Hunter, then. Why not?

The bodyguard came into the jewelry store without a look to either side and set the package down in front of Lauren. 'Mr. Dix wanted me to deliver this, Miss Hodges,' he said in a near monotone. 'And to tell you that the limousine will pick you up here before the concert tonight.'

Lauren nodded, and after he was gone she looked down at the heart-shaped, cellophane-wrapped box. Chocolates, she thought helplessly.

'Well, I guess candy is the obvious thing for the day,' Ward said. 'Too bad, of course, that you're allergic to chocolate. Doesn't he know that? Or doesn't he care?'

Lauren bit her lip, but she was determined not to let her disappointment show. 'I guess the subject just never came up,' she said mildly, and reached for the nearest pair of scissors to slit the cellophane. When she lifted the lid off the box, two slips of cardboard fluttered out— new, signed backstage passes for tonight's show. She handed one to Kim with an almost ceremonial bow.

Underneath was a single layer of rich, moist candies, each in a dark paper cup, each identified by shape and color and the professional swirl on the surface. They were obviously good quality, but they were still chocolates, and she couldn't eat even one of them or she would break out into a gigantic case of hives—her whole body would turn red, and puff up and itch. And Ward would have to go rushing down to the pharmacy for an antihistamine to get it under control again.

He sends me roses I can't smell and candy I can't eat, she thought. But it wasn't fair to blame Hunter for not considering her stupid allergy; how could he have known? And lots of people wouldn't have thought about her stuffy nose and the roses, either.

'Well, would you look at that!' Kim said breathlessly. 'What brand are these chocolates? I think I'd have Mr. Baines take a look at it, Lauren. It might be like the prize in a box of breakfast cereal.'

Lauren looked at her in astonishment. 'If you'd take your nose out of the box so I can see what brought on this torrent of enthusiasm, Kim. . .'

It was a ring, propped between two chocolate-coated butterscotch-crunch candies in the very center of the box.

It had fallen to one side, which was why Lauren hadn't seen it right away; the stone had nestled against the side of a caramel, and only the gold glint of the band had drawn Kim's attention.

Lauren plucked the ring out of the box. A ruby winked back from between her fingers—a large, heart-shaped ruby, at least a full carat in size. On each side of it were mounted three tiny diamonds.

Lauren stood there and held it, and wondered why she was feeling just a little sad. Then she knew. Hunter had promised that when he returned she would have all the trappings of romance, and in her mind's eye she had seen a pleasant little dinner with champagne and caviar and candlelight. And afterward, in some private little spot, Hunter would kneel and formally ask her to marry him, and then he would put a very special ring on her finger. . ..

Well, there simply wasn't time for that, she told herself stoutly. There were demands that couldn't be put aside. There wasn't time for a leisurely dinner before the concert, and it was stupid to be annoyed at him for not wanting to wait until afterward to present her ring!

Besides, she thought, it was a rare woman who had a personal concert on the evening of her engagement. It *was* her concert tonight, devoted entirely to her. How much more romantic that was than any mere dinner could ever be.

And the ring—yes, it was a very special ring. Nothing could have been more appropriate than a heart-shaped ruby. And if Hunter couldn't be here himself to put it on her finger. . . Well, she was sure that later tonight he would bless it with a kiss.

She slid the ring onto her left hand. 'Isn't it beautiful?'

She stretched out her hand on the top of the display case and studied the effect of the blood-red stone. A heart-shaped ruby. She hadn't seen many of those.

Ward touched the stone with the very tip of his finger, turning the ring to face the light. It moved easily; it was a little large for her tiny hand. But that could be fixed easily enough, Lauren thought. Perhaps even this afternoon, if Mr. Baines had time. . .

Ward was extremely cautious to touch only the ring and not let his hand brush against her skin. She stayed very still, her hand almost frozen against the glass top of the cabinet, until he pulled away.

'I hope both of you will have a good time at the concert of the century,' he said, and Lauren knew what he was really saying.

She drifted over to the window and watched as he walked down the street and stopped to chat with a customer and her little boy. And she told herself that it was foolish to feel sad because there hadn't been a chance to say a real goodbye. Very foolish, indeed. For what, really, was there to say?

CHAPTER FIVE

KIM OBVIOUSLY INTENDED to enjoy herself; the moment that the chauffeur ushered the two of them into the back of the limousine, she began playing with the buttons—turning the television on and off, tinkering with the telephone, and in general driving Lauren mad. Finally she settled back against the leather seat with a contented sigh. 'May I look at your ring again?'

'It depends,' Lauren said dryly. 'Are you admiring the ring, or checking to see if my finger has turned green yet?'

Kim grinned. 'That tabloid had me worried, you know. I really thought Hunter was just giving you a rush and that you were an idiot to fall for it. I never dreamed he was serious.' She was studying the ruby in the glow of one of the reading lights when Lauren grabbed for the switch and turned it off. 'Wait a minute,' she protested. 'I wasn't finished!'

'That's the convention center ahead,' Lauren said, 'and look at the crowd waiting. With the lights off, they can't see into the car.'

'She learns fast, doesn't she?' Kim said to no one in particular.

Lauren glanced at the tiny clock built into the limousine's entertainment center. It was later than she had thought, and on the stage inside the convention hall, the opening band would already be performing. Yet there was an incredible number of people still standing outside, jamming the walks and pressing against the police barricades that had been set up to keep the street clear.

Even inside the quiet car, Lauren and Kim heard the shout that went up when the limousine was spotted, and Lauren could feel the color draining from her face as people began to leap the barricades almost into its path. It was not fear of what they might do that made her turn white, but fear for their safety as the car swept through the crowd without reducing its speed. Once past the barricades, it dropped down the ramp to the hidden, protected parking area beneath the building.

Kim's eyes were wide, and she was clutching at the edge of her seat. 'So this is the way things will be from now on? I guess you won't be going to the grocery store very often, will you?'

Lauren laughed a little shakily. She had known intellectually that this sort of thing was likely to happen. But she hadn't really understood how it felt to be the pursued, and the experience had rattled her a little.

They thought it was Hunter in the car, she told herself; that's why the commotion was so great. I'm sure I'll get used to it eventually.

One of the bodyguards met the limousine and opened the door for them. Then he hurried them up another ramp to the main part of the building. 'There's a special box reserved for you just off stage,' he said. 'I'll take you there right now—the concert has already started and Mr. Dix is getting ready to go on, so he'll see you at intermission.'

But Lauren wasn't listening. She had managed to peek around his bulk, and in the wide hallway ahead she saw Hunter. He was leaning against an untidy pile of unrecognizable stage gear, and he was talking to a man a head shorter than he was.

He looked so different, she thought involuntarily. The tour had taken its toll.

He was thinner, and there were heavy lines almost slashed into his face, and his color was terrible—or was that only the stage makeup? It had to be harsh and garish, Lauren told herself, to stand up under the tremendously powerful lights he would face on stage. But he looked. . .awful. That was the only word for it. As if he needed a rest.

And he sounded worse. She didn't catch every word of what he said, but she got the substance of it. He was announcing that he detested the fans who were waiting for him to perform tonight, stupid fools that they were. He was tired of being at the beck and call of every pimply teenage girl who had the price of admission. . ..

'Hunter,' she said in a voice that was little more than a whisper.

He didn't hear her, but the man with him did, and he put an elbow in Hunter's ribs. Hunter frowned at him and turned and called, 'Sweet Lauren!' He came toward her, his arms outstretched. 'My precious girl. You're shocked at me, aren't you?'

'You sound so cynical. . .' Her throat almost closed up.

'You mustn't fret, sweet Lauren. Of course I don't mean it. It's stage fright, you see. I have to do this every time I face a crowd, or I'd never get my nerve up to go through that door when the curtain rises. But with you here now to give me courage. . .' He reached for her hands, and when he saw the ruby on her finger something in his face changed. Before she could move, his arms were tightly around her, and his mouth was hard against hers till she couldn't get her breath, and her lips felt bruised. She tried to protest, but his tongue probed deep into her mouth, eager and demanding. She felt almost violated at the very public nature of that kiss, and she had to tell herself quite sternly that of course he was a little exuberant tonight. He hadn't seen her in two weeks; the man had a right to a kiss from the woman he loved, the woman who wore his ring. If he had gone a little overboard, that was understandable, and flattering, in a way.

And after all, the bodyguard hadn't seemed to notice anything unusual, and the man in the hallway had just walked away as if nothing had happened.

Kim gave Lauren a sidelong look as they settled into the draped private box at the side of the stage, but she didn't say anything. It was impossible to talk, anyway; the opening act was already well into its performance, and the hall was too noisy for conversation. Or for thinking, Lauren told herself; this group of performers certainly didn't agree with Hunter on what music was supposed to be.

People were still coming in, the ones, perhaps, who had been waiting outside, not caring about the first act, in the hope of seeing Hunter. They hadn't seen him, only the limousine, but they were happy. They didn't know it had been only illusion.

The band finished with an earsplitting roar, took its bows and left the stage, and a crew moved in, crawling over the stage like so many giant ants as they tugged the equipment into new positions. The work went incredibly fast, and less than five minutes later the lights changed, the crew vanished, and the anticipation began to build as Hunter's band members came on stage one by one and began a heavy, pounding, rhythmic theme that grew slowly and steadily into a crescendo of sound. And then, at the height of it, two spotlights snapped on and intersected at center stage on Hunter. The crowd was on its feet, and over the screaming, he began to sing.

It had been the stage makeup that had made him look so odd, Lauren thought. From her seat almost in the wings, he looked tanned and rested.

Another illusion, she thought.

He sang about the joy of coming back, and when the song was done he swept them all a bow, and began to talk to the 'girder people'—the ones crammed into the very top of the house, almost against the steel rafters—telling them how important they were, and how delighted he was to be there to sing for them.

And that, too, Lauren thought, was illusion. For she knew, in the depths of her heart, that what she had overheard backstage had been the truth. He had meant every word of what he had said then. This charming Hunter, here and now, was the act—the one who was false.

But why should she be so surprised? He was a performer—a creator of illusion. That was what these people had come to see; they weren't disappointed.

But if all that was only a performance, she found herself wondering, then how much of what she had seen in Hunter was real, and how much was. . .just illusion?

It was almost as if each of Lauren's nerves had been rubbed with sandpaper and sensitized to falsehood, for she could hear it now in his voice. Even in songs she had loved for years, in lyrics she could quote entirely from memory. Tonight she was hearing a man who thought himself at the center of the universe and saw no reason that everyone else should not agree.

She glanced over at Kim, who was leaning forward, sometimes almost singing along, her eyes rapt. Obviously she didn't hear the egotistical undertone in this well-loved voice.

Was she being fair? Lauren asked herself. Any performer—any star—had to be certain of himself. How could anyone get up on that stage and bare his soul without that sort of self-confidence? Was she suddenly seeing him clearly for the first time, or was she just suffering from a case of cold feet?

She tried to swallow her confusion and simply enjoy the concert—her concert!—but she knew that the first half was almost over, and he was expecting her backstage at intermission.

Kim punched her in the ribs, and Lauren's attention snapped back to the stage.

'. . .a new song,' Hunter was saying, 'for a very special lady on Valentine's Day, to close out the first half of the evening. . .'

It was a beautiful melody, and the haunting lyrics spoke of love coming back into his life after he had thought his life was forever empty.

It was very good, Lauren thought, this song he'd written for her. It would be a hit, for it was enough to bring tears. Kim was crying. She would cry herself—if she still believed.

Perhaps Kim was the wise one after all, Lauren mused. *I like my heroes to stay on their pedestals,* she had said. Perhaps she too, should have left him there—a hero on a pedestal.

Kim stayed in the box at intermission, still sniffling and fumbling for her handkerchief. 'You're one lucky girl,' she said with a gulp, when the bodyguard came to get Lauren.

Lauren hugged her and smiled. Yes, she thought, she was. For she could see it all clearly now. That beautiful love song wasn't about her at all, but about him; her feelings and her desires had never entered his mind when he wrote those lovely words. And she could see now that the passionate kiss tonight had nothing to do with her, but with the need to conquer. And the urgency of his plea that she come with him tonight—why was it so important, after all, that it be now? *Because once I was away from the familiar, I would be dependent on him. And there are lots of other women who would have done just as well.*

The things he said and did had not been an expression of his love, but of his selfishness. There had been signs of it all along, now that she looked for them—the telephone calls at hours convenient only to him, the list of complaints of the way he was being treated on the tour, the way he had belittled the bodyguards. He obviously thought that rules—like restaurant dress codes—did not apply to him, and also that cash was a tonic to be applied to solve any problem.

But she had excused those things, overlooked them, ignored them, and concentrated on the romantic gestures instead—the champagne and the roses and the ring— things that in the end were meaningless. How much thought did it take, really, to tell a bodyguard to wire two dozen roses? And what did a ring mean, when it was delivered without a word about love or commitment— indeed, without any word at all?

She did not feel angry at him for betraying her, or for villainously plotting this entire scheme. She had asked for it, after all, and eagerly marched along to the tune he had sung. Besides, she thought that his self-centeredness was so complete that Hunter himself was incapable of realizing when he was using other people.

No, she was not angry. She was conscious of nothing but a soul-deep relief that she had come to her senses in time.

Backstage, Hunter moved to seize her for another kiss, but she sidestepped him.

He looked startled, and then he said, 'I see. A little more privacy?' and started to draw her into a dressing room nearby.

Lauren shook her head. 'That's not necessary. I came backstage to thank you for my concert, Hunter.' She pulled the ruby ring off her finger and dropped it into his palm. 'And to return this. I'm not sure what it meant, but I'm certain you didn't intend it to be an engagement ring. Did you?'

He was still stammering—it was an interesting phenomenon, Lauren thought, Hunter Dix without words!—when a tall redhead in elaborate makeup and a very short skirt sauntered up beside him and slipped her arm through his. 'You're in wonderful voice, darling,' she murmured.

'Who the hell let you in?' Hunter said roughly.

'You don't think I'm going to tell you, do you? You'd fire the poor soul.' But the woman wasn't looking at him; she was surveying Lauren through narrowed eyes. Lauren recognized her. So the tabloids hadn't had all the details right about his actress friend leaving him, after all, for here she was. . ..

'Who is *she?*' the woman asked. 'Honestly, Hunter,

not another groupie. I swear, every time you go on tour—'

'I'm no one you need to worry about,' Lauren said gently. 'Goodbye, Hunter.'

It was busy backstage, and easy to slip through the crowded hallways and out to the street, where the air was fresh. There were still a few people hanging about outside the convention center. One was a girl, clutching a promotional poster and a pen, waiting patiently for a moment with her hero—

Some kind of hero he had turned out to be, Lauren thought. She realized that her backstage pass was still in her hand, and she considered giving it to the girl. Then she shredded it into the gutter instead, for she could not square it with her conscience if she helped to feed someone else's hero-worship.

It was cold but not bitter, and as she walked away from the glow of the convention center's lights, the stars appeared, gleaming in the clear sky. Her heart was soothed a little, and when she saw a cab she hailed it and gave the driver her home address. She sank back against the ripped vinyl and began to think of the peaceful quiet of her own living room, and of the work that awaited her—putting back in place all the pieces of her life she had ripped apart in the past couple of weeks. The clothes, the photograph albums, the sentimental memories—the friendships.

It was too late, she told herself. She'd been such a fool—rude, obnoxious, stupid. How could any man forgive being called a miserable, suspicious creep? To say nothing of the other things she'd called him, the way she'd acted, the nincompoop she'd been.

Still. . .she had to try, didn't she? She could at least

say she was sorry, and clear her conscience, even if Ward didn't care to accept her apology.

She sat up straight and said to the driver, 'I've changed my mind. Take me to Poplar Street instead, please.'

'Nothing's open there this time of night, miss.'

'I know,' she said. 'That's why I want to go.'

The cabbie shook his head at the craziness, but he changed direction. Lauren had a sudden twinge of apprehension as the blocks went by. Bursting in on Ward like this might not be such a good idea.

Well, she told herself firmly, it was better than just turning up tomorrow at the pharmacy. He might say anything, then. And she couldn't apologize in public— not the way she should apologize. She probably couldn't tell him all the things she should, anyway. She certainly couldn't say that she was an idiot for not knowing what love really was!

But why couldn't she? she asked herself. It was the truth.

It was like waking from a nightmare, drenched with sweat, relieved to find that the bogeyman wasn't real, but finding that the whole world had assumed a greater clarity—every noise, every ray of light, every thought. . .

She'd let herself be so blinded by illusion, she thought, that she couldn't see reality. She'd fallen so hard for an image that she couldn't recognize real love when she saw it.

When she had been sick, Ward had been there, quietly doing what needed to be done. He had brought her food, and stayed with her, and risked her germs, and made sure she was cared for. How much easier it would have been for him to go back home, kick off his shoes, call the shop down the street and send her a bunch of flowers!

Romance isn't just a word, she mused, it's an attitude. It isn't lavish gifts, it's thoughtful ones. Sometimes it's not caviar, but chicken soup. And roses are beautiful, but crocus lasts forever, and renews itself each spring.

Why had she never seen Ward's gifts in that light before—in the light of love?

But was that truly what it was, she asked herself, or only what she wanted it to be? *Don't kid yourself, Lauren; he's never said a word about loving you.* And he had all the time in the world to tell her before Hunter ever came along. And he hadn't done a thing for her that he wouldn't have done for half of his customers.

There was a dim yellow glow in the windows of his apartment above the pharmacy. She stared up at the front of the building for a long moment, and then paid off the cab.

It was funny, she thought as she turned toward the stairs. At the convention center, she didn't feel a bit as if she'd burned all her bridges. Now, she did. What if she went up there and told Ward that birthday dinners at home and movies and Sunday afternoon drives were important to her, after all, even if that was all she'd ever have—and he said that he didn't want even that much anymore?

Ward opened the door six inches and stopped. There was no warm gleam in his eyes. 'To what do I owe this pleasure?'

She ducked her head. What did she expect, she asked herself miserably. Arms thrown wide in welcome? She had treated the poor man like dirt.

'Surely the concert isn't over yet, Lauren.'

She concentrated on the second button of his shirt. 'It's over for me.'

He didn't move. After a moment, he said, 'And since you didn't want to be alone with your self-pity, you came here for comfort?'

She looked up in surprise. 'No. Not at all. I came to tell you I've been temporarily insane, and I'm sorry.'

His eyes closed for a moment as if in pain, and Lauren's heart twisted. She thought, *He does know how to use those incredible eyelashes to good effect!* Or perhaps it was just that he didn't have to manipulate people, and so didn't use them. . ..

He stepped back then, and she followed him into the living room, cheerfully cluttered with books and records. There was a volume facedown on the coffee table, as if he'd put it hastily aside to answer the door.

Lauren took her coat off, and then didn't quite know what to do with it, for Ward made no move to take it from her. She sat down finally with the coat folded awkwardly in her arms, and Ward perched on the edge of a chair across from her. 'He didn't jilt me, you know,' she said, with a note in her voice that was almost a challenge.

Ward sighed. 'I suppose that's my cue to ask what *did* happen. If it's all the same to you, Lauren—'

'I told him goodbye,' she said simply. 'I told him. . .'

He did not move, or respond, and Lauren's eyes filled with tears. *It's too late,* she thought. She couldn't say that she blamed him for it, after the way she'd treated him. If he ever did love her, it was certainly gone now.

'Well, I'm proud of you.' Ward got to his feet. 'Thanks for letting me know, so I wouldn't think I was seeing a ghost when you came in for coffee tomorrow.'

'Do you have to be so mean and stubborn?' Lauren asked in fury. Then the anger died with a hopeless little gasp. What good would that do, now? 'It was obviously a mistake for me to come here,' she said stiffly. 'May I use your phone to call a cab?'

He waved a hand toward it without a word, and she fumbled with the telephone book, trying to find the number.

'You said I was a fool,' she said, 'and I came to tell you that you were right, you know. More than that, I was an idiot. You know that song he was writing for me?'

'Lauren—'

'Remember the old story about the guy who called up girls and asked them out for a day on his boat? 'It's a very special boat,' he'd tell each one. 'I named it after you.' And when they got to the dock, sure enough, there on the stern of the boat was painted two words—'after you'. That's what my song was like. It'll be a hit, and I'm sure Hunter knew exactly what he was doing. Any woman can pretend it's all about her.'

Ward took the telephone receiver out of her hand and hung it up just as the dispatcher answered. Then he put his arms around her. 'Lauren, I'm so sorry.'

'Dammit, don't you see that I don't want you to be sorry?' Her words were indistinct, between sobs, but they were the best she could do.

He led her over to the couch and held her while she cried tears of anger, frustration, fear and happiness all mixed in together. For nothing could be completely wrong when she was in his arms like this. He hadn't thrown her out. That was something, wasn't it?

Eventually he dried her face with his handkerchief and said, 'Better?' and smiled down into her eyes, a sad sort of smile. 'I'll take you home.'

It was oddly final. So, all those loving things he'd

done for her, she thought hopelessly, had been just friend-ship, after all. She'd been fooling herself; now that she had finally decided that he was what she wanted—the man she loved—he only wanted to get rid of her.

'No,' she said forlornly. 'I'm not better.' It didn't hurt her pride to admit it, for she had none left to be hurt.

'Lauren, what is it you want from me?'

She had started to cry again, silently and tormentedly. 'I want you to *care,* that's all.'

'Care that you're hurting? Or course I—'

'No. I want you to care about *me.*' It was so quiet that he had to bend his head to hear.

His voice was husky. 'Oh, I care, all right. Too much. It ripped me up to watch you these past two weeks, and know what a horrible mistake you were making, and that there was not one thing I could do to stop you. If I'd said something before he came along, but I couldn't, and so—'

'Couldn't?' That was an odd way to put it, surely. She mopped futilely at the tears on her cheeks. 'Why couldn't you?'

For a moment she thought he wasn't going to answer at all. 'What have I got to offer you?' he said quietly. 'I'm not talking about his kind of money. . .but the things you've got already that I could never afford, the things your parents left you. I'm up to my eyebrows in debt after buying the pharmacy, Lauren. Someday I'll be out of it, but it isn't fair to drag you down with me in the meantime.'

'It certainly—' she began.

'I can't take on the upkeep on your house—and I won't ask you to give the place up. I love you too much to ask you to make sacrifices like that.'

There was a little glow in her midsection. She had been right about one thing, at least. He was awfully stubborn. No, perhaps not actually stubborn, but he was firm in his beliefs. A woman would always know where he stood, and she could be certain that it was safe to lean on him, to trust him.

'Oh, hell, honey,' he said ruefully, 'I might as well be honest. I can't even afford your earrings, and I won't ask you to give up pretty things for the sake of...' His fingers brushed softly across her hair, pulling it back to expose the simple costume pearl in her earlobe.

'They were ten dollars,' she said, 'with my employee discount.'

'What happened to the diamond ones?'

'Those belong to the store. And since I wasn't planning to go back, I left them in the safe tonight, along with the opal necklace and the sapphire ring. Oh, Ward, how could you have thought I owned all that stuff? There was something new every week!'

'I know,' he said simply. 'And I added it up and it didn't fit very well in my budget. And I couldn't afford the kind of ring that would coordinate with all that glitter, so—'

'Ring?' she said demurely. 'What sort of a ring are we talking about?'

But for a long time after that they didn't talk about much of anything, except some whispered bits between kisses. And Lauren reflected—in the odd spaces when she could think at all—that if they gave a prize for knowing how to make a woman feel loved, and cherished, and adored, that Ward would surely win it. . ..

It was a great deal later when she said, with a twinge

of wry humor, 'Good heavens, I forgot to say goodbye to Kim. I just walked out on her at intermission.'

'Kim can take care of herself,' Ward said mildly.

'Oh, I'm not worried, exactly. She was going to take a cab home, anyway, since we didn't want to risk upsetting Hunter's plans for after the concert—' Then, as she abruptly remembered that it might not be a good idea to mention Hunter's name, she looked up at Ward warily.

He was smiling. 'I'd say you did a pretty good job of that all by yourself.' He stretched. 'Kim will get a surprise tomorrow, that's all—it will be good for her. I think I've got a bottle of champagne somewhere. If you'd like to celebrate, that is.'

'Oh, I'd certainly like to celebrate.' She hesitated, and then said firmly, 'But I'd rather have orange juice.'

'Orange juice? Lauren, that's the craziest—'

She silenced him with a finger across his lips, and then with a kiss. She'd explain it someday, she decided.

And she knew Ward would understand that some things were just too important to toast with mere champagne.

For Better, For Worse

by
Rebecca Winters

REBECCA WINTERS, an American writer and mother of four was excited about the new millennium because it meant another new beginning. Having said goodbye to the classroom where she taught French and Spanish, she is now free to spend more time with her family, to travel and to write the Mills & Boon® novels she loves so dearly.

Look out for THE BRIDEGROOM'S VOW by
Rebecca Winters in February 2002 in
Tender Romance™!

CHAPTER ONE

'I NOW PRONOUNCE YOU—' the chaplain frowned as he stumbled over the words printed on the special license '—Raf-fael de Mendez y-y Lucar, and you, Kit Spring, husband and wife.'

Even with the preoperative medication starting to take effect, Rafe's black eyes flickered a private message of love to Kit.

He'd searched frantically on two continents for eight hellish weeks to find her, not knowing if he would ever see her again. It wasn't until a friend of Kit's had remembered the name of Kit's birthplace that he'd finally caught up with her. His arrival the day before at the obscure motel where she was working brought their painful separation to an end, and now the long-awaited words had finally been pronounced. She could tell he was relaxed now, at peace.

Without waiting for the chaplain's directive, she leaned over the stretcher to kiss the pale lips she wanted so urgently to feel beneath her own. But the anesthetist assisting with the surgery prevented her from touching her new husband.

'I'm sorry, Mrs. Mendez, but I should have administered the Halothane five minutes ago.' He nodded to the orderly who helped guide the stretcher out of the emergency room cubicle and down the hall.

Kit hurried after them to the elevator, hardly able to believe it was Rafe's powerful body lying there so helpless, his normally olive-toned skin a sickly gray color. She couldn't even see his black, wavy hair, which was hidden beneath the surgical drapes.

The very real possibility that she could lose him forever prompted her to catch hold of the doctor's arm.

'Please,' she whispered, her eyes beseeching him, 'don't let anything happen to Rafe. I couldn't bear it. Not after—' Her voice broke as fresh pain welled up inside her. These two agonizing months of separation had taken their toll. Her tension was so great that she hadn't realized the Mendez crest on Rafe's signet ring, the one used for their marriage ceremony, was cutting into her palm.

'A subdural hematoma is serious, but the operation to relieve the pressure is fairly routine. I have no doubt he'll be fine.' Before the doors closed the surgeon flashed her what she suspected was his professional smile of reassurance, but she wasn't comforted.

'Mrs. Mendez?' The chaplain cupped her elbow. 'Since I know you'll be unable to rest until you learn the outcome, at least allow me to sit with you until the operation is over.'

The last thing she wanted right now was company. However, she couldn't be rude to Pastor Hughes, the chaplain who'd been on duty at the hospital and had performed the two-minute marriage ceremony on a moment's notice.

Still lucid after the freak accident that had caused his head injury, Rafe had refused to undergo surgery until he'd made Kit his wife. She wanted that, too—more than anything in the world. When it became clear that his agitated state could adversely affect the outcome of the operation, Dr. Penman, the neurosurgeon, had given in to his patient's demand and arranged for the ceremony to take place in the emergency room. In fact, everyone associated with the University Regional Hospital in Pocatello had been wonderful. Kit owed them a debt of gratitude she could never repay.

'Thank you, Chaplain,' she said, but as she took a step forward, she felt suddenly light-headed and had to lean against him for a few seconds.

He put a supportive arm around her shoulders. 'Are you all right?' he asked in a concerned voice.

After a moment, she murmured yes and together they walked to the waiting room area, where the chaplain guided her to a chair and brought her a cup of water.

'Here. Drink this.'

Since arriving at the hospital—she'd followed the ambulance in the rental car Rafe had been driving—Kit had refused anything to eat or drink. Now even the lukewarm water tasted good.

'That's better, isn't it?'

His kind smile reminded her to thank him for everything he'd done. It was then that she remembered Diego Silva, Rafe's pilot, who would still be at the airport wondering what had happened to them. She had to talk to him and explain about the accident.

Excusing herself for a moment, she went in search of a pay phone and, after some difficulty, succeeded in getting through to Diego. She'd met the good-looking pilot on one other occasion, when he'd flown her and Rafe to North Africa, ostensibly on business. But Rafe's work had only taken an hour to accomplish; it had been the necessary excuse to get away from his family for a short while, to have Kit all to himself. The rest of that day he had devoted to her, making those precious hours ones of enchantment.

Diego's distraught response to the bad news let her know how much he cared for his employer. When she told him that she and Rafe were now married, he wept over the phone, thanking her for making the *señor* so happy. His open devotion to both Rafe and herself warmed her heart. He kept murmuring a lot of unintelligible words in Spanish, a language she was trying to learn, though she wondered if she'd ever become fluent. He said something about wanting to come to the hospital at once, but she told him to wait until the doctor said Rafe could have visitors.

Diego rushed to assure her that he would get in touch with the family; she was to do nothing but look after the *señor*.

When she returned to the waiting room, the chaplain was still there. 'You know, I've had occasion to perform a few emergency wedding ceremonies here at the hospital, but I must confess your particular situation intrigues me. Your husband is obviously not an American citizen. Perhaps you would tell me about him over dinner. What brought you two together? I find it very romantic.'

Kit smiled through the tears that wouldn't stop flowing and ran an unsteady hand through her short, golden blond curls. 'If you really want to hear.'

'Of course I do. Shall we walk to the cafeteria and get ourselves a bite to eat? Dr. Penman said the operation would take at least an hour and a half, so we have plenty of time.'

His suggestion made sense, and Kit was glad she'd agreed to eat with him, after all. She actually enjoyed the potatoes and fried chicken, and the chaplain had an

easy, gentle manner that inspired her confidence. As time
went on, she found herself telling him things she'd never
told anyone else. She supposed it was because the events
of the past few hours had shaken her and she needed to
unburden herself to someone who cared.

'We were going back to Spain to be married. While
we were driving through an intersection on our way to
the airport, a Jeep and a van collided in the other lane.
The impact dislodged a kayak fastened to the top of the
van. It flew through the air and. . .and by some quirk of
fate hit Rafe's side of the car, striking his head through
the open window.' Her voice quavered as she spoke.

The pastor shook his head gravely.

'Rafe didn't lose consciousness, but I could tell by the
difficulty he had in talking that he'd been dazed. The
paramedics arrived and started an IV. At the hospital
they discovered that a clot had formed where he'd been
struck, so he was prepared for surgery. But Rafe insisted
we be married first.'

'Your husband sounds like a strong, determined indi-
vidual.'

'He's remarkable,' she murmured, wondering how
to explain Rafe to this sweet, unassuming Idaho
chaplain. Educated in the most prestigious schools in
Europe, conversant with several different languages,
sophisticated, wealthy, Rafael de Mendez y Lucar
appeared larger than life. He was a man whose roots
went back to the Spanish aristocracy; his family was one
of the most important landowners in Andalusia.

And he loved *her*, Kit Spring, an insignificant 25-year-
old American schoolteacher who was all alone in the
world. He loved Kit with a ferocity equal to her own
love for him. But it had been a forbidden love that had

torn the Mendez family apart, setting brother against brother, mother against son, changing the complicated fabric of their private lives forever.

Knowing that *she* was the reason Jaime was always at Rafe's throat, the reason Rafe and his mother were estranged, Kit had seen no other choice but to remove herself from their sphere. If she bowed out of their lives for good, Jaime, who had always walked in Rafe's shadow and had a propensity for self-destruction, would be spared the humiliation of losing Kit to his elder brother. Then they'd be able to put their family back together and go on as before.

At least Kit had prayed that her disappearance would effect a reconciliation, even if it meant the end of her world. Without telling a soul about her plans, she resigned her teaching job in Spain and flew back to the United States—to Inkom, Idaho, the tiny town of 850 people where she'd been born and lived with her parents who'd worked at the cement plant until they died. She doubted Rafe would be able to trace her there.

But in that assumption she'd been wrong. Yesterday afternoon, when she was on the verge of phoning Rafe to tell him she couldn't stand to be away from him any longer, he had miraculously appeared in the lobby of the tiny six-unit motel where she worked as a part-time receptionist. The owner, a friend of her parents', had been kind enough to let her live in one of the units and work for room and board.

When she heard the buzzer signaling that someone had come in the door, she looked up from the desk to discover Rafe walking toward her. The joy of seeing him again, combined with the thrill of alarm that coursed through her body at his furious expression, made her retreat until she'd backed up against the wall. 'H-How did you know I was here?'

'You *should* be terrified of me,' he said in his lightly accented English, ignoring her question. He levered his lean body over the counter with effortless grace. 'There've been moments in the past eight weeks when I wondered if I'd ever find you or hold you again. How could you have done this to us?' From the raw emotion in his voice, she could tell he'd suffered torment as great as her own.

'You know why I left,' she whispered, noting that he'd lost weight, yet was more darkly attractive than ever. 'I didn't want to make matters worse between you and Jaime.'

He closed the distance separating them and covered her body with his own. She felt *alive* for the first time in two months as the familiar weight of his hard thighs and chest pressed heavily against her. How had she thought she could live the rest of her life without him, without this?

His black eyes smoldered. 'Your sacrifice could make no possible difference to the situation between my brother and me. Our father made certain of that long before he died. A break was inevitable. Jaime has left the estate, *amorada,* to make a new life for himself. And now I'm taking you back to Spain with me, where you belong.'

He lowered his head and claimed her mouth with an intensity that left her clinging to him, unable to deny him any part of her self.

'What about your mother?' Kit murmured long moments later. 'She told me to. . .to go away and leave her sons alone.'

'That was her pain talking. She's an intelligent woman, and in time, she, too, will grow to love you. I've made her understand how I feel—that my life is not worth living without you. I have a special license so we can be married as soon as we get back to Jerez. Where is the person in charge of this place so I can tell him you're leaving with me today?'

'Here's some ice cream.' The chaplain broke in on Kit's private thoughts. She hadn't even realized he'd left the table.

'I'm sorry. You must think me extremely rude.'

'Not at all, my dear. When the most important person in our lives is in difficulty, how can we concentrate on anything else? Tell me how you came to know him.'

She took a few spoonfuls of ice cream. 'I met him through his brother, Jaime. Until a few months ago I was teaching math and English at the U.S. Naval Military Base in Rota, Spain. The town isn't far from Jerez where the Mendez estate is located. Jaime helps Rafe run the family business. They have vineyards and export their sherry all over the world.

'Last fall some friends from the base invited me to go to a sherry-tasting party Jaime was hosting. One thing led to another and we began dating.'

'But it was the other brother who captured your heart.'

She took a deep breath. 'Yes.'

'That must not have been an easy time for you.'

'It was awful. You see, Jaime asked me to marry him before I met Rafe, but I kept putting him off because I wanted to be sure that what I felt for him was love and that it would last. As soon as I met Rafe, I understood the difference between loving someone like a brother and being *in love*.'

On a rush of emotion, Kit found herself explaining her impossible position. She described Rafe's desire to bring everything out in the open and Jaime's heavy bouts of drinking after she turned down his proposal. Brokenly, she told of the painful exchange with their mother, which had precipitated Kit's flight from Spain. And finally she talked about Rafe's unexpected arrival in Idaho, after he'd traced her through one of her friends on the base. It felt so good to discuss all this with someone she could trust.

'I'm afraid Rafe and I have hurt Jaime very badly. It seems he's left Jerez and is living in Madrid. Who knows what he's thinking, what's happening to him right now? He's apparently cut himself off from everyone.' She shivered.

'But that's all to the good. Your husband was right, you know. This kind of situation has to be dealt with in an honest, forthright manner. He knew that would force his brother to face his life, which is what this Jaime is doing now. Instead of the end, it could be the beginning for him. One day he'll meet a woman who will love him in return. It's not your fault.'

Her eyes misted over. 'I know, but because of me the entire family is estranged.'

'Are you saying you wish you had never met your husband?'

'*No!*'

The chaplain chuckled at her vehement response, and she blushed. 'I didn't think so. And since I'm a great deal older than you, I'll tell you a secret. Life has a way of working itself out, and right now your husband needs your love and support as never before. After all, over the past few months he's searched nonstop for you, forsaking his business interests, everything. Don't you see? He's refused to let anything or anyone come between you. I would venture to say a love like that doesn't happen very often.'

'He's my whole life, Chaplain.' Her voice shook. 'He's *got* to be all right!'

'Where's your faith?' he asked quietly as his tuft-like brows lifted in query. He patted her hand compassionately. 'Why don't we go back to the emergency room and find out if there's been any news?'

Twenty minutes after their return, Kit heard her name called. She turned to find Dr. Penman at the front desk, still garbed in his surgical gown, smelling of anesthetic. She jumped to her feet and hurried over to him. 'Dr. Penman? How did the surgery go? Is Rafe going to be all right?'

CHAPTER TWO

'THE OPERATION was a success. Your husband came through it without complications.' The relief was exquisite and the doctor smiled at her reaction. 'He's in the ICU now. If he continues to do well, you'll be allowed to see him for a few minutes tomorrow morning. Call around eight.'

His words robbed her of some of her euphoria. 'Not until then?' It was only 10:30 p.m. Ten more hours. . ..

'I'm sorry. But you want your husband back as strong and healthy as before, don't you?'

'Of course. Thank heaven it went well,' she cried, grasping his hand. 'Thank you for everything.'

'Your husband is a fortunate man,' he said, eyeing her slender curves and fine-boned, delicate features with obvious and very masculine appreciation. 'I can't say I blame him for wanting to marry you on the spot. I've got a hunch you'll be the reason he recovers in record time, too. My advice is that you get some rest now, Mrs. Mendez. I'll be around to see both you and your husband in the morning.'

After he left the desk the chaplain turned to her, smiling. 'I told you that you had nothing to worry about, didn't I? Are you ready to leave? I'm on my way home, and I'd be happy to drop you some place.'

'Thank you. I appreciate your kindness more than you know, but our rental car's outside with the luggage. It was hardly damaged—just a dent. I'll find a motel and manage just fine.'

The chaplain recommended a nearby motel and wished her good-night and a safe drive.

But Kit hadn't realized how difficult it would be to get back in the car, to sit where Rafe had been sitting when he was injured. It brought back the horror of his accident all too clearly. A new rush of pain almost immobilized her, and she arrived at the motel too distressed to think of resting.

She'd never known a night could pass so slowly. Her sleep, when it did come, was fitful. In her anxiety she got up repeatedly to pace the motel room floor, staring at Rafe's gold and ruby seal ring, which was too large for her finger and kept slipping off. It had been passed down to the first-born son through four generations of Mendezes and given to him by his father, Don Fernando. Afraid of losing something so priceless, she reached for her handbag and put it in one of the zippered compartments where it would be safe.

By eight o'clock the next morning, she'd had some juice and a sweet roll provided by the motel, then gone straight to the hospital's emergency room desk. Relief flooded through her when she was given permission to go straight to the ICU. Dr. Penman met her at the door and took her aside.

'Your husband had a good night and is resting comfortably. So far, there are no complications, no fever. Even so, I'm only allowing you to see him for a moment because he's a little hazy and confused.'

'Is that normal?' Kit asked in alarm.

He nodded. 'Quite often we see post-op head-injury patients experience this reaction. It doesn't usually last very long. But every case is unique and no two patients respond the same way. I wanted you to be aware of this so you wouldn't say or do anything to upset him. Just behave naturally. Shall we go in?'

Her emotions ranged from longing and anticipation to fresh anxiety as she hurried into the room ahead of the doctor. Rafe lay perfectly still in the hospital bed, his head swathed in a white bandage, his hard-muscled body hooked up to monitors. He was awake, following their progress with his eyes.

The relief of knowing he'd come through the operation so well and that his color was so much better had her rushing to his side. 'Darling?' she whispered. She reached out to touch his upper arm where the bronzed skin was exposed below the hospital gown. 'How are you? I've missed you,' she said anxiously.

His interested gaze wandered over her mouth and eyes, the shape of her face. *But there was no hint of recognition.* Until this moment she'd never seen him look at her with anything but desire and passion. *And anger, when she'd told him she couldn't see him anymore because their relationship was destroying his family.*

The change in him staggered her.

She rubbed his arm gently, hoping the physical contact might help. 'Darling? It's Kit. I love you.'

'Kit?' He said her name experimentally, with that light Spanish accent she loved.

'Yes. Do you remember we were married last night? I'm your wife now.' He still didn't respond. She fought to quell her rising panic. 'How do you feel? Are you in pain?'

He muttered some Spanish phrases she couldn't understand, then closed his eyes. Dr. Penman signaled to her from the other side of the bed, where he'd been conferring with the nurse. In acute distress Kit followed him into the hall.

'He didn't know me!' She choked on the words. 'When you told me he was confused I thought—' She shook her head. 'I had no idea he wouldn't even recognize me.'

The doctor looked at her with compassion. 'This is only temporary. Do you remember the skier last year who fell during a race in Switzerland? She suffered a concussion and temporary amnesia after her fall. Give your husband another twenty-four hours and he'll be himself again, just like she was.

'Call the desk tonight after I've made rounds. If he's more lucid, you can visit him for a few minutes. If not, call again in the morning after eight.'

Kit phoned twelve hours later but there'd been no change in Rafe's condition. When seventy-two hours passed and he still had no memory of her or what had happened to him, Dr. Penman ordered another CT test, along with blood tests and a toxicology screen. But the results indicated that nothing was organically wrong.

Feeling as though she were in the middle of a nightmare, Kit met with Dr. Penman and a Dr. Noyes, the staff psychiatrist who'd been called in for consultation.

'Why doesn't he remember me, Dr. Noyes? What's going on? I'm frightened.'

'I don't blame you,' the psychiatrist replied. 'Memory loss is not only disturbing to the patient, but to his loved ones, as well.'

'Have you ever seen a patient take this long to snap out of it?'

He nodded. 'At the end of the Vietnam era, I was finishing up my residency in California. I worked with several patients who'd lost their memories as a result of a closed head injury during the war. These were men like your husband who had no prior physiological problem and no other complications.'

'How long did it take them to recover their memories?'

'I don't know,' he said, and Kit gasped quietly. 'Please allow me to explain, Mrs. Mendez. That was years ago and I only worked with them for a three-month period. Most likely all have regained their memories by now.'

'Three months?' She sat forward in the chair. 'How can you compare war injuries to an accident as straightforward as my husband's ?'

He studied her for a long moment. 'I was hoping you could tell me.'

'I don't understand.'

'In my opinion, your husband could be suffering from what we call psychogenic loss of memory. What that means in lay terms is memory loss when there is no organic disease present. In other words, the onset of amnesia by a head injury because of a stressful event *prior* to the injury. With soldiers, it's battle fatigue, terror, isolation—all things the mind would want to suppress.'

Taking off his glasses to rub his eyes he said, 'With most other people, the stress generally comes from serious financial problems or an insoluble family crisis such as a disturbed parent-child or sibling relationship. In such cases, the patient's amnesia serves to help him escape from an intolerable situation. He can't find a rational way to deal with the circumstances, so he retreats. Is there anything in your husband's past like that? A problem so serious that he'd want to suppress it?'

'Dear God,' Kit mused aloud and she sprang to her feet.

'What is it, Mrs. Mendez?'

Without pausing for breath she told the doctor everything about her association with the Mendez family, leaving out only the most personal, intimate details.

When she finished he nodded. 'In an aristocratic family such as you've described, duty and honor are of overwhelming importance. Your husband's intolerable burden no doubt comes from the conflict between his feelings for you and his sense of family responsibility. With an autocratic father and a vulnerable, dependent brother, not to mention a mother who by culture and upbringing remained helpless in the face of such tension—well, all of that could trigger the amnesia.

'And think of the trauma he must have felt when the woman he obviously loved enough to risk disturbing the delicate family balance ran away, making it all but impossible for him to ever find her again. What you have, then, is a man who couldn't take any more.'

'But he did find me!' she cried out. 'We were married before he went into the operating room.'

'That explains his almost irrational need to marry Mrs. Mendez before he went under the anesthetic,' Dr. Penman interjected.

'Exactly,' Dr. Noyes concurred. 'Mrs. Mendez, your husband's situation is classic. His injury occurred before your marriage which is why he's blocked the marriage from his memory. For the time being, he's wandered away because the pain of losing you over an intolerable family situation is too great. And according to you, it still isn't resolved.'

Kit was listening carefully. Though she was terrified of the answer, she had to know. 'How long will this amnesia last?'

Dr. Noyes did nothing overt, but she could sense she wouldn't like his answer. She couldn't help shuddering.

'Patients respond in two different ways. The first group emerges with a full resumption of identity and an amnesic gap covering the loss of memory or the fugue, as we call it.'

'And the second?' she whispered, her heart contracting with fear.

'In the second, which is very rare, patients have an awareness of their loss of personal identity, and an amnesia for their whole life.'

'No!' she cried out and clung to the desk for support. Dr. Penman was the first out of his chair to steady her.

'I realize this is a great shock to you,' Dr. Noyes said in a gentle voice. 'I'd like to tell you that his amnesia is temporary and will go away in a matter of hours. That may well be the case, but I just don't know. However at the moment, my concern is more for you than your husband, Mrs. Mendez.'

Kit lifted her head from her hands, wondering how he could say such a thing.

'The fact of the matter is, your husband has lost none of his motor skills or his ability to take care of himself. For example, he knows to brush his teeth and take care of his bodily functions. He knows it's Friday and that tomorrow is Saturday. He's even aware that he's in Idaho and that he comes from Spain. He functions like you and me and acts appropriately without drawing attention to himself by any abnormal behavior. In fact, he's no different from before the operation except that he can't remember the past. But he's not unduly distressed about it yet because no one is pressing him to recall incidents that his subconscious is suppressing.

'Whereas *you* have total recall. And you're a brand-new wife, married to a husband who has no knowledge of you. That's a very painful situation, Mrs. Mendez. Dr. Penman and I are here to help you deal with this in any way we can.'

'I don't have the faintest idea where to start!'

'We know that,' Dr. Penman said. 'No two amnesia cases are the same, which means that it's an extremely unpredictable disorder. But for the next while, your husband needs to recuperate from the operation. In a few days I'll have him transferred to a private room, where you can sit at his side day and night if you wish. It will give you time to come to grips with the situation. Until then, however, we feel it's best if you don't see him.'

Her expression must have prompted Dr. Noyes to say, 'Feel free to talk to me whenever you wish.'

'When I do see him, what am I supposed to say? How am I supposed to act?'

'Do what your instincts tell you. Be yourself. In the course of time, daily events will probably trigger something in his brain and he'll recover his memory. Your biggest problem will be to hide your anger from him.'

'My anger?'

'Oh, yes, Mrs. Mendez. You're going to get very angry before long. It's a natural part of the grieving process. And it's healthy as long as it doesn't last too long. We'll talk about it again before he's discharged from the hospital.'

After they left Dr. Noyes's office, Kit wandered through the halls in a daze. She thought back to the wedding ceremony, remembering the chaplain's words. *'From this day forward, do you, Kit Spring, promise to take this man, Rafael de Mendez y Lucar, as your lawfully wedded husband, to have and to hold, for better or for worse, for richer or for poorer, in sickness and in health, for as long as you both shall live?'*

With tears streaming down her cheeks, Kit relived her fervent response and made up her mind that from this day forward she'd do everything in her power to help Rafe recover his memory. And if he didn't, then she'd make him fall in love with her all over again. They'd face the future together, no matter how difficult or uncertain. Eight weeks' separation had shown that, for her, a life without Rafe wasn't a life at all.

CHAPTER THREE

SIX ENDLESS DAYS after the surgery—three days after her conversation with the doctors—Dr. Penman informed Kit that Rafe had been transferred to a private room and she could start visiting him. When he called her with the news, she happened to be standing in front of the motel room mirror. She gasped at the haggard-looking woman staring back at her. Her mouth was drawn tight and her eyes were noticeably dull. Many times in the past Rafe had told her how much he loved the fullness of her mouth and the slight almond shape of her gray-green eyes with their curling lashes. Right now he wouldn't have known her even if he'd *had* his memory!

Without wasting another second, she gave herself a thorough makeover. With her hair freshly washed and wearing a minimum of makeup, just enough to emphasize her golden tan, Kit felt more like the woman who had captured Rafe's attention from the very first moment he saw her.

She purposely wore the same dress he'd admired then, an expensive, form-fitting navy Italian knit that buttoned up the front from the hem to the square neck. A bright-red knit border at the hems and up the front gave it a sophistication and outlined her curves, drawing male interest wherever she went. But she wanted only one man's interest. . ... She dabbed on his favorite scent and fastened the gold earrings he'd bought her in Tangiers.

According to Dr. Noyes, Rafe's memory could come

back at any time and there was no way to predict exactly what would trigger it. Kit determined to do whatever it took to hasten the process. The possibility that he'd never regain his memory was something she refused to consider.

'What I'd give for your figure,' the nurse on duty murmured as Kit passed by the desk on her way to Rafe's room. 'In fact, what I'd give to be married to a gorgeous man like your husband.'

A smile curved Kit's mouth. 'When we met, I remember thinking that I'd never seen a more beautiful man. After I got to know him, I realized the person inside was even more wonderful.'

The nurse sobered. 'We've all heard about your husband losing his memory and we're praying it comes back soon.'

'Thank you. I am, too.'

'The orderlies brought him down a little while ago. He's getting restless. Now that he's out of ICU and his tests are over, he wants to leave the hospital. He insists he can do everything himself. He's a fighter, and I'd say that's a good sign.'

'I hope you're right. My husband has always taken responsibility for others. He's not used to depending on anyone.'

'Yes. I noticed.' She gave Kit a wry smile. 'He may have forgotten the past, but there's nothing wrong with the rest of him. . .if you catch my drift.'

Kit's eyes smarted, and she managed a weak smile in return. 'I intend to have a real marriage.'

'If you want my opinion, you won't have any problems, not looking the way you do.'

'Beneath this facade, I'm terrified.'

'I know you are. I would be, too.'

'Do you have any advice?'

The nurse cocked her head. 'You obviously love him, so show him that love in every way you can. I know that doesn't sound very professional, but in his case there's no guideline to follow.'

Kit nodded and started for his room, so nervous that she couldn't stop shaking. She'd only seen him once, that first morning after the operation. Since then, both doctors had asked Kit to be patient while they ran tests and learned as much of his history from her as possible. The rest of the time they talked with Rafe to work him through the first stages of accepting his memory loss.

To help pass the time, she ate most of her lunches and dinners with Diego in the hospital cafeteria. The chaplain joined them when he could. Diego stayed at a motel near the airport and, to Kit's everlasting gratitude, acted as the go-between for her and the Mendez family, regularly advising them of Rafe's progress. His kind words of encouragement and the chaplain's compassion were all that had sustained her through the long week of waiting, but now it was over.

When she entered the room, Rafe was sitting in bed in his hospital gown watching a television program. He looked perfectly normal. In fact, from her vantage point near the door, she couldn't see anything but a small patch of white bandage where the incision had been made. His luxuriant black hair covered most of it. He was more attractive than ever and certainly showed no sign of having undergone anything as serious as brain surgery.

When he saw her, he turned off the TV. His dark gaze appraised her in that familiar, bold manner of his. For a breathless moment she expected his eyes to ignite in passion, the way they always did when the two of them were together. But there was no melting warmth this time.

She wanted to cry aloud her frustration. Instead, she busied herself putting down her handbag and placing a small suitcase with some of Rafe's clothes in the room closet. Mustering her courage, she moved closer to his bed. 'Do you remember who I am?'

'I remember seeing your face when I woke up from the operation,' he said in a hesitant voice. 'Among many other things, the doctors have told me that you are my wife of one week. Kit.' He said her name experimentally. 'Why do you not use the longer name, Kitty, the way most women do?'

It was strange to think that his basic knowledge of life was in no way impaired, yet the amnesia had blotted out the tiniest memory of her from his mind. 'When I met you for the first time in January, you asked me the same question and I told you my parents named me Kit.'

He appeared to digest her explanation before muttering, 'January. It's April now.'

She nodded. 'The twenty-fourth.' She watched closely to see if the date held any significance for him. In the middle of May, less than a month off, the town of Jerez celebrated its vintage fair. According to Jaime, Rafe, as head of the estate, was expected to open the fair and parade his prized horses around the plaza before the crowds, a sight Kit had once hoped to see. Until everything fell apart. . ..

One dark brow quirked. 'In a four-month period, we met and married?'

Without stopping to think she blurted out, 'If it hadn't been for some complications, we would probably have been married after a few weeks.'

His eyes narrowed on her mouth. 'Have we slept together often? Do you carry my child?'

Rafe's direct way of talking about intimate things had always brought a blush to her cheeks, and today was no exception. It would be so easy to tell him they'd been lovers from the beginning, that it was a distinct possibility she was pregnant. But a marriage based on lies had no hope of enduring.

'The answer is no to both questions,' she said in a quiet voice.

'And why is that?' A puzzled expression crossed his face. 'You have golden hair and a beautiful body. Any man would desire you.'

But not you, Rafe. Not now . . .

His compliments should have brought her pleasure instead of deep, searing pain.

'Did I marry you because I couldn't get you in my bed any other way?'

Coming from his lips, the insensitive question sounded so alien that she could scarcely believe this was her beloved Rafe talking.

His mouth twitched with the faintest trace of cynicism. 'Am I to believe you are a virgin? That no man has ever seen or felt what lies beneath that becoming dress?'

She bristled in anger. 'I realize I'm a mere stranger to you, but I had hoped we could at least be civil to each other.'

'I thought I was being extremely civil,' he said with an arrogance she'd only seen him display on one other occasion—when Jaime had said something so offensive about her and Rafe that Rafe couldn't let it go. 'You come into my room purporting to be my wife, and since I have no recollection of my former life, I must accept everything you and the doctors say on faith. Naturally I have a few questions of my own, particularly when it concerns my private life, which I've supposedly shared with you.'

He had every right to be suspicious and upset. 'The only reason I'm still a virgin is because I never met a man I wanted to go to bed with until I fell in love with you. But there were problems that prevented us from. . .being together. You see—' she paused, wondering how to begin '—your younger brother Jaime was in love with me, too.'

At that point he leaned forward, resting his bronzed, muscled arms over his raised knees, giving her his full attention. 'How much younger?'

'H-he's twenty-nine, two years younger than you.'

'And how old are you?'

'I'll be twenty-six in October.'

'That still doesn't tell me why we didn't make love.'

She sucked in her breath. 'It's very complicated. Neither you nor I wanted to hurt him, particularly as he'd met me first and had asked me to marry him.'

His features formed a scowl. 'Since you didn't love him, why did you continue to torment him?'

Without knowing it, Rafe had just driven to the very heart of her nightmare. 'I liked Jaime. He's a wonderful man, so giving and full of life. I thought that in time my feelings would turn into love, but they didn't.'

'And all that time you and I were playing my brother false behind his back? Is that what you're saying?' He flung the grim accusation at her.

'No!' she responded emotionally. 'You and I didn't meet until Jaime and I had been seeing each other for about four months.'

'Why was that? If my brother was so besotted that he begged you to marry him, why weren't you and I introduced right away?'

Kit had trouble believing Rafe had lost his memory, because none of his natural instincts had been in any way changed or impaired.

'Jaime never took me to the hacienda to meet your family. Instead we went sightseeing on my days off from teaching. At first, I didn't think anything of it, but later I decided he was afraid to let the family know he was dating an American.' And something had told her Jaime didn't want her to meet his brother until she was safely married to *him*.

At Rafe's frown she tried to explain, 'In a family as old and wealthy and prestigious as yours, it's still a foregone conclusion that any sons will marry Spanish women of high birth whom the parents have already selected.'

'That's an archaic custom, one I do not espouse,' came the emphatic avowal. Was he remembering? Her heart leaped.

'That's true. And it's been a source of bitter conflict in your family because both you and Jaime have put off marriage rather than marry without love. This shattered your parents' lifelong dreams for you. In fact, when your father had his first heart attack several years ago, he blamed it on you, hoping your guilt would drive you to bend to his will.'

'*Madre de Dios!*' Rafe blurted out, his hands forming fists. Kit's heart went out to him. More than anything, she wanted to throw her arms around his neck and comfort him.

'Rafe, darling—'

His dark head reared back. 'What did you call me?'

She swallowed hard, furious with herself for allowing the endearment to slip out. 'Rafe. It's my nickname for you. Everyone else calls you Rafael. You once told me that your father named you for the archangel, Rafael, because he said that one day you would inherit everything, that you would be the guardian of the Mendez holdings. That was his ambition for you. You've also told me many times how important the family estate is to you, especially since his death.'

It still amazed her to consider that Rafe's destiny to head the Mendez family and fortune had been sealed at birth, that even his given name had been chosen with a specific purpose in mind. Was it any wonder that Rafe hated what his father had done to him—and to Jaime, who as second-born received no birthright? Who believed himself inferior and lacked any sense of self-worth?

His face darkened. 'You make my father sound like a monster.' His gaze fused with hers and the tendons stood out in his neck. 'Now that I have no memory of the past, how do I know this is not some invention of yours to manipulate me to your own advantage?

'From what I've learned, you're a penniless American schoolteacher from some back-country hamlet. A woman without means who probably isn't above using her one asset to exploit our family and to drive a wedge between me and my brother.'

Her cheeks caught fire. 'If you have so little faith in me, you can have our marriage annulled on the grounds of nonconsummation.'

In a white-hot rage, Kit reached for her handbag. Unzipping one of the compartments, she pulled out his ring, along with the marriage documents, and tossed them on the bed next to him.

'There's your precious seal and the proof that our marriage did take place. You lent me the ring for the ceremony until you could give me one of the family jewels—which I never wanted in the first place because your love was enough.' She fought to keep her voice steady.

'I'll leave an address with your pilot, Diego Silva, who's staying in town. He's anxious to fly you back to Spain as soon as the doctors say you're free to go. When you get there, have your attorney send me the annulment papers. I'll sign anything you want and we need never see each other again.'

On the verge of bursting into tears, she headed for the door.

'Where do you think you're going?' he demanded in such an imperious tone that she feared the entire floor could hear him.

Her body rigid, she turned toward him. 'To my back-country hamlet where no-account parasites like me belong. Where else, *Don Rafael de Mendez y Lucar?* That's the name printed on the marriage license you brought with you from Spain. It's your official title, and you wear it well. After all, you were born to it. Goodbye, *señor*.'

CHAPTER FOUR

NOT WANTING to see anyone after her fiery exchange with Rafe, Kit took the stairs rather than the elevator to the main floor. She slipped out a side entrance to the parking lot.

It wasn't until several hours later as she drove aimlessly through the streets of Pocatello reliving their explosive encounter that Dr. Penman's warning came back to haunt her.

'Oh, yes, Mrs. Mendez. You're going to get very angry. . .. And it's healthy as long as it doesn't last too long.'

By the time she returned to her motel room, she was sick with worry that her flash of temper, no matter how justified it had seemed, had done serious damage. How could she have lost control like that? She loved Rafe above all else and wanted his health and happiness at any cost. How could she have allowed herself to forget that?

A message from Dr. Noyes asking her to see him at the hospital as soon as possible made her feel guiltier than ever.

'What's wrong with Rafe?' she asked in an anxious voice when he invited her inside his office twenty minutes later. 'The second I got your message, I drove over.'

He eyed her with puzzled interest. 'Why, nothing that I know of.'

Kit blinked. 'He didn't tell you about our fight? It was

horrible. I didn't mean any of the things I said.' In a torrent of words, she related the essence of their argument to the doctor.

His grin caught her off guard. 'Quarreling already. I'm happy to hear it. That means your emotions are in touch, even if there is a memory gap.'

'Dr. Penman told me I'd get angry. At the time I didn't know what he meant. I'm ashamed of myself and frightened for Rafe. If I've said or done anything I shouldn't—'

'Nonsense. I wager there'll be many fights before both of you come to terms with his condition. The reason I called you in was to let you know that the psychiatry department at the University of Utah has come up with the names of a couple of psychiatrists in Spain, one in Madrid and another in Seville. I wondered if you wanted me to call either of them and discuss the case. It'll probably involve bringing in a translator. Would you like me to proceed?'

'Have you talked to Rafe about it?'

'I have, but he doesn't see the necessity. Your husband is not a man to lean on others. He carries his burdens inside. I believe you're the only person who has any influence with him.'

'If you could have heard him this morning—' Her voice cracked.

'I have no doubts that by now he's regretting the outburst and longing for your company. Remember, he has no memory of the past. But he does know you're his wife. And he knows that, for the present, you're the only rock he has to cling to. The fact that he's fighting you so hard proves it. He has to trust you, but he doesn't like it. That's because it goes against his upbringing and nature to place his confidence in someone from the outside, and he's going to test you every step of the way.'

'And you still think I can influence him to see a psychiatrist when we get to Spain?'

'I think that if we lay the groundwork now, in time you and your husband will reach a point where you'll want to talk to someone. It would be better if you're prepared with a doctor in mind.'

'I agree. Please go ahead and try to contact that psychiatrist in Seville. It's close to Jerez.'

'I'll make the call first thing in the morning.'

Kit got up from the chair. 'I'll be in Rafe's room if you need to talk to me.'

'Your being there will show him you're made of much stronger stuff then he might have thought. And it'll give him the security he craves, even if outwardly he resents you because he needs you so much.'

Talking with Dr. Noyes gave her a measure of calm, and she hurried to Rafe's room. She was eager to apologize for losing her temper and secretly determined that she wouldn't let him get to her again.

'How is my husband?' she asked the nurse who was coming out of his room. There had been a change in shift, and Kit didn't recognize the older woman, who looked harassed.

'It's a good thing you're here. He's been threatening to walk out of the hospital to find you if you didn't show up soon.'

The nurse's words were like a balm to Kit's wounded heart. 'I've been with Dr. Noyes.'

'Well, the next time you go anyplace, you'd better let your husband know exactly where you are.'

Kit frowned. 'Is there a problem?'

'His blood pressure was up a little, but I'm convinced that's because of your absence.'

'Then I'll make certain it doesn't happen again.'

'Men,' the nurse grumbled. 'They're never around when you need them and then they act like spoiled children when they decide they want your attention.' Kit didn't comment, only gave her a commiserating grin.

Rafe was sitting in much the same position as before, reading a magazine. When he saw her, he tossed it on the bedside table next to the papers and the ring. He hadn't put his ring on, though she didn't know why. By the set of his features and the glint in his eye she could tell that given the slightest pretext, he was ready to resume the battle.

'I'm sorry for walking out on you earlier,' she began, plunging ahead before he could say anything. 'I admit I got very angry. After I cooled off, I tried putting myself in your place and—I couldn't. Rafe, I don't blame you for not trusting me. I'm a perfect stranger to you. But if you'll let me, I'd like to be your friend. Forget that we're married. It's only a piece of paper and it doesn't mean anything without a commitment.'

His chest heaved from the force of his emotions. 'Are you saying you regret our marriage?' he asked in a grating voice.

'No!' she admitted without reservation. 'But I could understand it if *you* did.'

He raked a hand through his hair, disheveling it. 'I don't know what I think or feel, but for better or worse, it appears we *are* married to each other.'

She rubbed her palms nervously against her hips, a gesture his eyes followed with disturbing intensity. 'Only if you want to be. Leaving me out of it, you have an extraordinary life waiting for you back in Spain. Your roots are there and they run very deep. There's the estate, business matters that need your expertise, family affairs and concerns. You're one of the most influential and important men in all of Andalusia, respected and admired by everyone.'

If anything, her words turned his expression to thunder. 'You sound as if you're introducing the guest speaker at a state function, making me out to be some kind of paragon.'

'You are,' she murmured softly, touched once again by his humility. 'That's why I fell in love with you.'

The tension increased. 'This brother of mine. Tell me about him.'

Choosing her words carefully she said, 'He helps you run the estate.'

'Are we close?'

'You've always wanted to be, but there have been barriers.'

His features tautened. 'You're referring to yourself— and to my father.'

She nodded. 'From all that I've gathered through you and Jaime, your father doted on you from the moment you were born. When Jaime came along, he was an afterthought and continually pushed aside, ignored in preference to you, which in the end hurt both you and Jaime terribly.

'Jaime's envy of you has tainted his life. And it's placed an unbearable burden on your shoulders, because you could do nothing about it. Every time you tried to reach out to him, make amends for your father's lack of love and concern, he repulsed your gestures.'

There was an ominous silence. 'If Jaime never brought you to the house, how did we meet?'

Kit had been waiting for him to ask that question. She tried to quell the frantic beating of her heart. 'One evening Jaime and I had a date,' she began carefully, 'but his car was in the shop, so I told him I'd pick him up at the bodega after he'd finished work. When I arrived, you were the only one there.

'Apparently one of the workers had a message for me from Jaime saying there was a problem at one of the vineyards and he'd be unable to keep our date. Later in our relationship you confessed to me that you told your employee you'd pass on the message. You wanted to meet the American woman Jaime had been seeing, the woman everyone was gossiping about.'

Rafe studied her intently. 'Go on.'

'Almost as soon as I arrived in Rota, a town not far from Jerez, I heard about Rafael de Mendez. Your name is well-known in that part of the province. After I met Jaime at a sherry-tasting party with friends of mine from the base, it didn't take long for me to realize he lived in awe of you. But it was equally obvious that he also harbored a deep resentment. I decided I didn't like you very much because you were the source of his pain and I hated to see him hurt. My dislike of you wasn't rational, of course.

'When I finally met you, you were nothing like I'd imagined.' Her voice trailed off. In fact, just remembering the awareness that had instantly sparked between them sent a pleasurable quiver through her body. 'What made everything so much worse was that I felt an immediate attraction to you. It terrified me.'

'Apparently the feeling was mutual,' Rafe murmured, frowning as though deep in thought.

'Yes. You asked me to come to the hacienda to drink some of the sherry you reserved for special guests and family. Because of what I was feeling, I knew I shouldn't go, so I declined the invitation.' Her eyes slid away from his. 'But you insisted, saying that it was remiss of Jaime not to have brought me to your home before. I gave in, because I wanted to go with you, be with you.

'The minute I stepped over the threshold, I felt I'd betrayed Jaime, but the feelings you aroused in me defied logic. Your mother happened to be out with friends and you and I spent an unforgettable evening together. We drank your sherry and ate a simple meal and you showed me around the hacienda, which is virtually a museum of Spanish art history. By the time you escorted me to my car, I knew something. . .shattering had happened to me. I made a promise to myself never to see you again.'

'How long were you able to keep that promise?' he asked in a taut voice.

'Not long.' She gave a sad little laugh. 'You phoned me twice the following day and took me on a picnic lunch the next. After that, we ate breakfast before work, lunch in between, and saw each other several nights a week when business kept Jaime away.' She sighed and had to blink back tears.

'I started avoiding Jaime, turning him down on the pretext of extra work, seeing him only when there were other people around. I've never felt so guilty about anything in my life. And yet, I couldn't help myself. I was so deeply in love with you. . ..

'Once, about a month after we met, I accompanied you to Tangiers. We flew there in your company plane and played tourist all day long. That evening you took me to a small restaurant by the water and we talked about our lives and dreams until the stars came out.

'I don't think either of us noticed the food or the surroundings. Later, we walked along the beautiful white beach in front of the sultan's palace. You took me in your arms and you kissed me.' Her voice quavered in remembrance of that incredible night when their souls had seemed to merge. 'Then you asked me to marry you.'

'*Por Dios!*' he muttered. 'The paragon had feet of clay after all and lusted after his brother's woman.' She could have wept for the self-contempt she heard in his voice.

'No, Rafe. It wasn't like that! You're not that kind of person. Let me exp—'

'Mr. Mendez?' An orderly stepped inside with a dinner tray, cutting off the rest of her words.

CHAPTER FIVE

IN HER NERVOUSNESS, she jumped up from the chair and took the tray, placing it on the table that slid over Rafe's bed. She thanked the orderly and watched him leave before lifting the cover off the meat-loaf dinner. But Rafe grabbed hold of her wrist with one hand and shoved the table away with the other.

Despite the violence of his mood, the physical contact sent a curling warmth through her body. It had been six days, an eternity, since she'd known his touch.

'Do you think I could eat *now*?' Abruptly, he let go of her hand as if he'd grabbed the wrong end of a hot poker.

'How is it possible I could meet a woman my brother had been seeing for four months and propose marriage to her within four weeks?'

With his innate sense of honor, Rafe was clearly horrified by what he interpreted as an act of disloyalty toward the brother he didn't even remember. Kit couldn't bear to see him suffering like this; she had to fight the urge to draw his head to her chest to comfort him. The need to hold him close brought a moan to her throat.

'I have no explanation. The French have a phrase for it, though. They call it a *coup de foudre*. A bolt of lightning. Love at first sight. That's what happened to us. When you took me back to the base after that night in Tangiers, you told me you were going to break the news to Jaime. He deserved to know the truth, you said.

I agreed, but begged you to let me tell him in my own time. I owed him that much.'

'But something tells me you didn't.'

'No. Before I had an opportunity, you told your mother about us. She called me a few days later and arranged to meet me for lunch at a restaurant in Jerez. During the meal she implored me to leave the country and never come back. She said that the news of our relationship would destroy Jaime. But if I went away, Jaime would still be able to hold up his head. As for you, she said there was a lovely woman in Seville named Luisa Rios who expected to become your wife. She came from a fine family. . .' Kit swallowed painfully. 'Your mother intimated that you would soon get over me.'

A strange sound came from Rafe. 'Is my brother that unstable?' he demanded.

Kit took her time answering. 'I honestly don't know. He's lived in your shadow his whole life. Neither your mother nor I wanted to find out what would happen. So I resigned my job at the base and left for the States without telling anyone where I was going.'

Rafe glared at her for endless minutes. 'You ran away from me.'

'I had to. There'd been enough heartache in your home. I didn't want to be the cause of any more.'

'Then you couldn't have loved me as much as you claimed. Certainly not with the depth that I must have loved you—since it seems I was willing to risk everything, even the anger of my mother and the hatred of my brother. Yet you disappeared. You obviously weren't concerned about what *I* might have been feeling. According to Dr. Penman, I searched two months before I found you.'

'I *was* concerned. I was devastated and I—'

With cool disdain he interrupted her. 'What made you relent and decide to return to Spain with me?'

'You probably won't believe me. But after two months of not hearing from you or being with you, I couldn't bear the separation and decided that sacrificing our happiness on the strength of what Jaime might or might not do no longer made sense. I was on the verge of calling the hacienda to beg you to come to Idaho when you arrived at the motel.'

His smile was wintry. 'You're right. I don't believe you.'

'Then why do you suppose I married you?'

'I don't know, do I? Perhaps to comfort a man who might or might not make it through surgery? If I'm to believe everything you've told me, your reputation for self-sacrifice precedes you.' His voice sounded tired; Kit was afraid their conversation had worn him out.

'I think I'll go and get some dinner. Would you like me to come back or would you prefer to be alone?' She struggled to keep her voice calm and pleasant.

'It makes no difference one way or the other.'

'Then I'll say good-night and wish you a good sleep.' She opened her handbag to pull out a pen and paper, then wrote down the name and phone number of her motel. Putting the note on his bedside table, she said, 'I'm leaving this in case you need to get in touch with me.' She tried not to let him know how much his comment had hurt her.

Kit said nothing further as she left. And only with the greatest control did she prevent herself from turning around and flinging herself into his arms.

Back in her motel room, she called Diego, who was

overjoyed to learn he now had permission to visit his friend and employer. She assured him Rafe was in excellent condition and would probably enjoy his company.

Kit decided to stay away until midafternoon of the following day to give the two men plenty of time to become reacquainted. She received something of a shock when she got off the elevator and noticed Rafe, dressed in casual pants and black shirt, walking down the hall toward his room. No one watching him would ever have guessed he was a patient. His tall, powerful, body, his confident bearing and long, graceful strides made her ache with intense and sudden need. Her palms moistened just looking at him.

She'd gone to a great deal of trouble to make herself as presentable as possible. She wore a tailored khaki suit with a white silk blouse and brown leather heels. Around her blond curls she'd tied a paisley ribbon in shades of yellow and brown, and she'd applied a coral frost lipstick for accent.

He might not remember her, but she was counting on one thing—that underneath he was the same man he'd always been. The man who'd fallen instantly in love with her, the way she had with him.

When she entered his room, she found him standing next to his bed with the receiver of the wall phone in his hand. The second he saw her, his features hardened and he put it back, sending her spirits plunging.

'How kind of my wife to drop by.' His tone was heavily sarcastic.

She was about to remind him of his parting words the night before, but changed her mind because she didn't want to initiate any more conflict. 'I saw you walking in the hall a moment ago. You must be feeling much better.'

His dark eyes narrowed. 'You could have no conception of how I'm feeling. If you'd been here earlier when both doctors made their visit, you would have learned that I'm being released in the morning. That is what I wanted to talk to you about.'

'Th-That's wonderful, Rafe,' she stammered. She hadn't expected to hear this for another few days. 'How long did they say it will be before you can return to Spain?'

'I intend to leave tomorrow. I've already discussed the details with Diego, who by now will have informed my mother.'

Kit was aghast. All the arrangements had been made without her knowledge. Rafe had automatically turned to Diego rather than her for help. This latest revelation came as another crushing blow and raised new questions in her mind.

'Does Dr. Penman know about this?' she asked in alarm.

'Of course.'

He sounded so condescending that she grew upset. 'But it's only been a week since your surgery. I assumed you'd have to stay at the motel for a while. I don't want you to risk—'

'Then you assumed wrong,' he broke in coldly. 'If I'm to recover my memory, which may or may not happen, then staying in a place alien to everything in my past will only frustrate me further.'

'Surely a few more days—'

'What's wrong?' he drawled, flashing her a calculating glance. 'Afraid I'm going to find out you've been feeding me lies all this time? Is that why the color has drained out of that beautiful, innocent-looking face?'

Ignoring the compliment, which sounded more like an insult, she retorted, 'If you've had the chance to talk to Diego, then you know I've been telling the truth.'

'Do I?' he murmured in a nasty tone. 'It seems you and Diego share a great deal more than one would expect of a mere employee and my wife.'

'For heaven's sake, Rafe! Diego's your friend! He'd do anything for you. He's the man who helped you look for me for the past two months. He's been here day and night waiting to see if you'd be all right.'

She didn't like the dangerous glint in his eye. 'I find it interesting that he never stopped talking about you the entire time we were together. The man is enamored of you.'

'You're wrong! Diego has a wife and two children he absolutely adores.'

'Since when does that stop a man from wanting the woman he desires?' His gaze roamed freely, intimately, over the lines and curves of her body. In that instant, he reminded her of the Rafe she'd known before the accident. Except that such a look had always been accompanied by love. . ..

Kit hadn't realized how close they were standing to each other until he lifted his hand and traced the soft curve of her lips with his thumb. With that touch he created a burning need inside her. She longed to taste and feel his mouth on hers again.

Some of her lipstick adhered to the skin of his thumb. He rubbed it against his other fingers, almost as if he were savoring a memory. 'It's understandable that my brother isn't the only one to be entranced by your charms.' He paused. 'You are desirable, *mi esposa*. That much I can see for myself. Perhaps I'll berate myself later for returning to Spain alone.'

'*Alone?*' she gasped.

His mouth curled in a derisive smile. 'That's right. Before I come to a decision about continuing with this marriage, I'm going back home, to make a few observations for myself. I trust you, too, need time to reflect on what has happened. I assume you'll be able to get your motel job back or find a teaching position. Naturally, I will deposit enough money in your bank account that you need have no fears in that regard.'

Kit's body went rigid with anger. 'Whether you like it or not, you're my husband now, Rafe. I married you because I'm in love with you,' she said, despising the slight quaver in her voice. 'And you are—were—' she caught herself '—in love with me. In fact, your doctors will testify that you insisted on marrying me before you underwent surgery rather than wait until we could return to Spain. So if you leave me, I'll just have to use some of your money to follow you to Jerez. It would be simpler if we went together.'

After an ominous silence, he grasped her shoulders, his eyes blazing like a fire out of control. 'If you insist on coming with me, *amorada*—' he almost sneered the endearment '—then you must be prepared to take the consequences. If I find you have not been scrupulously honest with me, then you will be in trouble up to your lovely neck.'

As he spoke, his hands slid up to encircle her neck, caressing the tender hollow of her throat where she could feel her throbbing pulse under his fingertips. He leaned closer and she thought he meant to kiss her until he said, 'Be ready to leave by nine in the morning.'

Then he released her and turned away.

CHAPTER SIX

KIT SAT APART from Rafe in the back of the limousine, watching him out of the corner of her eye, hoping to see a reaction of some kind. For the past ten minutes they'd been driving on Mendez property. Not a touch or a word passed between them.

Luis, the silver-haired retainer Rafe had introduced to Kit as a trusted friend when he'd taken her to the hacienda that one and only time, had met them at the airport outside Jerez. He'd grasped both Rafe's hands in his happiness to welcome him back home, hugging his *patrón* with genuine warmth.

Rafe could have no idea of the love and esteem in which he was held by everyone. So it must have been painful for Luis and Diego when Rafe only tolerated the older man's spontaneous embrace and muttered a coolly polite thanks to his pilot before helping Kit into the car.

Her heart ached for her husband, whose face was creased with lines of anxiety and fatigue. She wanted to reach across the short distance separating them, to assure him he had nothing to fear from her or his family. But Rafe's fierce pride wouldn't let him accept help from anyone. He hadn't wanted her along in the first place and Kit sensed that he would have repulsed any overtures she might have attempted. So she made no move toward him.

In her opinion, they should never have flown here on the same day he'd been released from the hospital. But when Kit met with Dr. Penman for a final consultation and voiced her fears, he'd assured her that Rafe was fit enough to travel as long as he rested frequently.

The Mendez jet had a bedroom, and though Rafe spent most of his time there, she doubted he'd been able to sleep throughout the exhausting flight, even with the light sedative the doctor had prescribed.

If there'd been no accident, no injury, she and Rafe would have been in that bed together, lavishing their love on each other. Instead, she'd spent the trip sitting alone in the body of the plane unable to concentrate on any of the books or magazines she'd brought with her.

Diego hadn't asked her to join him in the cockpit to help pass the time. In any case, she wouldn't have accepted his invitation since she didn't dare risk adding to her husband's suspicion that she was on more than friendly terms with his pilot. Perhaps Diego, too, sensed Rafe's paranoia and wisely refrained from doing anything that could be misconstrued.

One glance at Rafe's taut mouth told her that being on Spanish soil meant nothing to him. Kit truly couldn't imagine what it would be like to lose her memory. She wondered what he was thinking about as his black eyes scanned the terrain that had once been so familiar to him.

Thousands of healthy grapevines stood in neatly planted rows, stretching from one end of the horizon to the other. A warm late-April breeze made the vines sway and undulate like a bed of sea grass. It was a sight Rafe had once told her he never tired of watching. Now, he barely seemed to notice.

As the car pulled through the gates leading to the estate buildings, the sun, a golden ball that lit up the Andalusian sky, began to slip out of sight. Evening had come upon them, and soon she'd be alone with her husband for the first time since their wedding.

Excitement and trepidation warred inside her. Afraid that her eyes would betray the intensity of her feelings, she avoided looking at Rafe. Right now, she couldn't tolerate his biting sarcasm, not when she loved him so much. She focused her attention first on the world-famous sherry bodegas ahead, then on the bell tower atop the family chapel, which came into view. In the distance she caught sight of the magnificent hacienda, parts of which dated back to the 1700s. This house and much of the property had always belonged to the Mendez family.

The one time Rafe had brought her here, Kit had been instantly charmed by its wrought-iron balconies and pottery roof tiles. Flowers of every hue and description clung to the walls and railings, lending the place an air of enchantment in the dusky twilight.

A fountain played in the tree-lined courtyard. Luis drove around it and drew up to the front entrance. Before he'd brought the car to a full stop, a slender, aristocratic-looking older woman, her black hair pulled severely back from her face, stepped out from the heavy doors and hurried toward them.

Kit noticed that Rafe's attention fastened on the woman. She'd been a great beauty in her day and was still striking. She wore a sophisticated royal blue suit and a long rope of pearls with verve and style.

Jaime, and to a lesser extent Rafe, resembled her in features as well as coloring. But after studying the oil painting of Don Fernando she'd seen hanging in the foyer of the hacienda, Kit could tell that Rafe had inherited his father's height and authoritative bearing.

'That's your mother, Rafe,' Kit whispered.

'I may have lost my memory, but I'm not blind,' he muttered beneath his breath. For an instant Kit wondered if she had imagined a teasing quality in his voice, reminiscent of the Rafe before the accident.

Gabriella Mendez rushed toward Rafe's side of the car and opened the door. Kit had it in her heart to feel sorry for the older woman. Although Diego had explained everything about Rafe's amnesia to her, Kit knew Dona Gabriella wouldn't really believe it until she'd talked to her son face to face.

'Rafael, Rafael, *mi hijo!*' she cried as Rafe climbed from the back seat to meet her. Kit could hear a mother's joy and longing in her voice as she flung her arms around her son and clutched him to her.

Again Kit noted the way Rafe merely tolerated the attention showered on him. She realized how painful this moment had to be for his mother—and for him.

Kit couldn't help but be moved by the older woman's display of affection and felt tears start to her eyes. Gabriella's love for her sons had never been in question. Rafe and his mother communicated in Spanish, with her doing most of the talking. Kit could only follow bits and pieces of their conversation.

Needing to release the nervous tension, which had been building since their arrival, Kit jumped from the car and went around to the trunk to help Luis with the luggage. To her surprise, Rafe broke away from his mother and interposed himself between Kit and the older man. His movement prevented her from reaching for her case. Dona Gabriella looked on with dark, accusing eyes.

'Leave that for Luis,' he said coolly. 'My mother is ready to show you to your apartment.'

Kit had been anticipating this moment, and her eyes

closed involuntarily. Rafe had allowed her to come to Spain with him, but he had no intention of letting her get close to him. However—despite what he and his mother might have wished—Kit wasn't about to be separated from her husband. Not after everything they'd been through.

In a low voice that would make it difficult for either Luis or Dona Gabriella to follow her English, Kit said, 'Don't you mean *our* apartment? I'm your wife, not a houseguest. I'll sleep where you sleep.'

If he was surprised at her tenacity, he didn't let it show. After staring at her for a long moment he turned to his mother and said in English, 'If you'll show us the way to my apartment? I believe Kit is tired and would like to freshen up before dinner.'

Kit had prepared herself for a fight; she certainly hadn't expected his swift capitulation. She wondered what was going on in his mind. She could tell that his mother was equally thrown by the change in plans. But the older woman chose not to argue with her son's suggestion, probably because she, like Kit, could see from the purple, bruiselike shadows beneath Rafe's eyes that he was exhausted and sorely in need of sleep.

'Come with me,' his mother said in accented English.

Kit tried not to let her surprise show when Rafe gripped her elbow to usher her inside. Unfortunately, her body betrayed her, trembling at his touch. She'd always reacted to his nearness that way. And he'd always known it.

But right now all she could assume was that he felt physically unsteady and needed something or someone to hold on to. As far as she was concerned, they couldn't reach his room fast enough.

The hacienda was exactly as she remembered it, a

masterpiece of Spanish architecture with its beamed ceilings, ornate furniture, tiled walkways, works of art, paintings and plants. But she was too concerned for Rafe's welfare to pay much attention as his mother showed them up a central staircase to the right wing of the hacienda, the one area Rafe hadn't taken her the night of her visit.

When she'd asked him what was there, he'd replied, 'My apartment. Would you like to see it?' Her face had burned with embarrassment and she'd remained silent, not daring to answer.

Even now heat washed over Kit as she remembered the velvety tone of his voice and the smoldering look in his eyes as he'd asked her the question. She had no doubts he would have shown it to her, and she freely admitted to herself that she'd wanted him to. From the very beginning, she had yearned to know every intimate thing about him.

'We are here.' The older woman's voice broke into Kit's reverie as she pushed open the double doors leading to Rafe's bedroom. Luis followed with the luggage, which he placed just inside.

The large room was more modern and simply furnished than the rest of the hacienda. No statuary or gilded frames here. Except for the dark, hand-carved double bed and armoire, the room had a lighter feel and was tastefully decorated predominantly in gray-blue and white.

A private study lined with books adjoined his bedroom; so did a bright, modern bathroom. As Dona Gabriella led them through the apartment, Rafe staggered and leaned heavily against Kit. Filled with alarm, she darted him an anxious glance, but he shook his head almost imperceptibly, warning her to say nothing to his mother.

Supporting his weight, Kit turned to her. 'Thank you for the tour.' Moistening her lips nervously, she said, 'I-I'm not feeling well, Señora Mendez,' which was very nearly the truth. 'Would you mind if I lay down for a while?'

Dona Gabriella contemplated Kit's request before addressing her son in Spanish. He answered in kind, but their conversation was too rapid for her to follow. Apparently whatever Rafe had said didn't sit well with her, but again his mother chose not to argue.

'I will instruct Consuela to bring you your dinner. Now I will say good-night, *mi hijo*.' After kissing her son on the cheek, she scrutinized Kit one more time, eyes cool and unwelcoming, before she left the room, closing the doors behind her.

By tacit agreement Kit helped her husband to the bed. He lay on his back, covering his eyes with his forearm.

'Are you in pain?' she cried softly and put a hand to his forehead. It felt warm but not alarmingly so.

Rafe pushed her hand away. 'I'm weak, that's all. The doctors told me I'd feel like this for a few more days.'

'Thank heavens you're home in your own bed. Let me help you change and get under the covers.'

'No.' The fierce look in his eyes stopped her in her tracks. 'That is the one thing you will not do. When this Consuela comes with our dinner, I will instruct her to show you to the apartment my mother has had prepared for you.'

'But outside—'

'Outside I could feel this weakness coming on. I didn't

want to use the little energy I had left discussing our sleeping arrangements.'

'Well, I'm not moving from this apartment,' Kit declared. 'You're my husband and I love you.' To her consternation, her voice quavered again. 'We took vows together. You said it yourself at the hospital—for better or for worse, we're married and we're going to live together. It's what we both wanted more than anything else in the world. It's the reason you flew all the way to Idaho to find me.'

More lines of weariness darkened his face and he grimaced. 'If you wish to live in my apartment, so be it, but you'll have to find a place to sleep other than my bed.'

She grasped at even that much headway. 'There's a couch in your study. I'll sleep there so I can listen for you in the night. If you need anything—'

'If I still needed a nurse, Dr. Penman would never have released me from the hospital.' Hurt by his response, Kit paused before saying anything else; in the interim there was a tap on the door. That would be their dinner.

Kit glanced at Rafe, who lay there perfectly still. The strain he'd been under had exhausted him and he had fallen sound asleep.

Before Consuela could leave, Kit quickly opened the door. After thanking the young woman for the dinner, she asked her to bring them some extra bedding. If Consuela thought it an odd request, she hid it well. She returned, laden with sheets and blankets, a few minutes later.

Soon Kit had made up a bed on the comfortable leather couch and covered Rafe with a light blanket. She placed his tray on the end table next to his bed. Judging from the deepness of his sleep, she doubted he'd awaken before morning.

Though she felt drained, she didn't want to leave his side. She sat down next to him to eat her meal, starting with a succulent piece of melon.

This was the first time, since the day of the accident, that she'd been able to look at him to her heart's content. Her eyes wandered freely over his face and hair, noting his long black lashes and the way his firm mouth softened in repose.

She felt a sharp, piercing ache as she gazed at the man she loved. Would she ever know the fire of his kiss again? Would she ever again hear him laugh or whisper those private endearments? Would they ever truly be husband and wife?

Salty tears scalded her cheeks and fell unheeded on her dinner plate. Unable to eat any more, she put the tray on another side table and got ready for bed. She eventually fell asleep, stifling her sobs with the pillow.

CHAPTER SEVEN

SUNSHINE FILTERED through the windows of the study and stole across Kit's face, warming her skin, rousing her from a dreamless sleep. She glanced at her watch through bleary eyes and saw that it was almost noon. She hadn't slept in this late since she was a teenager!

What about Rafe? Was he still in bed?

Throwing off the covers, she reached for her bathrobe, slung over the chair next to his desk, and tied the belt around her slender waist before padding into his bedroom.

Rafe was gone! Not only that, his bed was made, the dinner trays had disappeared, and there was no sign of their luggage.

When she opened his dresser drawers, she felt a small thrill of happiness to discover that her nightclothes and underwear had been neatly put away alongside his. Flinging open the armoire, she saw her clothes hanging next to his, her shoes lined up beside his. Anyone peering inside would imagine she and Rafe were an old married couple who shared everything.

She shuddered to think the reality of their situation was so far removed from these deceptive appearances—and from her dreams. But standing here paralyzed by the pain wasn't going to provide the solution to her dilemma. She was determined to make him fall in love with her all over again. That meant staying with him wherever he went, whatever he did, until she was all he could see or think about.

With renewed vigor, she showered and washed her hair, then dressed in a purple cotton skirt with a matching print, short-sleeved blouse, something airy and fresh that flattered her figure and coloring. She wore sandals in the same shade of purple and put on a light pink lipstick.

After leaving Rafe's apartment, she made her way down the hall to look for him. At the bottom of the staircase, one of the house staff directed her through a portico to the informal dining room, which was more like a patio garden with every kind of flower in bloom.

Kit's spirits plummeted when she saw Dona Gabriella, dressed more formally in a cream-colored crepe dress, seated at the round glass-and-wrought-iron table laden with fruit and rolls. '*Buenos días, señora,*' Kit said in her best Spanish.

Rafe's mother responded in English. 'I have been waiting for you so we could talk. Please, help yourself to breakfast. If you want an egg or meat, tell me and I'll instruct Nina.'

Kit shook her head. 'A roll and a peach will be fine.'

'Coffee?'

'No, thank you.'

Growing more and more uncomfortable under the older woman's scrutiny, Kit buttered her roll. She tried to act nonchalant as she peeled her fruit and started to eat.

'When Diego telephoned and told me the news about my son, I did not want to believe it. But after talking to Rafael this morning, I can see that the past, the family, the estate, means nothing to him. That *I* mean nothing to him.'

Dona Gabriella never minced words. She was a strong,

proud woman like her son, but Kit heard the quaver in her voice and looked with compassion into her dark eyes. 'Señora Mendez, Rafe doesn't remember anything or anyone, but the doctors assured me that in time he will probably regain his memory. We have to be patient.'

'For how long?' Dona Gabriella moaned. Kit knew exactly how she felt.

'No one can say. We can only hope and pray and do everything possible to help him adjust.'

The older woman looked pained. 'Why did you come back? He doesn't love you, he doesn't know you. You don't even sleep together. You have nothing between you but a meaningless document saying you are married, and that marriage not even in the Church.'

The sweet fruit suddenly felt dry and tasteless and Kit had to swallow hard. She wiped her mouth with her napkin. 'He may have lost his memory, but I'm more in love with him than ever. If he'll let me, I want to be a wife to him. He loved me before the accident. I'm hoping he will love me again.'

In a brittle voice the older woman said, 'You may have a long wait. I don't believe he will ever remember.'

'I disagree,' Kit retorted firmly. 'The psychiatrist told me that permanent amnesia is very rare. I refuse to believe Rafe won't make a full recovery.'

Dona Gabriella shook her head and her bottom lip trembled. 'When I talked to him about the business, he told me he wasn't ready to think about that yet, that he doubted it would ever interest him.

'With Jaime gone, the family affairs are in the hands of our estate manager, who is out with my son right now, showing him the property. But Rodrigo isn't capable of overseeing our international concerns the way Rafael did.

For the past few months while my son has been looking for you, the situation has deteriorated. I have been getting phone calls. There are problems.'

In an unexpected gesture, she reached out and grasped Kit's hand. 'If you truly love my son and if you still refuse to leave, then you must see that he takes his right-ful place once more. Everyone looks up to him, needs him.'

And you most of all, Kit surmised as she saw the tears gather in her mother-in-law's eyes. Dona Gabriella hadn't been brought up to take financial responsibility or understand the intricacies of running a business. Kit realized that the older woman's feelings of helplessness only compounded her grief.

Dona Gabriella suddenly removed her hand as if she was embarrassed for displaying any weakness, a charac-teristic so reminiscent of Rafe, Kit could have wept.

'*Señora,*' Kit began, then hesitated because the idea that came into her mind would probably upset Rafe's mother further. 'I honestly believe Rafe will get his memory back, but since we don't know how long it will take, someone capable needs to be in charge. Why not call Jaime and ask him to come home?'

Dona Gabriella stared at Kit as if she'd taken complete leave of her senses. 'Do you know what you are asking?' she muttered in a hoarse voice.

'Yes.' Now that Kit had started this, she wasn't about to back down. 'Jaime can run the estate competently— I'm convinced of it. But since either your husband or Rafe has always been here, Jaime's never had the oppor-tunity to really prove himself. I got to know your younger son quite well, and he loves this land, this business. Ask him to come home. Tell him he's needed.'

Kit wondered if Rafe's mother had even heard her.

'He'd never come,' she murmured at last. 'Not with you here.'

The bitterness in her voice brought back all the guilt Kit had been trying to resolve. Still, she had to ask, 'Does Jaime know what has happened to Rafe?'

'No.' She shook her dark head. 'I decided to say nothing to him until I had seen Rafael for myself.'

'*Señora,* you've just given me an idea,' she cried out, her heart pounding. 'Why don't you phone Jaime and tell him Rafe has been injured in a very serious automobile accident. Tell Jaime he's needed at home immediately, but don't tell him I'm here.

'You and I both know that deep down he loves Rafe, and he'll come. I'll stay out of sight until Jaime has had an opportunity to talk to Rafe himself. When he can see the situation for what it really is, he won't be able to walk out on either of you, and I don't think he'll let his pride and anger toward me make any difference.'

Dona Gabriella stared at Kit for a long, long time, and if Kit wasn't mistaken, she saw a glint of admiration. 'You give my Jaime a great deal of credit.'

Kit's eyes filled with tears. 'You've raised two remarkable sons. Jaime is a wonderful man. I love him like a brother. Please believe me when I tell you neither Rafe nor I ever meant to hurt him.'

After a slight pause, Dona Gabriella said, 'You're very convincing.' Then she pushed herself away from the table. 'If you will excuse me, I have some things to attend to. Consider this your home—for the time being,' she added as she walked off.

Kit had no idea if what she had suggested to Rafe's mother would produce results. In fact, when she really thought about it, Kit wondered if she'd been wrong to bring Jaime's name into the conversation. But it had seemed—still seemed—the only possible solution and Dona Gabriella hadn't said no. It was a start.

Left to her own devices, Kit had little choice but to find some way to pass the time until Rafe came home. Since she couldn't concentrate and the walls of the hacienda seemed to press in on her, she decided to go for a walk.

Beyond the walls of the back courtyard and garage, a dirt road led to the vineyards in the distance. She set off briskly, but the intense heat of the afternoon sun beat down on her and she gradually slowed her pace. She spent another half hour walking leisurely past rows of young grapevines planted in the chalky soil, which Rafe had told her was found only in this part of Spain.

She scanned the terrain, squinting in the bright sunlight. A group of outbuildings beckoned from the distance and she walked faster, eager for a drink of water.

Every so often she passed groups of workers tying vines who paused in their task to wave to her. She waved back. By now everyone on the estate must know Rafe had brought his wife home with him.

As she drew closer, she realized she had come to the stable where Rafe kept his prized horses. Rounding one corner, she noticed her husband immediately, although half a dozen dark-haired workers surrounded him. He and the man she presumed was Rodrigo had just ridden into the paddock on magnificent snowy white horses with black markings.

Rafe sat astride his horse with a princely bearing, commanding the attention of those around him. She thanked heaven that his memory loss hadn't prevented him from mounting one of his horses. For the first time since his accident, he seemed to be enjoying himself.

Kit didn't understand his Spanish because he spoke too fast, though she could tell that whatever he said held all of them spellbound and they responded with obvious affection and camaraderie.

She stood in the shadow of the tack shed, but the shade proved no barrier against the sun. Small rivulets of perspiration, caused by nervousness as much as heat, ran down her spine and between her breasts, and her blouse and skirt clung damply to her body. She found herself staring at him, mesmerized, and couldn't move away.

As the group drew closer, she smiled secretly because every other man paled into insignificance beside him.

He wore no hat, exposing his jet-black hair to the sun. Over the past few months it had grown longer and now it curled over his bronzed forehead in rakish abandon. Gazing at his profile brought to mind the image of the grand *hidalgos* of a hundred years earlier. When he turned to respond to a comment made by one of the men, Kit caught the full measure of his strong-boned face. The character it revealed went beyond mere handsomeness.

Forgetting her thirst, she stepped out of the shadows. It was like responding to a force outside her control. As she walked purposefully toward the corral, all talking ceased and every man turned and stared at her with unabashed male admiration, respectfully greeting her as Señora Mendez. *Rafael's wife.*

All the men except her husband. There was a sudden, unnatural quiet. When she looked up at Rafe, she saw that his face had lost its earlier animation. Perhaps it was a trick of the light, but she thought he went pale for a moment, as if he'd experienced a shock. *Had he remembered something from the past?*

His horse pranced in place but Rafe's body remained frozen in the saddle. His utter stillness unnerved her. It must have unnerved the others, too, for they quietly dispersed, including Rodrigo, who tipped his hat toward Rafe before dismounting, then led his horse into the stable.

She raised one hand to shield her eyes from the sun's rays. Looking up at him, she suddenly felt the breath squeezed out of her when his black eyes impaled her with a lightning glance. It was as if all his life's force and energy swirled in those depths, like thunderheads gathering for a tempest.

Something had happened to him while he was out riding, making him more suspicious of her than ever. She could feel it. His penetrating gaze took in her delicate features flushed by the sun, the shape of her body outlined by the sweat-dampened clothes, the gold of her curls tousled by the hot breeze. He seemed to resent the very look of her. 'Did you want something, *mi esposa?*'

He delivered his words with a sting that made her wince. 'I was out taking a walk when I saw you. Don't you think you should come back to the house now and rest? I'm quite sure Dr. Penman didn't expect you to go riding this soon.'

'I told you last night I don't require a nurse.'

Her throat was painfully dry, and she couldn't quite control the quavering of her voice. 'It's because I love you that I'm concerned. This heat is oppressive. Let's go back home together and enjoy a late lunch. Now that you've had a little tour of the estate with Rodrigo, I want to know what you're thinking and feeling.'

'If you're asking me if I remember anything, the answer is no.'

She tried to ignore his insensitive comment. 'I—I thought you might feel like company.'

'I've had a surfeit of it all morning, so I have to presume you're talking about something slightly more. . .intimate.'

'No. Not—not now.' Her voice caught on the words and a rush of heat stained her cheeks. 'Don't misunderstand me. I *want* to make love with you. I've wanted it from the first moment we met. But I'm talking about companionship, about being your friend until you can make sense of things.'

One corner of his mouth curved in mockery. 'What you ask is impossible. Let me know when that finally gets through to you. Tell my mother I will join her for dinner this evening.'

She felt as if he'd slapped her. 'I'm afraid you'll have to tell her yourself, since I won't be home until late.' She said the first thing that came into her mind. Wheeling around, she broke into a run and headed for the hacienda in the far distance, ignoring the heat.

Rafe called out, demanding to know where she was going, but Kit ignored him. In fact, she didn't care if all the men in the tack room were witness to the spectacle. If, through the house staff, Rafe's mother already knew that Kit and Rafe slept in separate beds, then by now it was common knowledge on the estate.

After today, the men would see for themselves that the recent marriage of the *patrón* to the American woman who had caused the trouble with Jaime was already in a precarious state. What an irony, when she and Rafe hadn't even been home twenty-four hours.

Dr. Penman had said she'd get angry, but he didn't know the half of it!

CHAPTER EIGHT

FOR THE NEXT three days Kit saw her husband only at dinner, which was a taciturn affair since Dona Gabriella was forced to initiate any conversation. Rafe's responses were polite but brief, and each night he excused himself after the coffee and liqueurs had been served.

In the mornings he left the hacienda long before Kit was up. He didn't return to his bedroom until she'd gone to bed in the study.

During the day Kit filled her time by borrowing Rafe's blue Mercedes and driving into Rota to visit with friends on the base and do a little shopping. That was what she'd done the afternoon of their confrontation, too, staying out for a late dinner and coming home close to midnight. Rafe was already asleep.

On the fourth morning, Dona Gabriella called to Kit as she prepared to leave the house. 'If I may have a word with you?'

Kit nodded and paused on the bottom step of the staircase. She could see the older woman's anxiety and understood her feelings only too well. The situation was becoming explosive. 'I called Jaime and he's arriving some time this afternoon.'

Kit could hardly refrain from embracing her mother-in-law. 'I knew he wouldn't refuse you,' she whispered in an emotional voice. 'That's wonderful.'

Dona Gabriella kept kneading her hands. 'It may turn out to be a tragic mistake.'

'No.' Kit shook her head. 'You don't really believe that and neither do I. Now that you've told me, I'm going to drive to Seville and visit with the psychiatrist I mentioned to you earlier. I think I'll stay overnight to give Jaime and Rafe a chance to talk.'

'That is a good idea, but my son wouldn't approve of you driving that far alone. I will call Diego and ask him to fly you there. He will be at your disposal. My son keeps a permanent suite at the Prado, so you don't have to worry about making accommodations. If you need to buy anything, he has accounts in all the good shops.'

'But the distance is nothing if that's what you're worried about!' Kit exclaimed, fearing Rafe's reaction. 'Back in America I've driven thousands of miles alone.'

'You're the wife of Rafael de Mendez y Lucar now, and can no longer behave in such a manner.'

'But he might get angry when he finds out I've been with Diego.' Deciding to tell the truth, she said, 'Before we left Idaho, Rafe accused me of being interested in his pilot.'

The older woman's eyes flashed. 'So my son's feelings for you aren't as dead as he would have me believe.'

'Oh, yes.' Kit's voice trembled. 'They are. Very dead.'

'Nonsense,' she scoffed. 'Do you think for one minute that my son would have let you come back to Spain with him or would have allowed you to sleep in his apartment if he didn't want you there? He follows you with his eyes when you're not watching. I would like to see his expression when I tell him you've flown to Seville with Diego. I know my Rafael. He is not indifferent to you. He never was,' she admitted in a strained voice.

Kit felt a closeness to Dona Gabriella she hadn't experienced before. 'I'll hurry and get ready.'

'While you pack, I'll telephone Diego. Luis will drive you to the airport.'

Before dashing up the stairs, Kit reached out and patted the older woman's arm. 'You must be so excited to see Jaime again. I'll pray that everything goes well.'

Rafe's mother lifted pained eyes to Kit. 'We will need the help of the Holy Virgin herself.' Her lower lip quivered. 'If there is a reconciliation, I will have you to thank,' she added, filling Kit with the small hope that the two women could become friends.

Within twenty minutes, Luis had brought the limousine out front and Dona Gabriella waved Kit off. When they reached the airport, Kit thanked Luis, then talked Diego into bringing his wife and children along.

He objected, at first, that the *señor* might not approve, but she told him he was as much her employee as Rafe's and that she wouldn't take no for an answer. She also told him she didn't mind waiting at the hangar until he could make all the arrangements.

Two hours later, the five of them were on their way to Seville. After getting acquainted with Diego's charming wife, Maria, Kit spent the rest of the day and evening playing with their two-and four-year-old children in Rafe's private suite, while the Silvas enjoyed some much-needed time alone.

The diversion helped Kit relax and keep her mind off of the situation at the hacienda. If she'd been alone with her thoughts, she would have gone crazy.

At ten the next morning, she met with Dr. Perez and they discussed Rafe's case in detail. He assured her things were progressing very well, citing instances of amnesiacs who went into severe depressions and refused to leave the hospital or the bedroom. The fact that Rafe was eating well and enjoyed getting out to spend time with his horses, if nothing else, showed he was in good mental health. He urged Kit never to give up hope and to continue doing exactly what she was doing.

Cheered by his optimism, Kit persuaded Maria to go shopping with her while Diego tended the children. When they returned to the hotel several hours later, their arms were laden with packages and toys, and Kit felt she'd made life-long friends of the Silvas.

It wasn't until they flew over Jerez with its tiled roofs burnished by the last golden rays of the sun that reaction to what might be awaiting her at the hacienda set in. She felt weak and nauseated and could only hope Rafe and Jaime hadn't come to blows.

Diego had phoned ahead to make certain Luis was there to meet Kit. But it wasn't the silver-haired Spaniard waiting outside the hangar when Kit emerged from the plane carrying her overnight bag and packages. It was her husband.

Her eyes fastened on him as he got out of his Mercedes wearing a dark, sea-green suit and tie. He strode toward her with a look of tightly controlled rage. Kit was so surprised to see him, so thrilled to think he'd come for her no matter the reason that she couldn't form words.

'I trust you've been enjoying yourself,' he bit out. Grabbing hold of her elbow, he jerked her closer to him. 'Of course it was too much to expect my wife to let me know she was leaving town. With my pilot, no less.'

Kit hadn't imagined the possessiveness of his touch or his words. *He was jealous!* She felt ecstasy and chagrin in equal parts.

'Since I haven't chosen to do so,' he muttered contemptuously, 'did *Diego* accommodate your needs?'

Kit would have responded, but Maria cried out excitedly, 'Señor Mendez!'

Rafe's head swiveled around in stunned surprise as the attractive young brunette stepped from the plane carrying a sleepy Pedro in her arms. Diego was close behind with fiery little Anita on his shoulders.

They rushed toward Rafe and both talked to him at once, their faces glowing. Diego introduced his wife, since he knew Rafe couldn't remember her. Their Spanish was so rapid that Kit despaired of ever truly picking up the language. She stood a little distance apart, watching Rafe's expression soften as he warmed to their friendliness and held Anita. According to Diego, their little girl adored Rafe, and Kit could believe it by the way she threw herself into his arms, patting his bronzed cheeks in delight, reciting every detail of their overnight outing.

In fact, the scene brought a lump to Kit's throat that wouldn't go away even after everyone had said goodbye and Rafe had helped her into the car.

But the second they were alone, Rafe's face sobered and he looked over at her with accusing eyes. 'I'm not going to apologize. You left the hacienda without a word to anyone. If Luis hadn't mentioned where he'd taken you yesterday, we would have had to call in the police. What was so important that you had to fly to Seville and spend the night?'

Dona Gabriella hadn't told him!

'I decided to see Dr. Perez, but he couldn't fit me in until this morning.'

Rafe's hand tightened on the steering wheel. She could see the white of his knuckles. 'I'm the one with the memory loss, not you.'

'Everyone could use the services of a good psychiatrist once in a while. I wanted some advice.'

There was an ominous pause. 'And did you get it?'

'Yes.'

With a grimace he started the powerful car and drove away from the hangar onto the main road. 'Don't you want to know what has been happening during your absence, or do you no longer care?'

His question triggered a sense of panic, and she had to fight to remain composed. 'You sound as if there's something wrong. Nothing has happened to your mother?' In truth, she was worried sick about Dona Gabriella.

'Jaime came home yesterday,' he muttered beneath his breath.

Adrenaline spilled into her system. 'That must have been a shock to you. H-How is he?'

She heard his quick intake of breath. 'Nicer, quieter than I had imagined. Very much like our mother and painfully honest. We talked into the night. You and I hurt him.'

'I know,' she said in a faint whisper, 'but never on purpose.'

'He's a finer man than I will ever be.'

Kit frowned. 'Why do you say that?'

'Because if I had lost you to him, I wouldn't be able to forgive such a betrayal, much less bear the sight of either one of you.'

'How do you know that?'

'I've learned things about myself in the past twenty-four hours. Apparently there's a great deal more of my father in me than I had supposed. You spoke the truth at the hospital. But the facts were unpleasant, and I chose not to believe you.'

'That's understandable, Rafe. I was a stranger to you. But please don't be so hard on yourself. Families are complicated, even the most normal and well-adjusted families. Nothing is black and white.'

'The Mendez dynasty does not fit the profile of what one would call a normal family.' He paused for a long, tense moment. 'What's really ugly about this is that having learned the truth, I know in my gut I'd hurt Jaime all over again to have what I wanted.'

Her heart thudded sickeningly in her chest. 'There's one thing you're forgetting. Jaime thought he loved me, but I never once said I loved him. What you and I felt for each other was instantaneous and inevitable. That's not betrayal.'

While they were stopped at a red light, he turned to her. In the darkness his eyes gleamed like hot coals. 'Jaime is moving back to the hacienda to take over the reins of the business before it starts to crumble. My mother tells me there's a vintage fair in a few weeks. I promised her I would stay home long enough to celebrate with the family, then I plan to leave.'

Kit knew better than to argue with him in this mood. 'Where will you go?'

'I'm not sure.'

The light turned green and they sped away from the city. Kit felt ill and didn't realize where they were headed until he pulled up to a small roadside inn on the outskirts.

'Why are we stopping here?'

Tension again filled the car. 'To be honest, I want to make love to you. And prefer to do it away from the hacienda.'

Until she got off the plane an hour before, Kit would have rejoiced at his words. but everything had changed drastically since then. The blood pounded in her ears. 'You mean, now that you know I'm not a liar, you've decided you want me.'

'Actually, I've wanted you since our first conversation in my hospital room. When I heard you'd gone off with Diego, I discovered that I didn't like the idea of your sleeping with anyone but me. I've been anticipating your return with more eagerness than I would have thought possible.'

But he hadn't mentioned one word of love. Kit had thought she'd be willing to do anything to keep Rafe, but without the love and sharing she craved, what hope did they have for a real marriage?

Trying to sound calm, she said, 'Unfortunately, your behavior at the hangar hurt me a great deal. The Rafe I knew before the accident would never have accused his wife and loyal friend of conducting a tawdry affair behind his back. I couldn't make love to you now.'

'We'll see,' was all he said before starting the car. It sounded like a threat.

CHAPTER NINE

THE MOMENT they returned to the house, Kit jumped from the car and, without waiting for Rafe, hurried inside. She learned from Consuela that Jaime was at the main shed going over the books with Rodrigo. Dona Gabriella had retired for the night.

The news came as a great relief to Kit, who was in no state of mind to face either of them. She dashed up the stairs, anxious to be alone where she could decide what to do about an increasingly impossible situation.

During the drive to the airport Luis had informed her that before retiring, the *señor* always spent his time grooming the horses. She assumed Rafe would head for the stables as usual and she would have the apartment to herself.

First, she needed a long shower. After that, she put on a pair of cotton pajamas and her robe, then brushed her teeth. Her curls were damp and would only take a few minutes to dry.

Turning off the light, she emerged from the bathroom but came to a sudden standstill. Rafe blocked her way to the study. He'd changed out of his suit and into a knee-length paisley robe she hadn't seen before, one that revealed the dark hair on his chest. His unconscious sensuality lowered her defenses as nothing else could.

'I—I didn't expect you to come back to the apartment this early. I'm sorry if you wanted the bathroom. It's free now,' she mumbled unnecessarily.

'I've been waiting for you.'

Her mouth went dry. 'If you don't mind, I'm tired and I'd like to go to bed.'

'My sentiments exactly.'

Something in his tone made her legs feel weak and trembling. 'You're in my way.'

His eyes narrowed on her mouth. 'I don't think so. It's time you slept in a real bed, with your husband.'

'I prefer the couch,' she answered in a less-than-steady voice.

'I don't suppose it matters where we sleep tonight, because I intend to make love to you,' he stated before moving toward her with purpose.

Kit started to back up and felt the footboard of his bed against her legs. 'I made my feelings clear in the car.'

'So did I.' In the next instant his hands slid up her arms and he began caressing her shoulders, drawing her closer with each movement. 'I've been thinking of nothing but your mouth, your beautiful body. . .' His tone was passionate, reminding her of Rafe before he'd lost his memory.

She could no longer remember why she was fighting him. He lowered his head, and Kit's parted mouth rushed to meet his in a cataclysm of feeling that left her clinging to him. His low moan traveled through her body, arousing her to a fever pitch, engulfing her until she had no will of her own.

His lips roamed over her face and throat with a voracious hunger. His mouth became the center of her universe, the focus of her sensations.

Kit was scarcely aware of her robe sliding to the floor or Rafe's strong arms carrying her to the bed, so caught up was she in the sheer excitement of his touch.

'I want you, *mi esposa*,' he confessed in a husky voice. 'I've been a fool to deny us what we've both wanted since I woke up in that hospital room.' He began devouring her mouth over and over again.

Through her euphoria, reason asserted itself long enough for Kit to break their kiss and cup his face in her hands. 'I've wanted you much longer than that, Rafe. I've been in love with you for months. I can't even remember a time when I wasn't,' she whispered against his lips. 'Are you saying you're in love with me now? That we'll leave here after the fair, together, and make a new life someplace else?'

Twining his fingers through hers, he removed her hands from his face and pressed them against the pillow above her head. 'For tonight let's forget everything except what we feel when we're together like this. *Por Dios,* how beautiful you are. I never knew pajamas could be so enticing.' He unfastened one button and pushed the thin fabric aside to kiss her shoulder.

He still hadn't answered her question. *Because he couldn't.*

'What we're doing is wrong if you don't love me, if you don't want me in your life forever,' she cried out even as her body clamored for fulfillment. He was delighting her with his kisses, plying his magic as only Rafe could.

'I know I want this,' he murmured, biting her earlobe with gentle insistence, 'and I can't think beyond this moment. No more talk, *amorada*. Tonight we will forget the world and create our own.'

Before she lost all reason, Kit took advantage of his weakness and slid out from under him. In an instant, she was on her feet, albeit unsteadily. She heard his groan and then a muffled curse as he struggled to a sitting position.

Afraid to trust herself alone with him any longer, she ran from his apartment. She could hear him calling her all the way to one of the guest rooms in the other wing of the hacienda.

This was how it always ended. With her running away and his pleading for her to come back. Kit feared it was the story of their lives, and for the first time since the accident, she felt a sense of real fear that they weren't destined to be together. He planned to leave the estate after the fair; he'd made no mention of taking her with him.

A numbing coldness crept through her body as she locked the door and climbed into one of the twin beds. She couldn't imagine ever being warm again, not when her heart felt as if it had turned to shards of ice.

The night brought no relief. After a fitful sleep, she got up at dawn and crept back to Rafe's apartment to get a change of clothes.

He lay sprawled across the bed on his stomach, his breathing heavy, the covers on the floor. She found no solace in the fact that he, too, had spent a restless night before succumbing to sleep. Kit tried not to disturb him as she gathered the necessary clothes, then slipped quietly out of the room.

Returning to the guest room where she intended to sleep from now on, she pulled on khaki cotton pants and a plain white T-shirt. A few minutes later she hurried out the front doors of the hacienda and started down the drive with no particular destination. All she knew was that she had to keep walking, keep moving, to work off the raw tension punishing her body. Now that it was

May, early morning was the best time for a walk, before the sun grew too hot.

She wasn't aware of time passing, but the sun was much higher in the sky when she drew abreast of the estate chapel. An aura of tranquillity seemed to beckon her, and on impulse she walked over to the building, wondering if it was open. To her surprise the heavy carved wooden doors gave easily at her tentative push. She stepped inside.

After the brilliance of the sun, it took several minutes for her eyes to become accustomed to the semidark interior. A warm, almost musty smell pervaded the place. And there was another scent, not an unpleasant one—perhaps incense and the tinge of sweet smoke given off by the burning candles near the altar. Someone had been here earlier.

The chapel was small, yet it was inordinately beautiful. Kit sank down on the nearest pew to absorb the beauty of the paintings on the walls and the ceiling and to pray for direction.

'*Kit?* I knew it had to be you,' a familiar male voice murmured behind her shoulder.

She jumped to her feet and whirled around. '*Jaime!*' He looked like a shorter, gentler version of Rafe. He was the same Jaime, but Kit immediately noticed some subtle changes in him. His dark, attractive face was more lined and he'd lost a little weight. 'I—I'm sorry if I'm intruding.'

'How could you do that?' His mouth broke into the familiar engaging smile. 'I was driving to another part of the property when I saw you, so I decided to follow you inside.'

Kit felt her eyes smart with tears. 'Jaime—'

'No.' He held up his hands. 'You don't need to explain anything. Or apologize. My brother has done enough of that since I returned.' On a deep sigh, he said, 'In the past couple of months I've had time to reflect. And drink,' he confessed with another quick smile. 'But drunk or sober, I came to the conclusion that neither one of you meant to hurt me.'

Kit tried again to speak, but he shook his head. 'Let me finish while I still have the courage. When you ran away, my brother was demented. Never in my life had I seen him out of control. Never had I seen him so desolate. That's when I realized you were everything to him, his very heart and soul.

'At first I admit I was angry and hurt. But in time, I realized how much you had come to care for me. Otherwise you would never have left my brother as you did to spare my feelings. Looking at you now, I can see you've been as inconsolable without him as he has been without him.'

Kit's shoulders started to shake and the tears ran unchecked down her cheeks. 'I love you in my own way, Jaime.'

'I know. And I love you. And we both love Rafael.'

'Yes.'

After a long pause he said, 'Mother tells me he may never completely recover his memory. No matter what happens, don't let him go, Kit. Don't ever run away again. Without you, he will be nothing.'

'He doesn't love me, Jaime.' Her voice caught painfully. 'He doesn't remember.'

'I don't believe that,' Jaime insisted. 'When Luis told him you'd flown to Seville with Diego, his face lost all color. The next thing we knew, he'd left the house and

I could hear his car in the courtyard. He drove out of here like a maniac. Isn't that how you Americans say it?'

'Yes.' Kit smiled through the tears.

'Kit, whatever our father did to me and Rafael, he's gone now. If we let his actions stand between us, then he has won. This is what I have told my mother and my brother.' In a silent move, Jaime grasped Kit's hands and kissed them. 'Help him, Kit. Help him understand that what went on in the past doesn't matter anymore.'

Her heart full, she threw her arms around his neck and hugged him for a long, long time. 'You're wonderful, Jaime. I'm so sorry it wasn't you.'

'No, you're not,' he murmured into her hair. 'And oddly enough, I'm not, either. Somewhere out there is a woman who'll love me the way you love my brother. And I intend to find her.'

Kit pulled away, sniffing and wiping her eyes. 'Every unmarried woman in Andalusia would like the opportunity, believe me.'

'You think so?' He grinned. 'My mother says the same thing.'

'She's right, you know.'

'Well, I have the rest of my life to find out. Now, before I get to work salvaging the family fortune, why don't I drive you back to the house? Something tells me Rafael will be looking for you—and bellowing loud enough to disturb the entire household.'

CHAPTER TEN

AFTER THANKING Jaime for the ride and his comforting words, Kit hurried inside the house. She almost collided with Dona Gabriella who met her at the front door and immediately seized her hands. That in itself was unexpected, but one look at the older woman's face, and Kit knew something was wrong. 'What is it, *señora?*'

'Have you seen Rafael?'

Kit's heart began to race. 'No. While I was out walking, I stopped to visit the chapel and Jaime found me there. We—made our peace.' The older woman crossed herself in gratitude, then grasped Kit's face and kissed her on either cheek. 'He brought me back before going to work, but we didn't see Rafe. How long has he been gone?'

'A half hour. When my son appeared for breakfast and discovered the two of you missing, he went off in his car and has never come back. I'm frightened.'

The despair in her voice reached Kit's heart, and she put her arm around the woman whose emotions at this point were as ragged and fragile as her own. 'Rafe gave his word he wouldn't leave until after the fair. He's an honorable man, and right now he has a lot to work out.'

Kit said the words, trying to believe them herself, but in truth, she was terrified. Last night she'd rejected her husband's advances; had his anger and confusion led him to do something foolish?

Even more of a concern was his possible reaction to

Jaime. No doubt he'd seen his brother's car parked near the chapel earlier. Had he stopped to investigate? Perhaps he assumed their accidental meeting was planned. Guilt, despair, fury—he might have felt any of those things.

She had no way of knowing what to believe, but like Dona Gabriella, Kit was imagining the worst. By night-fall, she had just agreed with his mother that they should call the police to trace his whereabouts when Rafe unexpectedly returned to the hacienda.

Though he didn't make an appearance in the dining room, Kit rejoiced that he'd come back. She exchanged a private look of relief with Jaime and his mother before excusing herself to see Rafe.

She burst into his bedroom, anxious to know if he was all right, and discovered him in a state of partial undress, obviously about to take a shower.

He stared at her with an indefinable expression on his face. 'Since you now sleep in another part of the house, I suggest you do not enter my apartment again unless you are prepared to sleep in my bed.'

Rafe would never know how tempted she was to give in. How tempted to take what he was offering, even if it was a matter of one week—or one night. 'You were gone so long that your mother's been beside herself with anxiety.'

'But not my *esposa?*' His voice was sharp, sarcastic.

'Naturally I have, too,' she admitted. By this time he had removed everything but his shorts. They rode low on his hips, revealing his splendid body to her gaze.

'You don't need to be,' he murmured in a silky tone. 'After seeing Dr. Perez this afternoon, I ran into an old acquaintance outside his office building—or rather, she ran into me.' His mouth curved with ill-concealed amusement, twisting Kit's emotions into knots. 'Luisa Rios is even lovelier than I'd heard. Not only that, she's eager to resume our. . .friendship.' He paused. 'Unless you can give me a reason to stay home tonight, I'm prepared to enjoy her company. She's let me know she's more than willing.'

Taking a deep breath, Kit said, 'A woman who would get involved with a married man is beneath you, Rafe. Maybe you always knew that. Maybe that's the reason you didn't marry her when you had the opportunity.'

His eyes turned glassy. 'The man you're talking about is gone. And after my talk with Dr. Perez, I'm more convinced than ever that he'll never resurface.'

'Is this your way of telling me it's over between us?' she asked in a dull voice.

'You made the decision when you left my bed. Now you must excuse me as I have another engagement.'

When she saw his hands go to the waistband of his shorts, she fled from his apartment. For the first time in their impossible relationship he didn't call her back. In some ways, she feared, that was the worst omen of all.

Throughout the next week they spoke only in passing. Every morning he would awaken early and drive off, rarely returning until after Kit had gone to bed. No one, including Jaime, knew where he went or what he did.

During the day when time hung heavily, Dona Gabriella tried to keep Kit distracted by discussing the costumes they would wear the following weekend, when the fair began. She called in the seamstress for fittings and Kit went along with her plans because she could tell it brought Dona Gabriella a little pleasure. It helped fill the empty hours, too; Kit no longer had the heart for her former trips into Rota or her long walks around the estate.

Rafe's mother proved to be a congenial companion, and she steadfastly refused to discuss anything unpleasant. Kit made an effort to keep up her end of their casual conversations. But they both knew very well that once the fair was over, Rafe would leave Jerez and everyone behind, destroying the family forever. Kit didn't want to think about that; she couldn't imagine a life without Rafe. Out of necessity she involved herself as much as possible with the preparations.

The carriage, which had been in the family for generations, had to be brought out of storage. When Kit saw the trappings for the horses, she marveled at the superb silver tooling in the handcrafted leather harnesses. Dozens of red tassels attached to the headdresses would accentuate the snowy white of the horses and sway to their movements.

Kit learned that she and Dona Gabriella would ride in the carriage to be driven by Esteban, head trainer at the Mendez stable. Rafe and Jaime, also in costume, would lead the parade astride their famous horses. Behind the Mendez family, the Rios carriage would follow and behind them, the carriages of other prominent Jerez families devoted to preserving the pageantry of bygone generations. People from all over the country, including tourists and dignitaries, had been pouring into the city to celebrate another successful vintage year.

The first day of the fair arrived. When Kit learned that Rafe was tending to the horses and wouldn't join the family until the parade was ready to start, something seemed to snap inside her. She could no longer put up a pretense.

She thought Jaime would understand that she couldn't

go through with it, couldn't ride in the family carriage as if she had every right to be there.

'Jaime, how can I smile and wave to the world when our marriage is a travesty? Luisa Rios, for one, knows the truth since she and Rafe have probably spent every evening together for the past week.'

'The fact that my brother has gone out of his way to humiliate you actually reveals the strength of his emotions. This won't last, I'm sure of it. But he's still trying to figure out exactly what he feels—and what *you* feel. It's the reason you cannot back down now. He's still testing your love.'

'*Testing your love. . .*' Only weeks before, Dr. Penman had said the very same thing. '*Show him you're made of stronger stuff,*' he'd admonished her.

In the end, Kit succumbed to Jaime's pleadings. Later that afternoon Luis drove her and Dona Gabriella through the streets of Jerez to the starting point of the parade, but Kit could scarcely appreciate the beauty of the town bedecked with all its festive finery. She merely went through the motions—smiling, commenting, trying to appear animated.

Above their heads, white and red lanterns had been strung on wires to create a carnival atmosphere. Hundreds of people dressed in bright colors milled around the shops and stalls, gathering under the traditional striped awnings to escape the sun. Everywhere Luis drove, Kit could hear the sounds of flamenco and castanets, the cheerful voices of the crowds, bursts of laughter now and then. But she felt nothing.

With her heart still numb, Kit gathered the many-tiered ruffles of her floor-length yellow dress and got out of the limousine. Esteban assisted Dona Gabriella, who wore a stunning black dress with a red-ruffled skirt. Before leaving the hacienda, Jaime had presented each of them with flowers to match their costumes. Dona Gabriella pinned a red rose corsage to her shoulder, while Kit fastened the yellow camellias behind one ear. Rafe's mother had insisted Kit wear yellow, since it went with her hair.

Kit knew her gray-green eyes and fair coloring stood out among all these beautiful black-haired, dark-eyed Spaniards. She'd be impossible to miss—the only foreigner among Jerez's best families, who could trace their lineage back to the time of Philip II and earlier.

Afraid to turn around in case she saw Luisa Rios in the next carriage—a woman who was one of the region's most celebrated beauties—Kit followed Dona Gabriella into the Mendez carriage. After making sure the older woman was comfortably settled, Kit took her own place. She found herself staring at the commanding figure of a man on horseback maybe fifty yards away, his head bent as he talked to someone in the crowd.

Rafe.

He looked so breathtaking that Kit could only gaze in wonder. He wore brown leather chaps over tight-fitting gray pants, and a form-fitting black jacket that revealed the power of his muscular chest and arms. He sat tall in the silver-tooled saddle, his dark head partially covered by the eye-catching gray hat with its flat crown and flat broad rim. He wore it at the jaunty angle so characteristic of the *hidalgo* of long ago.

His beautiful white stallion with the unique black markings pranced in place, setting the red tassels of his bridle in motion, as if he were impatient for his master to begin the festivities. It came to Kit as never before how much

Rafe was a part of this land, this life. *He couldn't give it up. She wouldn't let him!*

Suddenly he lifted his head and slowly walked his horse through the hordes of people toward their carriage. Jaime rode several yards behind, dressed in a similar fashion as Rafe, but all Kit could see was her husband's black eyes, singling her out of the crowd. Without acknowledging her verbally, he stared at her for a long, unsmiling moment. Then he passed by the carriage. In the next instant she heard a woman cry Rafe's name and felt the blood drain from her face.

'Ignore it, *mi hija*,' Dona Gabriella murmured. The older woman had just called Kit her daughter.

A lump rose in Kit's throat, making it difficult to swallow.

'Greet the crowd with a smile. You have nothing and no one to envy. Every woman here would like to be in your shoes this day—particularly Luisa Rios.'

When the older woman extended her ringed hand, Kit grasped it and clung, loving her mother-in-law with all her heart.

Then the parade finally began, and for the next hour Kit smiled and waved to the thousands of faces lining the streets. Her eyes never left her husband, who rode beside Jaime. At every turn in the road, the sight of the beloved Mendez brothers produced loud cheering and applause from the exuberant crowd.

Several times throughout the parade, Jaime rode back to the carriage to talk to Kit and his mother, keeping pace with them. Only once did Rafe follow suit, but he flanked his mother's side of the carriage. Kit looked away and waved to the crowds on her side, unwilling to let him know how his lack of attention pained her.

But she couldn't blot him out altogether. At one point she felt his gaze travel over her face, somehow compelling her to turn to him. When she did, she surprised the strangest expression in his eyes. He stared at her as if he'd never seen her before, almost as if he couldn't believe what was in front of him.

It all happened within a few seconds, and before she knew it, he had urged his horse forward and joined Jaime again. But it left Kit feeling alone and isolated, and more heartsick than ever. She realized with new and shattering clarity that she would probably always be a stranger to him.

By the time the parade was over, and the music and street dancing began, Kit had lost sight of Rafe. He seemed to have disappeared among the throng. She imagined that now he had done his duty by the family, he'd gone back home to pack. Considering his state of mind, she wouldn't have been surprised if he left the hacienda without saying goodbye to any of them.

Dona Gabriella excused herself and asked Luis to drive her home at once. Kit wanted to go with her but refrained from saying anything in case Rafe's mother wanted to be alone with her son once more before he left.

Kit knew Jaime was equally worried about Rafe, but he had an obligation to fulfill here at the fair. He insisted Kit dance with him, and she agreed, proud of him for the way he was handling things, for the way he'd taken charge.

After a short while, Diego appeared on the scene and claimed a dance with Kit, while Jaime twirled Maria in his arms.

'May I say you look beautiful this afternoon, *señora?* The *patrón* is a fortunate man.'

'I wish he felt the same way, Diego.' Kit couldn't prevent herself from admitting the truth to someone she trusted. 'Since you're going to find out, anyway, I might as well tell you—'

'If you don't mind, Diego, I need to talk to my wife,' a deep familiar voice broke in. 'Privately.'

Kit gasped in surprise and spun around, unable to credit that Rafe was here instead of halfway to the hacienda. His stern expression sent a chill of foreboding through her body. Diego, as well, seemed to sense that something was wrong and simply nodded to his *patrón* without a smile or a word.

While Jaime danced with Maria somewhere in the crowd, Rafe put his arm around Kit's waist; holding her tightly against him, he ushered her to a back street where his Mercedes stood parked. With formal politeness, he helped her inside, then went around to the driver's side.

'You're leaving Jerez, aren't you?' she asked in a tremulous voice, feeling as if she'd come to the end of her life. She'd promised herself not to make a scene when the time came, but faced with the hard reality that her marriage was over, she found it impossible to act on her good intentions. She was on the brink of losing complete control. 'Once you'd performed your duties, why didn't you just go and let me enjoy the rest of the festival?'

The brim of the hat hid his eyes from her gaze. 'Because there are a few matters we need to discuss before anyone goes anywhere and I don't want an audience,' he replied in a low, determined voice. He started the engine, pulling out into the stream of traffic moving away from the city center.

'You might as well know now that I'm planning to

stay at the hacienda and get my old job back at the base in Rota. Your mother and I have become good friends. It's her wish—and Jaime's—that I remain and th-that's the decision I've made.'

Taking a shallow breath, she rushed on. 'I am your wife, Rafe, and I intend to stay married to you. The Church disapproves of divorce, but if you want to be free that badly, if you want to marry Luisa Rios, then you'll have to be the one to file. As I understand it, divorce proceedings take much longer in your country, so you could have a lengthy wait.'

'I don't know where you got the impression I would want to marry Luisa Rios,' came his mocking reply. 'Not when you yourself pointed out to me I could have done so at a much earlier date.' Away from the parade route the traffic had thinned and they headed in the direction of the Mendez estate.

Almost suffocating from jealousy and heartache she cried out, 'Is she going away with you? Is that what kept you at her side through most of the parade—announcing to all of Jerez that you preferred her company to your own wife's?'

The car's speed increased. 'As I recall, my own wife refused to sleep in my bed. That is part of the marriage vow, *mi esposa*.'

'And you know why I refused!'

'Are you saying you are now prepared to fulfill your marital obligations?'

Her body trembled. 'That's a moot point considering you're going away.'

'And if I weren't?'

'It's still irrelevant because if you slept with me, I would know it wasn't motivated by love. When you grew tired of me, you'd turn to Luisa and who knows how many other women.'

He made no answer and for several miles they traveled in silence. When the car finally passed through the gates of the estate, he spoke again. 'And if I promised to remain true to you, what then?' he asked in a curiously offhand voice.

'Just how long do you think you'd be able to keep your word?'

'Perhaps longer than you think.'

'You're only saying that to spare my feelings.' Tears stung her eyes; she blinked hard to keep them from falling, but they slid down her cheeks nonetheless. 'Let's face it, Rafe. You've been trapped since you woke up in a strange hospital room. Your own home was equally unfamiliar, and your friends and family were all strangers. And. . .you were married to a woman you couldn't even remember. I wouldn't wish that experience on my worst enemy.'

She wiped the tears from her cheeks and opened the door on her side of the car. 'I—I didn't mean what I said about staying on here. That was my anger talking. Dr. Penman warned me about it. The accident that caused your memory loss changed both our lives, only I haven't wanted to admit it until now.' She looked away from him. 'I'll leave Spain as soon as you have the divorce papers drawn up for me to sign. Tomorrow, if you like.'

By some miracle she didn't trip on the ruffles of her yellow gown as she dashed from the car to the entry of the hacienda. Without looking back she flew up the stairs to the guest bedroom she'd been using since that night he'd wanted to make love to her.

She should have let him. Then at least she'd have had

one memory of shared intimacy to sustain her through the empty years ahead.

Quickly, before she could give in to the urge to collapse sobbing on the bed, she got out of the fancy dress and slipped off the black high heels. Her only thought now was to change into clothes suitable for walking. She planned to escape as far from the hacienda as possible.

She was just pulling off her slip when she heard the door open and close. She glanced up, then let out a little cry as her husband came into the room, wearing the paisley robe instead of his festival clothes.

She gazed into his black eyes, no longer hidden by the hat, and saw that they smoldered with a fire she hadn't seen since before the accident. A rush of desire for him engulfed her, but she remained where she was, unmoving.

'Rafe—' She brought one hand to her throat. 'I—I don't know what you think you're doing in here, but you'd better go.'

He kept on advancing. 'I'm doing what I should have done as soon as I'd recovered from the operation. I'm going to make love to you.'

She retreated from him and ended up with her back to the dresser. 'Th-This won't solve anything,' she cried in panic as his hands ran sensuously up and down her arms. When he drew her against him, the feel of his body seemed to break her last tenuous link to rational thought. She'd needed him for too long to fight him any longer, and her body soaked up his touch like parched ground drinking in the rain.

He was behaving very much like the Rafe she remembered from before the accident; it confused her and set her heart tripping over and over itself. 'Has something happened?' She half moaned the question because he was kissing the side of her neck and throat, making it impossible for her to remain coherent. 'Y-You seem different.'

'*Por Dios,* Kit!' He said her name with all the love and longing she'd missed over these painful weeks. 'When I looked into the carriage a while ago and saw your golden hair capturing the light, I wanted to carry you off like the *conquistadores* of old. I wondered how I would be able to wait until I got you home alone.'

'Rafe—'

Her hands stilled against his chest and her gaze flew to his. She stared into the depths of his eyes long and hard, and what she saw made her tremble. The look of *recognition,* of passionate desire and intense love, was there again.

'*Your memory*—' she whispered in awe, '*it's come back.*'

For a moment she feared she might be dreaming, that none of this was real.

'*Rafe—it's come back!*' she shouted for joy and threw her arms around his neck. With an exultant cry he picked her up in his arms and crushed her against his heart, burying his face in her hair.

Her cries turned to heartrending sobs and for a long time they simply clung to each other while Kit tried to absorb the miracle.

'*Amorada,*' he whispered feverishly, covering her face with hungry kisses before claiming her mouth. When they finally gazed into each other's eyes again, she saw that his were as wet and shining as her own. She ran her fingers through his black curls. 'When did it come back, darling?'

'During the parade,' he murmured. 'While I was riding beside Mother, it came to me that I had done this many times before. The sounds, the smells, the horses, Jaime, everything—it was suddenly all familiar. I experienced instant recall, exactly the way Dr. Noyes said it would happen. And then I saw you.' His voice grew husky and he pressed a hard kiss to her mouth, a kiss that spoke of his deep need and his suffering.

Kit responded fervently, recalling the moment. He'd stared at her as if he'd never seen her before, but at the time she hadn't understood.

'I felt a surge of intense emotion because I knew I didn't have to look for you anymore. You were right there at my side, the way I'd dreamed from the moment I first met you. It was like coming home after a long, arduous journey. The feeling was indescribable.' He gave a deep, shuddering sigh. 'I love you, Kit,' he whispered with tears in his voice. 'I adored you even when I couldn't remember. But I was afraid to tell you, afraid I might lose you if my memory never came back and I couldn't be the same man you'd fallen in love with.'

'But Rafe,' she cried softly, molding her hands to his face, tracing every feature. 'Don't you know your memory loss didn't change you? Not in the ways that matter. You were and always will be the same man I lost my heart to. If anything—' her breath caught and she swallowed a little sob '—I was terrified of smothering you with my love.'

'*Smothering* me? You mean like this?' He clasped her even more tightly than before and rolled her over so she was lying on top of him, leaving her in no doubt that he wanted her very badly. 'When you left my bed, Señora

Mendez, I almost came after you and did something you would have found unforgivable.'

'I want to forget the past, all of it,' she said softly, arching against him. 'I want to start living our future. I'm your wife, Rafe. For better, for worse, you'll never be free of me.'

'Kit—' Her name seemed to pour from his soul and in the next breath their mouths and bodies fused in hunger. For a time nothing mattered but the need to love and be loved. 'I feel like I've been reborn,' he whispered.

'So do I,' Kit moaned her euphoria. 'But Rafe—' She kissed his throat and jaw, not able to get enough of him. 'Jaime and your mother need to be told right away. By now, they're probably beside themselves with grief, thinking you're going to leave the estate for good.'

Rafe chuckled deep in his throat, sending delicious chills through her body. 'My adorable *esposa,* if you had seen my mother's expression as I raced up the stairs after you like the lovesick man that I am, you would know she's beside herself not with grief but with happiness. I can guarantee that at this moment she's busy planning our wedding ceremony.'

Suddenly a look of pleading entered his black eyes. 'You don't mind saying our vows again, do you? I scarcely remember anything before the anesthetic set in.'

He'd just expressed the desire of her heart, and she murmured her assent against his mouth, which he kissed with an aching tenderness. After another timeless moment, he lifted his dark head and his expression grew solemn. 'You've already proven that you take your vows seriously, otherwise we would never have made it through the "for worse" part of our marriage. No husband ever had greater testimony of his wife's devotion and loyalty.' He brushed his lips against her eyes and nose and mouth, seemingly insatiable. 'Now I want to repeat those vows and show you the "for better" part, for the rest of our lives. We've only just started to live, *amorada*.'

Modern Romance™
...seduction and
passion guaranteed

Tender Romance™
...love affairs that
last a lifetime

Sensual Romance™
...sassy, sexy and
seductive

Blaze
...sultry days and
steamy nights

Medical Romance™
...medical drama on
the pulse

Historical Romance™
...rich, vivid and
passionate

29 new titles every month.

*With all kinds of Romance for
every kind of mood...*

MILLS & BOON®

Makes any time special™

MAT4

Medical Romance™

6 brand new titles each month

...medical drama on the pulse.

Available on subscription every month from the Reader Service™

GEN/03/RS2

Historical Romance™

4 brand new titles each month

...rich, vivid
and passionate

Available on subscription every month
from the Reader Service™

GEN/04/RS2

Sensual Romance™
4 brand new titles each month
...sassy, sexy and seductive.
Available on subscription every month from the Reader Service™
GEN/21/RS2